H. Ward Silver, NØAX

ARRL's
HANDS-ON
RADIO
EXPERIMENTS

Basic electronics instruction from the pages of **QST** *magazine*

Compiled by Steve Ford, WB8IMY

Production: Jodi Morin, KA1JPA
Cover Design: Sue Fagan, KB1OKW
Proofreader: Kathy Ford

Published by:

ARRL *The national association for* AMATEUR RADIO

225 Main Street • Newington, CT 06111-1494

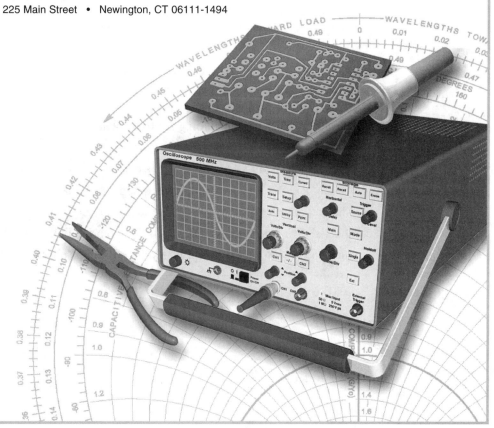

Updates

There is often additional information regarding the Hands-On Radio experiments — you can find it on the Hands-On Radio Web page at **www.arrl.org/tis/info/HTML/Hands-On-Radio/**. The contents include links to reference articles and sources of supplies and equipment. There is also a Frequently Asked Questions section that provides explanations about many of the experiments. Readers have contributed their observations and sometimes tools and links that relate to the topic in the experiment. You may find the information helpful as you perform the experiments in this anthology.

www.arrl.org/tis/info/HTML/Hands-On-Radio

Contents

Foreword

Back in late 2002, then-*QST* Publisher Mark Wilson, K1RO, was looking to replace my monthly *QST* "Radio Puzzler" column with something of broader interest. We kicked around a few ideas and came up with a short, monthly experiment involving electronic fundamentals. It wasn't at all clear that experiments would be a popular topic, but we agreed to try them "for a few months" and watch the response. The name "Hands-On Radio" was selected and I prepared a column that was about as fundamental as electronics gets: "The Common-Emitter Amplifier". Well, here we are after five solid years and the experiments have turned out to be a hit as hams heat up soldering irons, plug in components and learn what makes their radios work. The response has been extremely gratifying and I am pleased to know that experts also keep a sharp eye on my writing, occasionally pointing out a slip or suggesting an improvement. Many readers have suggested putting the column in book form and I am indebted to them for their enthusiastic letters and encouragements. Hams have always given freely of their considerable technical expertise. The hands-on ethic certainly lives on in ham radio!

From the early days of radio, technical articles have been a mainstay of *QST* and the *ARRL Handbook* is known as an authoritative reference around the world. Those authors have been responsible for educating and inspiring thousands and thousands of amateurs and experimenters, of which I am one.

The articles of Doug DeMaw, W1FB and Bill Orr, W6SAI, among many others, inspired me to tinker and build and eventually become a professional engineer. As I turn in my second career to writing and instruction, I feel both indebted and privileged to carry that tradition forward--a tradition of which all hams can be proud.

H. Ward Silver, NØAX
January 2008

Other Books by Ward Silver, NØAX

Other books by the author include three in the popular *For Dummies* series; *Ham Radio for Dummies, Two-Way Radios and Scanners for Dummies*, and his latest, *Circuitbuilding Do-It-Yourself for Dummies*. All are available through ARRL Publications at **www.arrl.org/catalog**. Ward has also written *The NOAX Puzzler* (another ARRL publication) and two antenna performance test reports; *HF Tribander Performance - Test Methods and Results, 2nd Edition* and *HF Vertical Performance - Test Methods and Results*, both available from **www.championradio.com**.

About the ARRL

The seed for Amateur Radio was planted in the 1890s, when Guglielmo Marconi began his experiments in wireless telegraphy. Soon he was joined by dozens, then hundreds, of others who were enthusiastic about sending and receiving messages through the air—some with a commercial interest, but others solely out of a love for this new communications medium. The United States government began licensing Amateur Radio operators in 1912.

By 1914, there were thousands of Amateur Radio operators—hams—in the United States. Hiram Percy Maxim, a leading Hartford, Connecticut inventor and industrialist, saw the need for an organization to band together this fledgling group of radio experimenters. In May 1914 he founded the American Radio Relay League (ARRL) to meet that need.

Today ARRL, with more than 150,000 members, is the largest organization of radio amateurs in the United States. The ARRL is a not-for-profit organization that:

- promotes interest in Amateur Radio communications and experimentation
- represents US radio amateurs in legislative matters, and
- maintains fraternalism and a high standard of conduct among Amateur Radio operators.

At ARRL headquarters in the Hartford suburb of Newington, the staff helps serve the needs of members. ARRL is also International Secretariat for the International Amateur Radio Union, which is made up of similar societies in 150 countries around the world.

ARRL publishes the monthly journal *QST*, as well as newsletters and many publications covering all aspects of Amateur Radio. Its headquarters station, W1AW, transmits bulletins of interest to radio amateurs and Morse code practice sessions. The ARRL also coordinates an extensive field organization, which includes volunteers who provide technical information and other support services for radio amateurs as well as communications for public-service activities. In addition, ARRL represents US amateurs with the Federal Communications Commission and other government agencies in the US and abroad.

Membership in ARRL means much more than receiving *QST* each month. In addition to the services already described, ARRL offers membership services on a personal level, such as the ARRL Volunteer Examiner Coordinator Program and a QSL bureau.

Full ARRL membership (available only to licensed radio amateurs) gives you a voice in how the affairs of the organization are governed. ARRL policy is set by a Board of Directors (one from each of 15 Divisions) elected by the membership. The day-to-day operation of ARRL HQ is managed by a Chief Executive Officer.

No matter what aspect of Amateur Radio attracts you, ARRL membership is relevant and important. There would be no Amateur Radio as we know it today were it not for the ARRL. We would be happy to welcome you as a member! (An Amateur Radio license is not required for Associate Membership.) For more information about ARRL and answers to any questions you may have about Amateur Radio, write or call:

ARRL—the national association for Amateur Radio

225 Main Street
Newington CT 06111-1494
Voice: 860-594-0200
Fax: 860-594-0259
E-mail: **hq@arrl.org**
Internet: **www.arrl.org/**

Prospective new amateurs call (toll-free):
800-32-NEW HAM (800-326-3942)
You can also contact us via e-mail at **newham@arrl.org**
or check out ARRLWeb at **http://www.arrl.org/**

Fundamentals

Experiment #29: Kirchhoff's Laws

Who is this Kirchhoff guy and why are his laws so important? They form the basis of understanding circuits, even as simple rules of thumb. In this experiment, I'll introduce the two laws and show you how they're used—without a bar exam!

Terms to Learn

- *Branch*—a circuit path with two terminals through which current can flow
- *Node*—the junction of two or more branches
- *Loop*—any closed path through a circuit that visits nodes and branches only once

Introduction

Circuit analysis (an intimidating pair of words) is founded on Gustav Kirchhoff's Current and Voltage Laws, which he announced in 1845 as an extension of Georg Ohm's pioneering research. These two laws are consequences of the law of energy conservation. In an electronic circuit, just like anyplace else, electrical energy produced must be equal to energy consumed.

To understand the laws, it is important to use the right terms to describe a circuit. First, a *branch* is a circuit path with two terminals through which current can flow—a wire, a resistor, a coil or a box containing some arbitrary circuit. A *node* occurs where more than one branch comes together. A *loop* is a complete path through a circuit, beginning and ending at the same node, but not visiting a node or branch more than once.

Kirchhoff's Current Law (KCL)

Kirchhoff's Current Law is the easiest to understand and it is applied at nodes, where currents combine, as shown in Figure 1. Even the simple connection between R3 and R4 is a two-branch node. (Don't confuse schematic connection "dots" with nodes because there may be more than one dot for a single node as shown at the bottom of the figure.)

KCL says that the sum of currents entering and leaving a node must equal zero. That seems reasonable, since electrons don't pile up at a circuit junction! KCL is a way of stating that energy must be conserved or balanced. The energy it takes to push currents through circuit branches into a node must equal the energy consumed in the branches through which the currents flow out of the node.

As an equation, KCL can be written as *incoming currents = outgoing currents* or *incoming currents – outgoing currents = zero*. You can assign a positive value to either incoming or outgoing current, so that currents flowing into and out of the node have opposite signs. Current is the same everywhere in the branch—you can't reverse current from one end of a branch to the other or change its value.

An example will help. Figure 2 shows a simple circuit with an arbitrary current assigned in each of the five branches. I1 through I5 are called *branch currents*. The three nodes are labeled 1, 2, and 3. We don't know which way the actual branch currents flow because we don't know whether V is positive or negative. The assigned direction doesn't matter! If we draw the arrow in the wrong direction, the calculated value for the branch current turns out to be negative.

Let's "do a KCL" for all three nodes. Ignore the gray loop markings for now. At node 1, I1 is assumed to flow in and I2 and I4 to flow out. At node 2, I4 flows in and I3 and I5 flow out. At node 3, I2, I3, and I5 flow in and I1 flows out. If we decide that current flowing into a node is positive:

Node 1: $I1 = I2 + I4$
Node 2: $I4 = I3 + I5$
Node 3: $I2 + I3 + I5 = I1$

KCL is used when analyzing parallel connections in a circuit, such as when figuring out how current divides between two unequal resistances or determining the effect of combining currents.

Kirchhoff's Voltage Law (KVL)

KVL is also a consequence of the law of conservation of

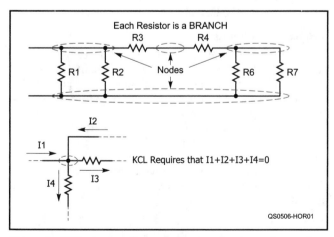

Figure 1—KCL requires the sum of currents at a node equal zero.

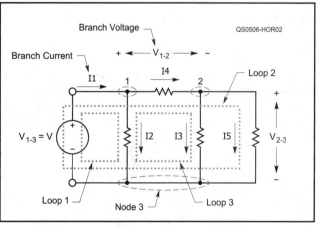

Figure 2—This circuit illustrates nodes, branches and loops—the keys to analyzing circuits.

energy. The opposite of KCL, KVL is applied to loops and states that *the sum of branch voltages around a loop is equal to zero*. A *branch voltage* is the voltage from one end of the branch to the other, such as V1-2 between nodes 1 and 2 in Figure 2. For example, if we follow loop 1 from the power supply's positive terminal at node 1, through the branch for I2, and back to the supply's negative terminal at node 3, the voltages must all sum to zero. It would be the same if, instead, we followed loop 2 through I4, then I5, and back to the negative terminal.

Why does this conserve energy? Take the perspective of a single electron leaving the positive terminal of the power supply that gives the electron all of its energy. If the electron chooses to follow branch current I2, all of its energy is dissipated by that resistor before returning to the supply. It might also follow loop 2 and spend its energy in those resistors. In either case, the energy imparted by the supply has to be sufficient for the electron to "make it home." If the electron didn't expend all of its energy, it would arrive home with energy to spare, increasing the energy stored in the supply! KVL describes how energy is exactly balanced between *sources* (that supply energy) and *sinks* (that consume or dissipate energy).

As with KCL, you must keep polarities straight. By convention, voltages across an energy sink (such as a resistor) are assumed to be positive in the direction of the current—voltage is plus to minus across a resistor in the direction of current flow. Voltages through an energy source (such as a power supply) are negative in the direction of the current. Just as for KCL, if you don't know a voltage's polarity, you're allowed to guess and, if you're wrong, it turns out to be negative.

Let's do another example. In Figure 2, "doing a KVL" around loops 1, 2, and 3, the equations are:

Loop 1: $I2 \times R2 - V = 0$ or $I2 \times R2 = V$
Loop 2: $I4 \times R4 + I5 \times R5 - V = 0$ or $I4 \times R4 + I5 \times R5 = V$

We can move the energy sources to the other side of the equal sign and treat them as positive quantities, which is a little more convenient.

Loop 3: $I4 \times R4 + I3 \times R3 - I2 \times R2 = 0$

Note that there is no energy (voltage) source in loop 3. Furthermore, we encounter the voltage across R2 as negative to positive because of the assigned direction of I2. Bonus—there are three more possible loops in the circuit. Can you find them?

KVL is used when analyzing (or troubleshooting!) circuits using their voltages. For example, when looking at the collector circuit of a common-emitter amplifier, the resulting KVL equation balancing energy sources and sinks is $V_{CC} = I_C R_C + V_{CE} + I_E R_E$.

Extending the Laws to AC Circuits

KCL and KVL work just as well when resistance is replaced by impedance, which includes both resistance and reactance. Impedance generally changes with frequency, so the equations for circuit voltages and currents will also depend on frequency.

For example, if a resistor and capacitor are connected in parallel, KCL will show that at dc, all the current goes through the resistor, gradually shifting to the capacitor as frequency increases. In the series connection of a resistor and inductor, KVL will show that the voltage across the resistor is a maximum at dc and gradually drops as frequency increases.

Exercising Kirchhoff's Laws

Now test KCL and KVL in a real circuit! The solutions for this circuit are found on the Hands-On Radio Web page:

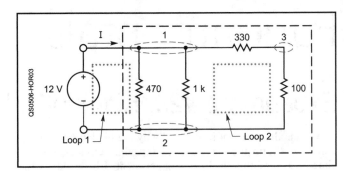

Figure 3—Build this circuit to test your understanding of KCL and KVL.

www.arrl.org/tis/info/HTML/Hands-On-Radio.

- Using the circuit of Figure 3, combine the values of the series and parallel resistors until you have one single equivalent resistance, R_{EQ} replacing everything inside the dashed line.
- Solve for $I = V / R_{EQ} = 12 \text{ V} / R_{EQ}$.
- What current flows in the 470 Ω and 1 kΩ resistors with 12 V across them?
- What current flows through the series combination of the 330 Ω and 100 Ω resistors?
- Build the circuit of resistors (no power supply yet) on your prototype board and measure the resistance from node 1 to node 2 to see if your calculated value of R_{EQ} is correct.
- Apply 12 V as shown and measure the power supply current, I. Compare the value to your calculated value.
- Measure all of the currents going into and out of the three nodes and confirm that KCL works. Either measure the currents directly, using the current scale of your meter, or indirectly, by measuring voltage across the resistors and using Ohm's Law.
- Measure all of the voltages in the two loops and confirm that KVL works. Don't forget to always measure voltage in the same "direction" around the loop.
- Experiment by changing the resistor values, then doing the calculations and measurements again. Identify the two remaining loops and "do a KVL" around them. Try replacing the 330 Ω resistor with a diode!

Shopping List

- 100 Ω, 330 Ω, 470 Ω, and 1 kΩ ¹/₄ W resistors

Suggested Reading

The section on series and parallel resistances in Chapter 4 of *The ARRL Handbook* (2005) covers Kirchhoff's Laws and also has all the equations for combining series and parallel resistances if you're a little rusty on those. While you're at it, browse through the following section on Thevenin equivalents—we'll be tackling those in the future. Rick, KB1HUE, also contributes the following Web site reference, which, if you have a Macintosh (or Mac simulator software), will provide hours of fun: **www.inform.umd.edu/EdRes/Topic/Chemistry/ChemConference/Software/ElectroSim/index.html**.

Next Month

We'll learn about another special type of IC—the charge pump. These handy critters can turn positive into negative or even double a voltage, just with a clever arrangement of switches and a couple of capacitors.

Experiment #32—Thevenin Equivalents

You can't buy a Thevenin Equivalent at the local electronics emporium, but it exists behind every pair of terminals—a fairly simple concept that you can use in many circumstances, a part of every electronic designer's tool set.

Terms to Learn

- *Duality*—the symmetry of opposite quantities, such as voltage and current or resistance and conductance, that allow electrical circuits to be described in terms of either.
- *Equivalent*—a circuit that behaves exactly the same as the original

Introduction

You've already encountered one aspect of Thevenin Equivalents by measuring the output impedance of the common-base amplifier circuit in Experiment 28. (All previous experiments are available at **www.arrl.org/tis/info/HTML/Hands-On-Radio**.) The output of the amplifier was acting like a perfect signal source in series with the measured resistance. Output impedance is just one instance of the more general idea of source impedance.

There are two kinds of sources that supply electrical energy in the form of voltage or current. An *ideal source* is one that can supply any amount of energy required while maintaining its rated voltage or current. For example, the ideal voltage source, shown in Figure 1, can satisfy Ohm's Law ($I = V/R$) through the attached resistor, whether the resistor is 1 MΩ or 1 $\mu\Omega$.

An ideal source would be a handy thing; it doesn't really exist but needs only to be approximated. If I am trying to build an op-amp filter, my voltage source (that is, the power supply) may only have to supply a few mA to act as close to ideal as I need. To build a power grid, I need the Grand Coulee Dam's generators instead!

An actual voltage source can only supply a limited amount of power and still have a constant voltage or current. If I draw current from a battery, with a light bulb, for example, in Figure 1, the output voltage will drop. This voltage drop is caused by the battery's internal or source impedance. I can model the battery as an actual voltage source—an ideal source (V_S) in series with the internal impedance (R_S). The voltage at the battery's terminals, V_L, is reduced as the output current flows through the internal resistance:

$$I = V_S / (R_S + R_L) \qquad\qquad \text{[Eq 1]}$$

$$V_L = V_S - I\,R_S = V_S - V_S\,R_S / (R_S + R_L)$$
$$= V_S\,[1 - R_S / (R_S + R_L)] \qquad\qquad \text{[Eq 2]}$$

Equation 1 shows that for an actual voltage source as R_L increases, the output voltage will drop and vice versa. If R_L is infinite (no load), the output or terminal voltage will be the same as that of the ideal source, since no current flows through the internal impedance. If R_L is zero (a short circuit), then the current is limited to V_S / R_S.

Thevenin's Insight

From the Wikipedia (**www.wikipedia.com**): "Leon Charles Thevenin (1857-1926) was a French telegraph engineer who extended Ohm's law to the analysis of complex electrical circuits." Thevenin's main legacy is a simple but powerful statement: For a circuit made up of any combination of voltage sources and resistors, the behavior at a pair of terminals to that circuit can be completely replicated by a circuit consisting of a single ideal voltage source, called the Thevenin voltage (V_{TH}), in series with a single resistance, called the Thevenin resistance (R_{TH}). That is Thevenin's Theorem, and the source and resistance comprise the Thevenin Equivalent in Figure 1.

That's a pretty powerful idea! If the original circuit, no matter how complicated, was out of your sight with only a pair of terminals visible, you couldn't tell whether the circuit was the complicated one or its Thevenin equivalent. All you know about it is the behavior at its external terminals. Thevenin's Theorem also works for ac signals and circuits, using ac signal sources and impedances. In general, the theorem is true as long as all of the sources and components respond linearly to voltage and current—no diodes or relays, for example.

Equivalence, More or Less

When you're designing or analyzing a circuit, it's handy to be able to replace parts of it with simplified circuit bits that act the same but are easier to analyze. These are equivalent circuits. For example, if I'm working on an amplifier circuit, I need to know the characteristics of what is connected to its input terminals. I don't really want to deal with the whole circuit of the signal source, so I replace it with its Thevenin equivalent. The Thevenin resistance is what you measured as output impedance in Experiment #28.

An equivalent circuit doesn't need to be a Thevenin equivalent. If you can replace a circuit of resistors in parallel with a

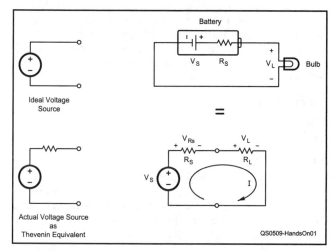

Figure 1—The Thevenin equivalent circuit is constructed from an ideal voltage source in series with a resistance.

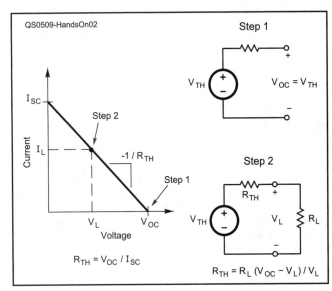

Figure 2—The values of the Thevenin equivalent circuit can be determined by simple measurements of voltage and current.

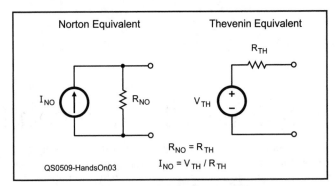

Figure 3—The Norton Equivalent and Thevenin Equivalent circuits exhibit exactly the same behavior at their outputs and can replace each other directly.

different circuit that has resistors in series, the new circuit is the original's series equivalent. (Going the other way, there's also a parallel equivalent.) A circuit that responds the same only at dc is the dc equivalent. All "equivalent circuit" means is that you can replace a circuit with its equivalent without affecting the external behavior.

Measuring a Thevenin Equivalent

Let's figure out the Thevenin equivalent circuit for a battery by determining V_{TH} and R_{TH}. A battery makes a pretty good voltage source, but it still has some internal resistance. How can you figure out what that internal resistance is? We'll use almost the same technique as was used to measure output impedance. Figure 2 illustrates the two steps and how the measurements allow you to determine both V_{TH} and R_{TH}.

- Obtain a 1.5 V AAA or 9 V battery. Do *not* use a larger battery because they can supply enough current to cause a burn or damage themselves.
- The load will be a 100 Ω, 1 W resistor; either buy one or make it from several lower-power resistors. Measure the exact value with your voltmeter. It doesn't have to be exactly 100 Ω; anything from 25 to 100 Ω will do. Don't use a light bulb; the resistance changes dramatically as it heats up.
- With no load connected at all, measure the open-circuit voltage of the battery. Since no current flows in R_{TH}, this is the same voltage as V_{TH}.
- Connect your voltmeter to the resistor leads, and using pliers or tweezers apply the resistor leads directly to the battery terminals without using clip leads or other connectors. Don't hold the resistor or its leads in your fingers, as it may get hot!
- The voltage will drop by some amount to V_L. For fresh batteries the voltage may not drop much. You can increase the voltage drop by lowering R_L, taking care to provide enough power dissipation. ($P = V^2 / R$)
- Use the equation in Figure 2 to determine R_{TH}. Congratulations: You just determined the Thevenin equivalent of your battery! Whatever is inside your battery—more batteries, chemicals, or a tiny hamster on a wheel—can be replaced by an ideal voltage source, V_{TH}, and series resistance, R_{TH}.
- Experiment with fresh and depleted batteries of the same type to see how their Thevenin circuit changes with energy level. Try different types of batteries, as well, taking care to avoid excessive heat dissipation in the load resistor.

The graph in Figure 2 illustrates the process of determining V_{TH} and R_{TH}. With no current drawn from the source, the open-circuit and Thevenin voltages are equivalent. If you short-circuit the output terminals, the current is limited to I_{SC} by R_{TH}. The negative reciprocal of the slope of the line between V_{OC} and I_{SC} is equal to R_{TH}. It's often not advisable to use a short circuit because of the potential damage to the circuit being tested or the circuit tester. Use an intermediate point with a safe current and determine R_{TH} from the slope of the line between that point and the open-circuit point.

Norton Equivalent

There is another way to create an equivalent circuit using an ideal current source and a resistance in parallel; this is called a Norton Equivalent, shown in Figure 3. The ideal current source supplies a fixed amount of current to whatever load is connected to its terminals. Surprisingly, R_{TH} has the same value in both the Norton and Thevenin equivalent circuits!

If you short-circuit a Thevenin circuit, $I_{SC} = V_{TH} / R_{TH}$. If the output is open-circuited, the voltage across the terminals is $I_{SC} \times R_{TH} = V_{OC} = V_{TH}$. Construct the Norton Equivalent by replacing the Thevenin voltage source with a current source of value I_{SC} and place R_{TH} across it. You get exactly the same graph of current and voltage at the output terminals—the definition of an equivalent circuit.

Dual Challenges

Thevenin and Norton circuits are a window into the world of *duality* in electronics where electrical behavior can be defined in terms of current or voltage. Other dual quantities include resistance and conductance, impedance and admittance, series and parallel, and node and mesh (from Experiment #29). The use of one parameter or the other is just a matter of convenience and always leads to the same answer for electrical energy and power.

Shopping List

- AAA or 9 V battery
- 100 Ω, 1 W resistor

Suggested Reading

Thevenin and Norton equivalents are discussed with examples on pages 4.5 and 4.6 of *The 2005 ARRL Handbook*. A more extensive discussion is available on-line at **www.allaboutcircuits.com/vol_1/chpt_10/7.html**. That Web page also has extensive links to other aspects of electrical circuits.

Next Month

In October, we'll get to know the magnetic personality of one of the electronic world's most common components—the transformer.

Experiment #33—The Transformer

Terms to Learn

- *Coupling*—The degree to which primary and secondary windings share a common magnetic field.
- *Step-Down/Step-Up*—The voltage across a step-up transformer's secondary is greater than that across its primary, the opposite of step-down.
- *Turns Ratio*—The ratio of turns on the secondary winding to the primary winding.

Introduction

The first transformer was made by accident, when an early experimenter ran some current through a wire and then noticed that a nearby wire "picked up" some of the energy from the first wire whenever the current was changing. Later, it was noticed that wires wound into coils were even better at transferring energy. The transfer became better still when the coils shared a common core. This was all due to the phenomenon of inductance. The principal investigators during those early days of discovery included Hans Oersted (1777-1851) of Denmark; Michael Faraday (1791-1867) of England, and Joseph Henry (1797-1878) from America.

The inductance of a wire, L, results from the magnetic field created by current in the space around a wire. That magnetic field "pushes back" against the generating current in a kind of electrical inertia just as physical matter "pushes back" against a force trying to get it to move. A wire that is configured so that the magnetic field can "push back" more effectively, such as by coiling the wire, has more inductance. For ac currents, the push back creates reactance.

When a changing magnetic field encounters another conductor, it causes (or induces) current to flow, transferring energy from one wire to the other. This sharing of magnetic field creates *mutual inductance*. The degree to which the magnetic field is shared is called *coupling*. Coils that share a lot of their magnetic fields are termed *tightly coupled*, with less sharing termed *loosely coupled*.

Transferring energy in the form of ac from one coil to another turns out to have very useful applications and so the pair of coils have become a common electronic component—the transformer. Transformers come in many shapes and sizes, but all have the common characteristic of (at least) two coils, called *windings*, sharing a common magnetic field. Most transformers are designed so that the coils share the field as much as possible and so use a core that concentrates the field inside the windings.

Of Primary Importance

Transformers can transfer energy between their windings in either direction. Usually, the transformer is used to send energy in just one direction. The winding to which energy is supplied is called the *primary* and the winding (or windings) from which energy is extracted is called the *secondary*. The transformer doesn't care; you could use it in a different circuit with energy going the other way. No severe tire damage will result!

In most transformers, the coils are so tightly coupled that nearly all of the energy is transferred between them. If I apply a voltage

Transferring energy from one side to another with amazing efficiency; converting voltages and currents and handling impedance shifts with aplomb—it requires no power supply or control circuits. This device has a magnetic personality that is unmatched in electronics ...meet the transformer!

to such a transformer's primary winding with inductance, L1, and measure the voltage across the secondary winding with inductance, L2, I will find that:

$$V2 = V1 \sqrt{(L2/L1)}$$

We know that the amount of inductance in a coil, L, is directly proportional to the number of turns (N) squared, or N^2. If the coils share a common core, the ratio L2/L1 is the same as $(N2)^2 / (N1)^2$ and that makes:

$$V2 = V1 (N2/N1) = n (V1) \text{ and } n = V2/V1 \qquad [1]$$

The letter n denotes the secondary to primary turns ratio, N2/N1. Equation 1 leads to another interesting relationship because the power going into the primary winding, P1, has to be the same as the power coming out of the secondary, P2. (Actual transformer cores dissipate a few percent of the power as heat.) P1 = (V1)(I1) and P2 = (V2)(I2), so (V1)(I1) = (V2)(I2) and V2/V1 = I1/I2. Since n = V2/V1, we also know:

$$I2 = I1 / n \qquad [2]$$

Thus, n is also known as the transformation ratio, showing the relationship between primary and secondary voltages and currents. Figure 1 summarizes all of these transformer relationships. Time for an exercise!

Exercises

If a transformer has 110 V ac on its primary winding and 12.6 V ac across its secondary winding, what is the turns ratio?

$$n = V2/V1 = 12.6 \text{ V} / 110 \text{ V} = 0.115$$

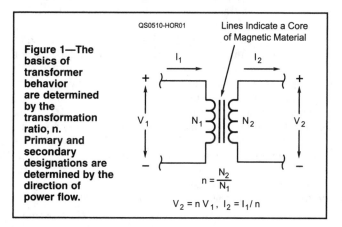

Figure 1—The basics of transformer behavior are determined by the transformation ratio, n. Primary and secondary designations are determined by the direction of power flow.

QS0510-HOR01   Lines Indicate a Core of Magnetic Material

$$n = \frac{N_2}{N_1}$$

$$V_2 = n V_1, \quad I_2 = I_1 / n$$

Given a transformer with a *transformation* ratio of 0.25, if I apply 10 V ac to the primary, what is the secondary voltage?

$$V2 = n (V1) = 0.25(10)$$
$$= 2.5 \text{ V ac}$$

And, if I measure 100 mA flowing in the primary, how much current must be flowing in the secondary?

$$I2 = I1 / n = 0.100 / 0.25 = 400 \text{ mA}$$

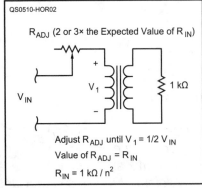

QS0510-HOR02

R_{ADJ} (2 or 3× the Expected Value of R_{IN})

V_{IN} V_1 1 kΩ

Adjust R_{ADJ} until $V_1 = 1/2 \, V_{IN}$
Value of $R_{ADJ} = R_{IN}$
$R_{IN} = 1 \text{ kΩ} / n^2$

Figure 2—Measuring the impedance at the transformer primary is done with an adjustable voltage divider. When $V_1 = \frac{1}{2} V_{IN}$, then $R_{ADJ} = Z_1$.

The Electrical Gearbox

Another important transformer relationship is impedance, V/I. The primary and secondary windings appear to external circuits as impedances $Z1 = V1/I1$ and $Z2 = V2/I2$. Because n can be used to convert V2 to V1 or I2 to I1 (and vice versa) we also find the novel relationship that:

$$Z1 = Z2 / n^2 \qquad [3]$$

This equation says that the impedance my power source sees at the primary connections due to a load on the secondary is inversely proportional to the square of the turns ratio. The transformer behaves as an impedance converter, too, acting just like a mechanical gearbox as it transfers power between different ratios of speed and torque. To find a required turns ratio based on two different impedances, $n = \sqrt{(Z2/Z1)}$.

Core Considerations

The ability of the core materials to store and transfer magnetic energy changes with the frequency at which the field is changing. For example, soft iron works best at ac power and audio frequencies. At RF, soft iron becomes lossy; dissipating the magnetic energy, so ferrite ceramics are used instead. Even air stores magnetic energy, and is used in some transformers, but air cores allow a lot of the magnetic energy to leak away.

Putting a Transformer to Work

The most common use of a transformer in electronics and radio is to convert power at a high-voltage to power at a lower voltage so that transistors and ICs can use it. This is the ubiquitous step-down transformer found in power supplies and ac line-powered equipment. Connected to 110 or 220 V ac at the primary, the secondary output of 6 to 25 V ac is connected to rectifier circuits that convert ac to dc power and regulate it for use by electronic circuits.

Step-up transformers do the reverse, turn line current into high-voltage power for use in our transmitters and amplifiers. A transformer may either be step-up or step-down, depending on which winding you connect as the primary. Caution—don't try to get high-voltage out of a transformer intended for electronics step-down use by connecting 110 V ac to the secondary. The insulation of the primary winding is generally not rated to withstand the resulting higher voltages and you might destroy the transformer or create a shock hazard.

Transformers are also used to convert impedances between different sections of an electronic circuit for low-level signals. For example, a simple transistor audio amplifier may have an output impedance of about 1000 Ω, while speakers typically

have an 8 Ω impedance. A transformer with a turns ratio of $\sqrt{(1000/8)} = 11.2$ will make both amplifier and speaker happy. Since not much power is involved, the transformer can be much smaller than a power transformer.

Transformers can also *isolate* circuits by transferring energy between them without a direct connection. This is often done for safety reasons or to keep noise and interference from traveling between pieces of equipment. If you use the HF digital modes, for example, the connection between your radio and computer sound card uses a pair of small audio transformers with a turns ratio of 1:1 to pass receive and transmit audio without directly connecting them. No voltage or impedance change is made.

Demonstrating Transformer Action

For this part of the experiment, you can either use a small power transformer or an audio transformer. If you have a transformer with more than two windings, just choose any two. If your transformer has a tapped winding (a winding with multiple outputs), use the pair of leads with the most turns between them (farthest from the tap).

• First, determine the turns ratio by connecting one winding to your function generator. Apply a 100 Hz sine wave of several volts and measure the voltage across the remaining winding. You may have to swap the windings if the turn ratio is large.

• Based on the turns ratio, calculate a couple of combinations of input and output voltages, then verify your calculations by measurements. Do the same with the input and output windings reversed.

• Calculate the impedance transformation ratio, n^2, between the two windings. How would you connect the transformer to reduce an impedance value? Try this by connecting the transformer in that configuration to a 1 kΩ resistor and measuring the input impedance as described in Figure 2. (The process is described in Experiment #28—The Common Base Amplifier at **www.arrl.org/tis/info/HTML/Hands-On-Radio**.)

• Swap the windings and calculate the transformed value of the 1 kΩ resistor, then verify by measuring the transformer's input impedance.

• Experiment by trying different transformers (or different windings on your transformer). Sweep the frequency of your generator through the audio range while watching the transformer's output voltage across the 1 kΩ resistor to see over what frequency range it works best!

Shopping List

• Power transformer (such as RadioShack 273-1365) or audio transformer (such as RadioShack 273-1380).
• 1 kΩ resistor.

Suggested Reading

The transformer is thoroughly covered in Chapter 4 of the current version of *The ARRL Handbook* (and in most prior editions). Armed with your new understanding, read about losses and autotransformers, too. Thanks to reader John Nall, AF4WM, there is now a complete shopping list for all of the Hands-On Radio experiments! You can download it from the Hands-On Radio Web site mentioned above. Thanks, John!

Next Month

Technical references—everybody needs them, but how do you find them? I'll discuss a few of my favorites. We'll also take a tour of the ARRL Technical Information Service, a Web site all Hands-On Radio readers should have on their list of browser Favorites.

Experiment #41 — Damping Factor

Terms to Learn

• Frequency response — a graph showing a circuit's output to input ratio at different frequencies.

• Overshoot — the output of a circuit exceeding the desired value.

• Step response — the response of a circuit to a sudden and persistent shift in input.

• Transient response — the response of a circuit to a sharp, short disturbance in input.

• Undershoot — the output of a circuit falling below the desired value.

The goal of this article is to introduce you to damping factor — an important circuit design parameter. Damping factor determines how circuits manage the energy stored in their components. Filter designers use damping factor to describe how the filters behave near their cutoff or center frequencies.

Damping Factor

As the name implies, a circuit's damping factor tells you how quickly oscillations and transients in a circuit die away. A higher damping factor (sometimes also known as damping ratio) means that the energy of the oscillations and transients is dissipated faster. Damping factor is represented by the symbol ζ (the Greek letter zeta).

Imagine bumping an undisturbed cup of liquid. The liquid will slosh back and forth in the cup until friction with the walls of the cup and within the liquid itself eventually dissipates the energy from the bump. The liquid eventually returns to the quiet state it was in before being bumped. If the liquid is water, the sloshing might go on for some time. If the liquid is motor oil the sloshing will be slow and quick to die out. The cup of water has a low damping factor and the oil a high damping factor.

Figure 1 illustrates the effect of damping factor in a parallel resistor, inductor, capacitor (RLC) circuit. Assume that a battery has been connected across the circuit for long enough that it has reached a stable value so that the inductor is completely "charged up." This is called the steady state. If I disconnect the battery and watch the voltage across the three components, I can watch the energy "slosh" around in my circuit (maybe this is why RLC circuits are called "tank circuits"). The more damped the circuit is, the longer it takes for the energy to finally be dissipated and the circuit to return to "rest."

The figure shows the three types of damping. The light gray (top) line shows the overdamped case in which $\zeta > 1$. The response is sluggish and takes a long time to die out. The underdamped case with $\zeta < 1$ is shown at the bottom — you can see the circuit *ring* as the energy flows back and forth until it is finally dissipated. In the middle is the critically damped case, with $\zeta = 1$. The critically damped circuit returns to the undisturbed state as quickly as possible without ringing — that is, when the energy flows back into the inductor from the capacitor.

If the inductor and capacitor were perfect components and without any losses, then the only energy dissipation would occur in the resistor. If I removed the resistor, then the energy would flow from inductor to capacitor and back again forever, creating an undamped circuit. The voltage in that case would look like a sine wave that continued without ever getting smaller. The damping factor for such a circuit is zero.

Step Response

Another way of observing the effects of damping factor is to examine the response of a circuit to sudden changes at its input. For example, we can apply a sharp, short transient (the transient response) or a sudden shift in voltage or current that persists for a long time (the step response) to our circuit. Figure 2 shows the effect of damping factor on the step response of a series RLC circuit.

In this figure, the switch is closed at the time shown by the dotted line on the graph and the capacitor voltage starts reacting. Eventually, the capacitor will charge up to the battery's voltage, V_{BATT}, but the damping factor determines how long that will take and what the voltage waveform will look like as it charges. As in Figure 1, the overdamped waveform approaches V_{BATT} slowly. The underdamped waveform first overshoots V_{BATT}, then undershoots, overshoots once again, and finally approaches V_{BATT}.

Observing ζ with Filter Response

The situation in which damping factor most often makes a difference to hams is in the response of filters. An underdamped filter may ring and an amplifier may oscillate. In fact, an oscillator is really an amplifier with a negative damping factor! The easiest way to observe the effect is by building a filter circuit yourself and adjusting its damping factor. Luckily there is a great circuit for this purpose.

The Sallen-Key circuit is a popular type of active filter, such as those we met in Experiments 3 and 4 (see the Hands-On Radio

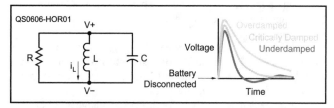

Figure 1 — The response of the circuit shows how energy is dissipated while being transferred from the inductor to the capacitor. An underdamped circuit allows the energy to partially flow back into the inductor before finally being dissipated by the resistor.

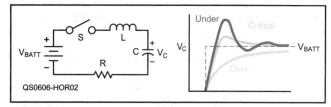

Figure 2 — Step response is important because it shows how the circuit will respond to sudden changes in input voltage. Overdamped circuits respond slowly while underdamped circuits have both overshoot and undershoot before settling on a final value. Critical damping is a compromise.

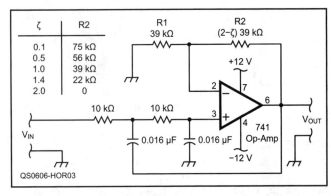

Figure 3 — The Equal-Value Sallen-Key low-pass filter circuit allows damping factor to be adjusted with a single resistor value. By adjusting the value of R2, different values of damping factor can be selected, although circuit gain also changes.

Web site at **www.arrl.org/tis/info**). The second-order (meaning two frequency-determining sub-circuits) filter is very flexible and can be designed in many different ways. The "Equal Values" low-pass filter circuit shown in Figure 3 is just right for our needs.[1] The name comes from keeping both of the input resistors and capacitors the same value. The gain of this circuit is fixed at $3 - \zeta$. To change damping factor, adjust the value of R2 as shown in the table. This also alters the circuit gain, but that is not important for this experiment.

Build the circuit as shown in Figure 3 with R2 = 22 kΩ ($\zeta = 1.4$). Connect the input to your signal generator and the output to an oscilloscope or voltmeter set to measure ac voltage.

The input resistors and capacitors are chosen to give a cutoff frequency of 1 kHz. Apply a sine wave of about 1 V$_{pp}$ and measure the input and output voltage at several frequencies from 200 Hz to 5 kHz. Take several measurements between 800 Hz and 1.5 kHz.

Plot the frequency response of the circuit using the spreadsheet provided on the Hands-On Radio Web site in the FAQ section for Experiment 18. (You do not need to plot phase information so ignore those entry cells.)

You should see a smooth low-pass frequency curve with a cutoff frequency (−3 dB from the 200 Hz response) around 1 kHz. Gain at 200 Hz should be $3 - \zeta$ or about 1.6. Be sure the circuit works properly before proceeding further.

You'll need an oscilloscope for this step. Change your input to a square wave and reduce the frequency to about 10 Hz. Adjust the horizontal position so that the rising edge of the input square wave is about 2 divisions from the left-hand edge of the screen.

Increase the sweep speed and take a close look at the rising and falling edges of the output waveform to see the circuit's step response. You should see an overdamped waveform as the output rounds off the input waveform corners. (You will have to speed up the sweep speed to faster than 1 msec/div, stretching out your waveforms to see this clearly.)

Replace R2 with a 56 kΩ resistor, changing damping factor to 0.5 (underdamped). Return the signal generator to a sine wave and measure frequency response again. This time, you will see a pronounced peak in the response around 1 kHz. Look at the step response by using a square wave as before. This time, you should see some ringing due to the underdamped response.

Experiment with the different values for R2 shown in the table and compare the different frequency and step responses to Figures 1 and 2.

Substitute a 100 kΩ potentiometer for R2 and adjust the damp-

ing factor while watching the effect on step response.

You can listen to damping factor's effect on audio by connecting your radio's audio output to the filter's input (see Experiment 4 for guidance). Overdamped responses will be slightly muffled. Underdamped responses emphasize frequencies around 1 kHz more than others.

What happens if you use a value of more than 3×39 kΩ for R2 ($\zeta < 0$)?

Shopping List

741 op-amp.
10 kΩ (2 ea.), 22 kΩ, 39 kΩ, 56 kΩ, 75 kΩ ¼ W resistors.
2 ea, 0.016 µF film or ceramic capacitors.
100 kΩ potentiometer.

Recommended Reading

I've mentioned Don Lancaster's *Active Filter Cookbook* before. It offers a succinct, easy-to-read presentation of common filter types and circuits that makes it a perennial favorite of experimenters. Walter Jung's *Op-Amp Cookbook* is another useful text to have around.

Next Month

As long as we're busy with op-amps and filters, let's try an interesting filter you'll find in your radio — the notch filter!

---

[1]D. Lancaster, *Active Filter Cookbook*, Howard W. Sams and Company.

Experiment #47 — Toroids

Open up just about any modern HF radio, tuner or filter and you'll see quite a number of toroidal inductors — circular cores wound with wire — or just plain "toroids" for short. Why are toroids so popular and what makes them better than "regular" cylindrical or solenoidal coils? That's our topic for this month.

Terms to Learn

Bifilar, Trifilar, Quadrifilar Winding — Two, three or four parallel wires, respectively, of the same length, wound with the same number of turns, in the same direction and at the same pitch.

Ferrite — A type of ceramic material that exhibits magnetic properties.

Self-Shielding — An inductor whose interaction with nearby components is minimized because the magnetic flux is contained within its core.

Permeability — A measure of the ability of a material to concentrate a magnetic field.

The Magnetic Donut

As discovered by Ampère, current flow produces an accompanying magnetic field around the conductor. Even straight wires have inductance! Apply the *right-hand rule* to find out in what direction the magnetic field is oriented. Make a fist with your right hand and stick your thumb out perpendicular to your fingers. If your thumb points in the direction of the current flow, your fingers show the direction that the magnetic field wraps around the wire. This is based on *conventional* (positive) current, rather than electronic current.[1]

If the wire is wound into a cylindrical coil, called a solenoid, the magnetic field is now oriented one way inside the coil (the core) and the opposite way outside. Make the same fist with your right hand, with your fingers curling in the same direction that current is flowing in the wire. Your thumb now points in the direction of the magnetic field inside the coil. As with the straight wire, the magnetic field extends out into space around the coil.

A core made of ferromagnetic material such as iron concentrates the magnetic field because the permeability (symbolized by μ) of the material is higher than that of air. The permeability of the core and the number and shape of the turns and their *pitch* (number of turns per unit of length) determine the inductance — the coil's ability to store magnetic energy.

Regardless of what material forms the core of a solenoid, there will still be a magnetic field outside the coil. In fact, there is just as much energy outside the

coil as inside, although it is dispersed throughout a larger volume. That field can transfer energy to other conductors through mutual inductance and it can cause problems in an electronic circuit. For example, a microphone cable will pick up 60 Hz magnetic energy as hum from a nearby power transformer's magnetic field.

One way of minimizing mutual inductance is to prevent the magnetic field from leaving the coil. If a magnetic core focuses the field inside the coil, it will do the same if extended outside as Figure 1 shows. If the core is circular, we have the familiar toroid. Very little of the magnetic energy leaks outside the core, called *self-shielding*, so toroids can be used in very cramped enclosures and near other components with little interaction.

Calculations for Toroids

The inductance of a coil, whether a solenoid or toroid, is proportional to the square of the number of its turns. It is also directly proportional to μ and depends as well on the size and shape of the core material. The constant A_L (the inductance per turn factor) accounts for the core geometry and is used to calculate inductance for a particular core. A_L is specified by the core's manufacturer as

Table 1

A Subset of the Complete Table of A_L Values Found in *The ARRL Handbook*

			Mix			
Size	15	1	2	7	6	10
T-12	50	48	20	18	17	12
T-16	55	44	22	na	19	13
T-20	65	52	27	24	22	16
T-25	85	70	34	29	27	19
T-30	93	85	43	37	36	25
T-37	90	80	40	32	30	25
T-44	160	105	52	46	42	33
T-50	135	100	49	43	40	31
T-68	180	115	57	52	47	32

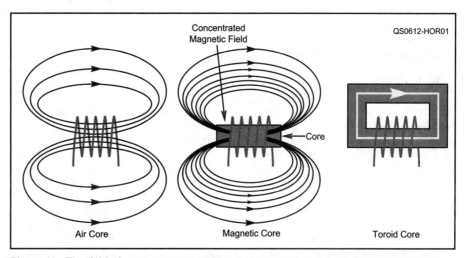

Figure 1 — The field of an air-core solenoid coil disperses into the space around the coil. Using a magnetic core concentrates the field, but it is still dispersed outside the coil. A toroid core contains almost all of the field.

[1]Conventional current is the flow of positive charge in the direction of positive to negative voltage. — **en.wikipedia.org/wiki/Current_(electricity)#Conventional_current**.

a ratio of inductance per turn. The industry standard is to state A_L as µH per 100 turns, so the proper formula is:

$$L = A_L \times n^2 / 10,000, \text{ or}$$
$$n = 100 \times \sqrt{(L / A_L)}$$

It would be great if this were all we needed to design toroids, but core materials don't act the same at all frequencies. Manufacturers offer a wide variety of material compositions (mixes) optimized for uses at different frequencies and power levels. Amateur Radio circuits use cores of ferrite or powdered iron. A core must also be large enough to handle the expected energy without overheating from internal losses. The result is a family of toroid cores for different uses.

The most common way of specifying a toroid core is to use the Micrometals system of identification. The part number for each different type of core begins with "T" followed by the outside diameter in hundredths of an inch, a dash and then a number identifying the material. For example, a T-37-6 core has 0.37 inch outside diameter and is made from a type-6 mix intended for use between 10 and 50 MHz. Table 1, extracted from *The 2007 ARRL Handbook*, Table 7.9, lists some typical mixes and A_L values for different sizes of cores.[2]

How about an example of a toroid design? What if we wanted to replace the air-wound solenoid coil of experiment #44 with a toroid?[3] The original inductance was 2 µH and the frequency was 7 MHz. Type-2, type-7 or type-E powdered iron cores and type-61 ferrite are recommended for 7 MHz. Let's choose a type-7 core because it has good temperature stability for oscillators. This is a very low-power application so we can use a small core. The T-37-7 is a convenient size to work with. A_L = 32 µH / 100 turns for this core so the number of turns is n = 100 × √(2 / 32) = 25 turns. Now you try — calculate the number of turns for the T-50-2 core with A_L = 49 as shown in Table 1. The answer should be fewer turns, since A_L increased. Experiment by picking different cores and inductances.

Winding Toroids

Aren't toroids hard to wind? As long as you're not trying to put 100 turns on a 0.25 inch outside diameter core, it's not nearly as bad as you might think. Start by being able to see what you're doing. For those of us (including me) with poor close-up vision, an inexpensive head-mount magnifier, available from craft stores, really helps.

Next, use the right amount of wire. Take a short length of the wire you'll be using to wind the coil — usually #20 to #28 — and wind five complete turns on the core, keeping each turn fairly snug. Mark the beginning and end of the windings, unwind it, measure between the marks, and divide by five — that's your length per turn. Multiply by the total number of turns and add 3 or 4 inches for connections and mounting.

Since you'll be using solid wire, prevent kinking to avoid breaks. If the total length of wire is short, you can pass the full length of

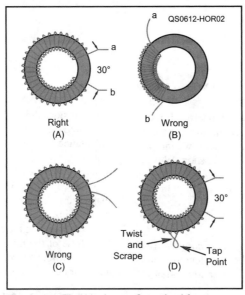

Figure 2 — The maximum-Q method for winding a single layer toroid is shown at A. A 30° gap is best. Methods at B and C have greater distributed capacitance. D shows how to place a tap on a toroidal coil winding.

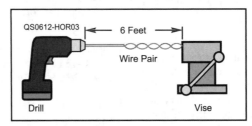

Figure 3 — A variable-speed drill can be used to twist sets of wires to make multifilar windings. These twisted pairs are also handy for other electronic projects as well.

wire through the central hole for each turn. For longer lengths, a bobbin is recommended. A length of ice cream stick or coffee stirrer will do nicely. Trim the width to about ⅔ of the toroid's inside diameter. Cut a notch in each end of the bobbin and wind the wire on it.

Holding the toroid and one end of the wire between your fingers, pass the bobbin through the core for each turn, keeping the wire slightly taut. Each pass through the central hole counts as one turn — there are no fractional turns. Spread the turns out around the core as shown in Figure 2. Practice on any small toroid you can scrounge up and save the bobbin design that works best for you.

Do The Twist

For some toroid designs, multiple wires are wound at the same time. These are bi- (two wire), tri- (three wire) or quadrifilar (four wire) windings. These are used when it is important that all windings be exactly the same length and distributed equally on the core. It's very difficult to do by winding the wires separately, so they are twisted together first.

While you can purchase pre-twisted wire or strip out sections of ribbon cable, it's more fun to make your own. You'll need a variable-speed hand drill and a bench vise or C-clamp. Once the multifilar winding is on the core, it can be difficult to figure out which wire is which, so try to find wire with different color enamel or insulation. Start with a single, twisted pair. Cut two pieces of wire about 6 feet long and clamp them in the vise or under the C-clamp. Stretch the wires out and capture them in the drill chuck so that there is approximately equal tension on both wires as shown in Figure 3. This is important so that each wire gets twisted about the same amount. Now slowly get the drill turning while maintaining light tension on the wires for an even twist. Run the drill until the wires are twisted about 8 times per inch. Fun, isn't it?

Recommended Reading

There is plenty of information on toroids in publications such as *The ARRL Handbook* and *Experimental Methods in RF Design*.[4,5] On-line you can browse sources such as the excellent set of application notes at **www.micrometals.com/appnotes_index.html**.

Next Month

Next month we're going to build on what we've learned about toroid cores to build some impedance transformers and unwind a couple of the mysteries associated with baluns.

[3]All of the previous Hands-On Radio experiments are available to ARRL members at **www.arrl.org/tis/info/HTML/Hands-On-Radio**.

[4]R. D. Straw, Editor, *The ARRL Handbook of Radio Communications*. Available from your ARRL dealer or the ARRL Bookstore, ARRL order no. 9760. Price, $44.95 plus shipping. Telephone 860-594-0355, or toll-free in the US 888-277-5289; **www.arrl.org/shop/; pubsales@arrl.org**.

[5]W. Hayward, W7ZOI; R. Campbell, KK7B; R Larkin, W7PUA; *Experimental Methods in RF Design*. Available from your ARRL dealer or the ARRL Bookstore, ARRL order no. 8799. Price, $49.95 plus shipping. Telephone 860-594-0355, or toll-free in the US 888-277-5289; **www.arrl.org/shop/; pubsales@arrl.org**.

[2]A fairly complete table of toroid core characteristics is given in the chapter "Component Data and References" of *The ARRL Handbook*.

Semiconductor Basics

Experiment #1—The Common-Emitter Amplifier

Our first experiment will feature the *common emitter* (CE) *amplifier*. Why the CE amplifier? It is the most common amplifier configuration of all—it is found in analog and digital circuits, from dc through microwaves and it is made of discrete components and fabricated in integrated circuits (ICs). If you understand the CE amplifier, you've made a good start in electronics.

Background

The CE amplifier (Figure 1) is used when modest voltage gain is required along with an input impedance (the impedance seen by the circuit supplying the signal to be amplified) of a few $k\Omega$ or more. The output of the CE amplifier is inverted from its input. (We call this 180° of phase shift.) As the input signal swings positive, more current flows into the transistor's base, which also causes more current to flow from the collector to the emitter. This causes more voltage drop across Rc and so the voltage at the collector also drops. The reverse is true when the input signal swings negative.

In order for the circuit to amplify both positive and negative swings of the input signal, its collector current (I_c) must be offset from zero so that it can both increase and decrease. An amplifier that has a continuous output current, even with no input signal, is called a Class A amplifier. The method of controlling this continuous current is called biasing. Resistors in the voltage divider R1 and R2 cause a small amount bias current to flow into the base and thus keep the collector current flowing at all times. The amplifier is then said to be operating in its "active" region. The resulting continuous collector current equals the base bias current multiplied by the transistor's current gain, β. Using Ohm's Law to find the voltages across R_c and R_e, the transistor's collector-to-emitter voltage (V_{ce}) is also determined by the bias current. The combination of continuous I_c and V_{ce} is called the Q-point of the circuit, where Q stands for "quiescent." When an input signal is applied, output voltage and current changes are centered around the Q-point.

As the collector current changes in response to an input signal, the circuit's output voltage is developed across the collector resis-

tor, R_c. For a given input signal, a larger R_c means a larger output voltage change—a higher voltage gain (A_v). The function of R_e is to set the transistor's Q-point such that the collector voltage can make wide swings without running up to the power supply voltage (V_{cc}) or down to ground. By being in the collector current's path, along with R_c, larger values of R_e work against R_c to reduce voltage gain. In fact, the voltage gain is approximately the ratio of R_c to R_e.

Figure 1 shows capacitors at the input (C_{in}) and output (C_{out}). This is called an "ac coupled" design. The capacitors block the flow of dc current to the load or to the circuit driving the amplifier. These capacitors also cause the gain at very low frequencies to be reduced, as the impedance of a capacitor increases at low frequencies—hence the gain at dc is zero. For this experiment, all capacitors will be 10 μF—a value large enough to act as a short-circuit for most audio signals. If polarized capacitors are used, the positive side should be connected to the circuit.

Terms to Learn

A_v—Voltage gain, the ratio of output to input voltage.

Beta (β)—DC current gain, the ratio of collector current to base current.

Cutoff—Collector current reduced to zero.

I_b, I_c—Base and collector current, respectively.

Q-Point—Quiescent or resting values of collector current (I_{cq}) and voltage (V_{ceq}) with no applied input signal.

V_{ce}, V_{be}—Voltage from collector-to-emitter and base-to-emitter, respectively.

Key Equations

$$I_c \approx I_e, \quad I_c = I_b \times \text{Beta } (\beta) \tag{1}$$
$$V_{cc} = (I_c \times R_c) + V_{ce} + (I_e \times R_e) \approx I_e \times (R_c + R_e) + V_{ce} \tag{2}$$
$$A_v \approx R_c / R_e \tag{3}$$
$$V_{R2} = V_{be} + (I_e \times R_e) \tag{4}$$

Designing the Amplifier

1. Choose the circuit's operating requirements:

V_{cc} = 12 V *(our power supply voltage)*.

A_v = 5 *(a medium value of gain)*.

Q-point of I_{cc} = 4 mA *(a value to keep power dissipation low)* and V_{ceq} = 5 V *(rule of thumb—about one-half of V_{cc})*.

Assume the transistor's β is 150 and base-to-emitter voltage, V_{be} = 0.7 V. *(The actual range of β can be read from the transistor's data sheet and V_{be} is typically 0.7 V for silicon transistors.)*

2. *From equation 2*, $V_{cc} = I_c (R_c + R_e) + V_{ce}$

$(V_{cc} - V_{ce}) / I_c = R_c + R_e$, so $R_c + R_e = (12 \text{ V} - 5 \text{ V}) / 4 \text{ mA}$ = 1.75 $k\Omega$

3. *From the above*, R_c = 1750 Ω – R_e and with A_v = 5, R_c / R_e = 5 *(equation 3)* so

R_c = 5 R_e and $(1750 \Omega - R_e)$ = 5 R_e, so 6 R_e = 1750 Ω and R_e = 1750 $\Omega / 6$ = 292 Ω *(use 270 Ω, a standard value)*.

4. *From equation 1*, base current, $I_b = I_{cq} / \beta$ = 4 mA / 150 =

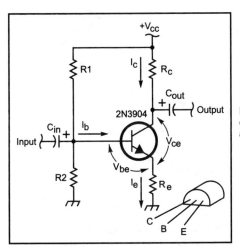

Figure 1—The common-emitter amplifier.

Figure 2—The experimental setup, showing the prototype board and connections to the power supply, oscilloscope and voltmeter. Note that the signal instrument grounds are all connected to a single point—this helps to prevent noise pickup and ground loops.

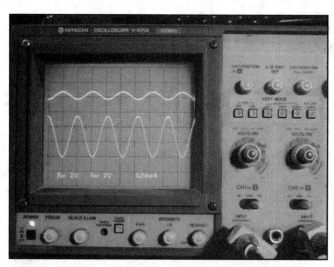

Figure 3—The oscilloscope shows the input (top trace) and output (bottom trace) waveforms. The output is inverted with respect to the input and the voltage gain is approximately 5.

26.67 μA (27 μA). Set the current through R1 and R2 equal to 10 times I_b or 270 μA. (*This is a rule of thumb simplifying calculations and keeping I_b stable with a "stiff" bias supply.*)

The voltage across R2 = V_{be} + I_c (R_e) = 0.7 V + 4 mA (270 Ω) = 1.8 V ($I_c \approx I_e$ *and equation 4*).

By Ohm's Law, R2 = 1.8 V / 270 μA = 6.7 kΩ (*use 6.8 kΩ, a standard value*).

The voltage across R1 = V_{cc} – 1.8 V = 10.2 V (*voltage divider*)

By Ohm's Law, R1 = 10.2 V / 270 μA = 37.8 kΩ (*use 39 kΩ, a standard value*).

Testing the Amplifier

1. Connect the power supply only after double-checking all connections, especially the transistor leads.

2. Use a VOM to measure the dc voltage from collector to emitter (it should be about 5 V), from base to emitter (0.6-0.7 V), and from collector and emitter to ground (7 V and 2 V, respectively).

3. Replace R1 with the 100 kΩ potentiometer, set to about 39 kΩ. Confirm that all the dc voltages remain about the same. Connect the VOM between collector and ground and observe what happens as R1 is decreased and increased (raising and lowering base current). Use Ohm's Law to determine what is happening to the collector current as you adjust R1. Reset the pot to 39 kΩ.

4. Set the signal (function) generator to output a 1 kHz sine wave of 200 mV$_{p-p}$, then connect it to C_{in}. If you are using an oscilloscope, you should see a sine wave at the output of C_{out} with an amplitude of about 1 V$_{p-p}$ and inverted (180° of phase shift) with respect to the input. (A VOM measuring ac RMS voltage will show values of about 70 mV RMS at the input and 350 mV RMS at the output—a gain of 5.)

5. Adjust R1 in each direction and observe the output signal with the oscilloscope. As you lower the collector current, you will begin to see the output waveform clip on positive peaks as the collector current is cut off. Raising collector current will eventually result in distortion on negative peaks as the transistor enters the saturation region.

6. Return R1 to 39 kΩ and increase the input signal to observe distortion on the output. If you are using a VOM, note that the RMS

output increases more slowly as the signal is clipped.

7. Turn down the input signal as far as possible. Connect the third 10 μF capacitor across R_e. (Connect the negative side of a polarized capacitor to ground.) Slowly increase the input signal and observe the new gain of the circuit. By bypassing R_e, the dc operation of the circuit is unaffected, but now the emitter circuit is effectively grounded for ac signals. The gain is now limited only by the internal impedance of the transistor emitter.

8. Now that you have a working circuit—experiment with it!

● Rework the math for a Q-point with 10 times more and 10 times less collector current.

● Raise and lower the input frequency to see where the gain drops to 70% of the peak value. These are the –3 dB frequencies that determine the amplifier's bandwidth. (These frequencies may be out of range, depending on your instruments.)

● Depending on your generator's capabilities, try different waveforms, such as square or triangle waves, at different frequencies. Does the amplifier faithfully reproduce them?

● Substitute other transistors of the same type and of different types to see what happens to the dc and ac performance.

Suggested Reading

"Transistor Amplifier Design—A Practical Approach" in Chapter 8 of *The ARRL Handbook.* For a more complete discussion of the common emitter amplifier, check out Chapter 2 of *The Art of Electronics.*

Shopping List

You'll need the following components:

● 100 kΩ potentiometer.

● ¼ W resistors of the following values: 270 Ω, 1.5 kΩ, 6.8 kΩ, 39 kΩ.

● 3—10 μF capacitors with a voltage rating of 25 V dc or more (electrolytic or tantalum are fine).

● 2N3904 transistor.

Next Month

The common collector amplifier, also known as the emitter follower, will be the subject of next month's experiment. With the exception of a few more resistor values, you'll be able to reuse the components from this month's exercise. See you then!

Experiment #2—The Emitter-Follower Amplifier

Our second experiment will again focus on a transistor amplifier—the emitter-follower. This handy amplifier doesn't offer much in the way of voltage gain (it has none), but it provides buffering or isolation for sensitive amplifiers and muscle to output circuits for driving loads like headphones or coaxial cables. It has relatively high input impedance with low output impedance and good *power* gain, as we'll see later.

Background

The emitter-follower (EF) amplifier configuration, also called the common collector, is found in applications where an amplifier must have both high input impedance (to avoid loading a sensitive or low-power circuit) and low output impedance (to drive a heavy load).

The EF provides no voltage gain; in fact, its voltage gain is always less than 1. The collector of the transistor is connected directly to the power supply, without a resistor and the output is taken across the emitter resistor. There is no 180° phase shift as seen in the common-emitter configuration of experiment #1—the output signal follows the input signal with 0° phase shift. This is the origin of the name—the emitter voltage "follows" the input signal voltage.

Why does the EF configuration have a high input impedance? Let's start by looking directly into the base of the transistor at base voltage, V_b and base current, I_b. Remember that β is the transistor current gain, or the ratio of collector to the base current.

$\beta = I_c / I_b$ so $I_c = \beta I_b$

$I_e = I_b + I_c$

Therefore, $I_e = I_b + \beta I_b = I_b (\beta + 1)$

$V_b = V_{be} + I_e R_e = V_{be} + [I_b (\beta + 1)] R_e$ [1]

The base impedance, Z_b, is the ratio of the change (Δ) in V_b to the resulting change in I_b. Biasing will keep the transistor current "turned on" so V_{be} doesn't change much and can be treated as constant. So, small changes in V_b due to the input signal will cause a corresponding change in I_b.

$\Delta V_b \approx \Delta I_b (\beta + 1) R_e$ and... [2]

$Z_b = \Delta V_b / \Delta I_b \approx (\beta + 1) R_e$ [3]

This equation shows that the small changes in I_b amplified by β effectively also multiplies R_e by the same amount. The base impedance (not counting the biasing network R1 and R2) is essentially the current gain, β, multiplied by the emitter resistor, R_e.

The input source doesn't just drive the base, of course; it also has to drive the combination of R1 and R2, the biasing resistors. From an ac point of view, both R1 and R2 can be considered as connected to "ac ground" (the power supply supplies a constant dc voltage; it should present a low impedance, which is effectively an ac short) and they can be treated as if they were connected in parallel. When R1 // R2 are considered along with the transistor base impedance, Z_b, the impedance the input signal source "sees" is:

$Z_{in} = R1 // R2 // Z_b = 1 / [1/R1 + 1/R2 + 1/R_e (\beta + 1)]$ [4]

Let's figure the output impedance, Z_{out}, too. Looking back into the connection between the transistor emitter and R_e, Z_{out} is made up of three components. The first is R_e, which is connected to ground. The second, Z_e, is the series combination of the transistor's internal emitter impedance, r_e, (note the lower-case "r" which distinguishes it from the external resistance, R_e) and the combined impedance of the signal source, R_s, and the biasing resistors R1 and R2. Using the same explanation of current gain's effect on input impedance—in reverse this time—the impedance presented at the emitter, Z_e, is:

$Z_e = (R_s // R1 // R2) / (\beta + 1) + r_e$ [5]

From the physics of silicon transistors, at room temperature, $r_e = 25$ mV $/ I_{eq}$, where $I_{eq} \approx I_{cq}$ in mA, so, for most designs, r_e will be much less than 50 Ω. Similarly, in our experiment, R1 and R2 are likely to be much higher than R_s, the signal source impedance—which is usually less than 1 kΩ. When R_e and Z_e are combined, the output impedance of the circuit becomes:

$Z_{out} = Z_e // R_e$ [6]

We see, therefore, that our emitter follower has a relatively high input impedance and a low output impedance, making it ideal for driving low-impedance loads.

Terms to Learn

Input (Output) Impedance—the equivalent ac impedance looking into the input (output) of a circuit.

Cascade—two circuits connected such that the output of the first is connected to the input of the second.

Power Gain—the ratio of output power to input power.

Buffer—an amplifier used to provide isolation between two circuits.

//—in parallel with.

Key Equations

$I_c \approx I_e, I_c = I_b \beta$ [7]

$V_{cc} \approx V_{ce} + I_c R_e$ [8]

$V_b \approx V_{be} + I_c R_e$ [9]

Designing the Amplifier

Choose the circuit's operating requirements:

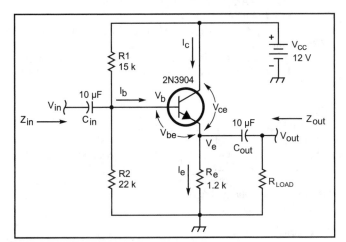

Figure 1—The common emitter circuit. This is a current or power amplifier, offering high input impedance and low output impedance. It is useful for driving low impedance loads, buffering and isolation.

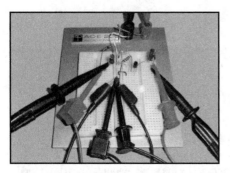

Figure 2—This photo shows the construction of the EF (emitter follower) circuit. Note that the input connection is on the right and the output connection is on the left. This keeps the input and output leads away from each other and helps prevent oscillation. All ground leads (black clips) are connected together at a single point.

Figure 3—An oscillating circuit—with a 1 kHz sine wave input, both the input (top) and output (bottom) signals show significant oscillation at more than 1 MHz. Experiment with lead placement and circuit component placement to learn what causes and prevents oscillation.

V_{cc} = 12 V *(our power supply voltage)*

Q-point of I_{cq} = 5 mA and V_{ceq} = 6 V *(rule of thumb, ½ V_{cc} allows the maximum output voltage swing)*

Assume the transistor's β is 150 and base-to-emitter voltage, V_{be} = 0.7 V

1. $R_e = (V_{cc} - V_{ceq}) / I_{cq}$ = 1.2 kΩ *(Eq 8)*

2. Base current, $I_b = I_{cq} / \beta$ = 33 µA *(Eq 7)*

3. Current through R1 and R2 = $10 I_b$ = 330 µA *(a rule of thumb simplifying calculations and keeping I_b stable with a "stiff" bias supply).*

4. Voltage across R2 = $V_{be} + I_c R_e$ = 0.7 + 5 mA (1.2 kΩ) = 6.7 V *(Eq 9)*

R2 = 6.7 V / 330 µA = 20.3 kΩ (use 22 kΩ). *(Ohm's Law)*

5. Voltage across R1 = V_{cc} – 6.7 V = 5.3 V. *(Voltage divider)*

R1 = 5.3 V / 330 µA = 16.06 kΩ (use 15 kΩ). *(Ohm's Law)*

$Z_{in} = 1 / [1/R1 + 1/R2 + 1/R_e (\beta + 1)] \approx 8.5$ kΩ *(Eq 4)*

Assuming R_s = 50 Ω, $Z_{out} \approx r_e // R_e$ = 5 Ω // 1.2 k$\Omega \approx 4.99$ Ω *(Eq 5 and 6)*

That's where our emitter follower shines!

Testing the Amplifier

Connect the power supply after double-checking all connections, especially the transistor leads. Figure 2 shows the breadboard circuit.

1. Use a VOM to measure the dc voltage from collector to emitter (it should be about 6 V), from base to emitter (0.6 – 0.7 V) and from emitter to ground (6 V). Replace R1 with a 100 kΩ potentiometer, set to 15 kΩ. Start with a value of 10 kΩ for R_{load}.

2. Set the signal generator to output a 1 kHz sine wave at 1 V_{p-p}, then connect it to C_{in}. You should see a sine wave at the output of C_{out} with an amplitude of about 1 V_{p-p} and in phase with the input. (A VOM measuring ac voltage will show 700 mV rms at the input and output.)

3. You will find later that the emitter follower has a very high bandwidth. This can lead to oscillation at several hundred kHz or higher, if you're not careful. This instability is visible as the "fuzzy" oscilloscope trace shown in Figure 3. Those of you using voltmeters only might see intermittent or jumpy ac signal voltages. It's important to keep input leads away from output leads and use the single-point ground as shown in the breadboard circuit of Figure 2. Sometimes, just moving the leads around will cause the oscillation to start and stop, so don't be afraid to experiment.

4. Increase the input signal to 5 V_{p-p}. Adjust R1 in each direction and observe the output signal with the oscilloscope. As you lower the collector current (V_b decreasing), you will see the output waveform clip on negative peaks as the collector current is cut off. Raising collector current will eventually result in distortion on positive peaks as the transistor enters saturation.

5. Substitute 1 kΩ, 100 Ω, and 10 Ω resistors for R_{load}, reducing the input voltage at each value, so that the output waveform remains undistorted. Lower resistance loads can only be driven at lower voltages because the ac currents in the transistor are much higher at lower values of load resistance. You can read about ac load lines in the reference texts for a detailed explanation. You'll also see the output signal begin to "lag" behind the input signal at these low load values. Why? The impedance of the output coupling capacitor at 1 kHz becomes significant for loads below 100 Ω, introducing phase shift in a series RC circuit.

6. If the input power is $(V_{in})^2 / Z_{in}$ and the output power is $(V_{out})^2 / R_{load}$, compute the power gain of the amplifier for the maximum undistorted values of input and output voltage at the different loads.

Power Gain = $P_{out} / P_{in} = [(V_{out})^2/R_{load}]/[(V_{in})^2/Z_{in})]$　　[10]

If $V_{in} \approx V_{out}$, then power gain = Z_{in} / R_{load} ! See how closely this approximation agrees with your measurements.

7. Now that you have a working circuit—experiment with it!

• Rework the math for a Q-point with 5 times more and 10 times less collector current. Calculate Z_{in} and Z_{out} for those currents.

• Raise the input frequency to see if you can find where the gain drops to 70% of the peak value; this is the upper –3 dB frequency of the amplifier.

• Drive both the CE and EF amplifiers with a square-wave at the highest frequency your generator can reach, using a 1 kΩ load resistor. Use the 'scope to determine which circuit will follow the input more accurately thus indicating wider bandwidth.

Suggested Reading

• "Transistor Amplifier Design—A Practical Approach" in Chapter 8 of *The ARRL Handbook*.

• "Low-Frequency Transistor Models" in Chapter 10 of The *ARRL Handbook*.

• For a more complete discussion of the Emitter-Follower amplifier, check out Chapter 2 of *The Art of Electronics*, by Horowitz and Hill.

Shopping List

You'll need the following components:

• 100 kΩ potentiometer.

• ¼ W resistors of the following values: 10 Ω, 100 Ω, 1 kΩ, 1.2 kΩ, 10 kΩ, 15 kΩ, 22 kΩ.

• 2-10 µF capacitors with a voltage rating of 25 V dc or more (electrolytic or tantalum are fine).

• 2N3904 transistor.

Next Month

We shift gears next month to operational amplifiers—usually known by their nickname "op amps." Be prepared to buffer, invert, add and subtract!

Experiment #6—Rectifiers and Zener References

Background

This month begins a three-part series of experiments on power supply circuits. We'll start with a basic rectifier and a Zener diode voltage reference. In the second step we'll experiment with some voltage multipliers. Finally, we'll design a linear voltage regulator.

Terms to Learn

- *Anode*—diode electrode into which current flows.[1]
- *Cathode*—diode electrode out of which current flows.
- *Half-wave or Full-wave*—rectification during one-half of or an entire ac cycle, respectively.
- *Peak Inverse or Reverse Voltage (PIV or PRV)*—the maximum voltage from cathode to anode a diode can safely withstand.
- *Avalanche Breakdown / Conduction*—current flow from cathode to anode when a diode's PIV or Zener voltage is exceeded.

The Basic Rectifier

The term *rectifier* can refer to either a semiconductor device (a diode) or to a circuit. Both convert alternating current (ac) into direct current (dc). The diode performs no other function besides controlling current flow, while the rectifier circuit may include several other functions. For this experiment, the term *rectifier* will refer to the circuit.

For a diode to be used in a power rectifier, we need to know two basic things about it: its PIV and its average forward current ratings. Diodes convert ac to dc by preventing current flow from cathode to anode. If ac is applied to a diode, current will flow only during the half-cycle in which the voltage from anode to cathode is positive.

During the non-conducting half-cycle, the diode blocks current flow as long as the voltage from cathode to anode does not exceed the PIV rating. At higher voltages, the diode will begin to conduct in its reverse mode and may suffer damage.

The diode's average current rating specifies how much power the diode can dissipate while conducting current without overheating. When conducting, a regular P-N silicon diode will have about 0.7 V *forward voltage drop* from anode to cathode[2] and will dissipate a power of $(0.7 \text{ V} \times I_{avg})$ W.

Now let's go on to the rectifier. Figure 1 shows three types of diode-based rectifier circuits—a half-wave, a full-wave center-tapped and a full-wave bridge. In our experiments, we'll use a function generator as an ac signal source, but the principles are the same for a transformer in a real power supply. We'll use 1 kHz (1000 Hz) as our ac frequency (because it's convenient and the filter components are smaller)—a transformer in a real power supply will usually be operating at the ac power line frequency of 60 Hz (as commonly used in the Western Hemisphere). Resistor R_L is the load.

The half-wave rectifier with its single diode can only supply current to the load during one-half of each applied ac cycle—thus the term *half-wave*. The full-wave center-tapped requires two out-of-phase voltage sources with a common center connection, such as a transformer's center-tapped secondary winding. Each source supplies current to the load on opposite half-cycles—thus the term *full-wave*—and doubling the output voltage.

The full-wave bridge achieves full-wave rectification by using an extra pair of diodes. On the first half-cycle, the full-wave bridge conducts through D1 and D3. On the next half-cycle, D1 and D3 are *reverse-biased* and don't conduct current, while D2 and D4 are *forward-biased* and supply current to the load.

[1]Notes appear on page 58.

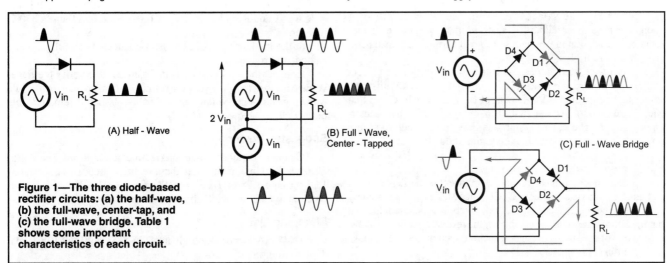

Figure 1—The three diode-based rectifier circuits: (a) the half-wave, (b) the full-wave, center-tap, and (c) the full-wave bridge. Table 1 shows some important characteristics of each circuit.

(A) Half - Wave

(B) Full - Wave, Center - Tapped

(C) Full - Wave Bridge

Table 1

Important Characteristics of Rectifier Circuits (V_{in} is the input RMS voltage and I_{avg} is the average load current)

Rectifier Type	Number of Diodes	Average Output Voltage	Power Loss	Diode PIV Required
Half-Wave	1	$0.45 \, V_{in}$	$0.7 \times I_{avg}$	$2.8 \, V_{in}$
Full-Wave, Center-Tap	2	$0.9 \, V_{in}$	$0.7 \times I_{avg}$	$2.8 \, V_{in}$
Full-Wave Bridge	4	$0.9 \, V_{in}$	$2 \times 0.7 \times I_{avg}$	$1.4 \, V_{in}$

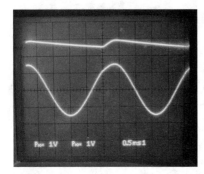

Figure 2—The bottom trace in this photograph shows the sine wave input from the signal generator. The upper trace shows the voltage across the load with a 1 µF capacitor. Note that the charging peaks in the upper trace correspond to the positive peaks of the input voltage.

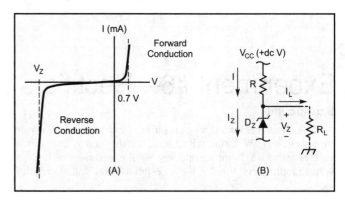

Figure 3 (A)—The Zener diode's current-voltage characteristics. Current from anode to cathode is considered to be positive or forward current and voltage from anode to cathode is positive. (B)—A common circuit for making a voltage reference with a Zener diode.

Testing the Half-Wave Rectifier

• Because function generator outputs usually have a ground-referenced output, we will only test the half-wave rectifier. Build the half-wave circuit of Figure 1a using a 1N4148 diode and a 3.9 kΩ load resistor.

• Set the function generator to output a sine wave of 5 V_{peak} (3.5 V_{rms} on the DMM's ac scale) at 1 kHz. The DMM will show about 1.3 V dc across the load resistor. An oscilloscope will show the load voltage pulsing on every positive half-cycle of the input sine wave. Note that the diode doesn't conduct for exactly one-half cycle because of the 0.7 V forward drop.

• Connect a 1 µF capacitor with at least a 10 V rating in parallel with the resistor. The DMM will show a load voltage of about 3.6 V dc because the capacitor stores energy during the non-conducting half-cycles. The 'scope will show the load voltage as a series of short ramps (as the capacitor charges through the diode) followed by long ramps (as the capacitor discharges through the resistor). This can be seen in Figure 2.

• Experiment by trying different input voltages, load resistors, and capacitors. Try different input waveforms—square and triangle waves, for example. Observe the shape of the charging ramp as you try different waveforms. If you have a function generator with a ground-independent (or *floating*) output, try building the full-wave bridge rectifier.

Rectifier Characteristics

Why would one select a particular rectifier circuit over another? There are certain differences, or *trade-offs*, in the characteristics of each that make them suitable in various circumstances, as shown in Table 1.

The full-wave bridge, because it has two diodes in the current path, is dissipating twice the power of the half-wave and full-wave center-tapped rectifiers. The benefit of the full-wave bridge is that each diode needs only one-half the PIV rating of a full-wave, center-tapped circuit. The other two circuits have fewer diodes and less power dissipation, but they require higher diode PIV ratings.

Zener Diodes

Another important power supply component is the Zener diode, named after American physicist Dr Clarence M. Zener. If an ordinary diode's PIV rating is exceeded, the diode enters avalanche conduction, but the Zener is designed to conduct in the reverse direction at a low, but stable voltage. In the normal, forward direction, the Zener looks like an ordinary diode.

The Zener is a very useful voltage reference. Figure 3 shows that even though the reverse current through the Zener may change substantially, the voltage across the diode changes very little. In the circuit of Figure 3, if enough current (I_z) is supplied to the diode through R, small amounts may be drawn by R_L without affecting the Zener voltage.

Using a Zener diode as a voltage reference requires several simple design steps:
1) Add up the currents that will be used by the load—this is I_L.
2) Determine the supply voltage, V_{cc}, and the Zener's power rating, P_z.

3) Select a current I_z so that $P_z = V_z \times I_z$ is, at most, less than one-half of the Zener's rated power—this is for safety and to keep the Zener voltage from changing with temperature.
4) Find I by adding I_L and I_z. Use Ohm's Law to find R.
   R = (minimum $V_{cc} - V_z$) / I

By using this procedure, R is set so that even at the minimum value of supply voltage, there is enough current to supply the Zener and the loading circuitry. Give it a try!

Testing a Voltage Reference

• Use a 12 V supply voltage (V_{cc} minimum is 12 V) and a 5.1 V 1N4733A 1 W Zener diode. (The letter following the Zener type number usually refers to the Zener's voltage tolerance, "A" being ±10%, "B" being ±5% and no following letter being ±20%.) Assume that the circuitry loading the voltage will draw 1 mA.

• Follow the design procedure, limiting the Zener's power dissipation to 100 mW.

5.1 V × I_z = 100 mW, so I_z = 19.6 mA. Now, I = 19.6 + 1 mA = 20.6 mA and R = (12 – 5.1 V) / 20.6 mA = 335 Ω; use a 330 Ω resistor.

For the load, use a 5.1 kΩ resistor connected from the Zener's cathode to ground.

• Connect the components as in Figure 3B and verify the Zener voltage is close to 5.1 V. Vary the supply voltage up and down while watching the Zener voltage on a DMM—it should remain stable until V_{cc} falls below $V_z + (I \times R)$.

Suggested Reading

• Chapters 8 (diodes) and 11 (rectifier circuits) of *The ARRL Handbook* go into great detail about rectifier circuits as do sections 1.25 through 1.28 of *The Art of Electronics*. The Web site for our series is: **www.arrl.org/tis/info/html/hands-on-radio/**.

Shopping List

• 1N4733A Zener (RadioShack 276-565) and 1N4148 signal diodes (RadioShack 276-1122)
• 1 µF, 16 V capacitor
• 330 Ω, 3.9 kΩ, 5.1 kΩ ¼ W resistors

Next month we'll learn about the voltage multiplier. From tiny diodes and capacitors, mighty voltages come!

Notes
[1]Electronics texts typically use "conventional current" or the flow of positive charge. The actual flow of electrons or "electronic current," is in the opposite direction.

[2]Other types of diodes, such as PIN, Schottky, or those made from germanium have different forward voltage drops when conducting.

Experiment #9—Designing Drivers

Transistors make great switches as well as amplifiers. In fact, computers are built of millions of transistors acting as switches. Any circuit that controls or supplies power to a heavy load is called a *driver*. In this experiment we will learn how to make a transistor switch that can turn a heavy load on and off reliably. (Thanks to George, KF6VSG, for suggesting the topic.)

Terms to Learn

- *Cutoff*—the point at which collector current reaches zero
- *Linear Region*—when a transistor is operating between cutoff and saturation, it is in its linear region.
- *Saturation*—the point at which increases in base current do not cause a further increase in collector current
- *Transconductance*—the change in output current in response to a change in input voltage

The Transistor as a Switch

The goal when designing amplifiers is to make the transistor's collector current linearly and faithfully follow (proportionally) its base current. This requires that the transistor stay within its *linear region*—conducting some current at all times. A switch has completely different properties—its output current is either zero or some maximum value. Figure 1 shows both a bipolar and metal-oxide semiconductor field-effect transistor (or MOSFET) switch circuit. You'll notice that there are no bias resistors in either circuit.

Before we proceed, a primer on the MOSFET—just "FET" from here on—is in order. The FET drain corresponds to the bipolar collector, the gate to the base and the source to the emitter. The FET's drain-to-source current, I_{DS}, is controlled by the gate-to-source voltage, V_{GS}.

Similar to the NPN or PNP bipolar transistor, the FET comes in N-channel and P-channel flavors. (The arrowhead points into the symbol for N-channel devices.) Unlike the bipolar transistor, the FET has both depletion and enhancement modes. An enhancement mode device is similar to a bipolar transistor—it does not conduct without an input signal. In an enhancement-mode FET, as V_{GS} increases, so does I_{DS}. The depletion mode acts just the opposite. The FET symbol in Figure 1 is of an N-channel, enhancement mode device.

When a bipolar transistor's collector current reaches zero, the transistor is said to be in cutoff. As base current increases, so will collector current until the transistor reaches saturation. In saturation, collector current can't increase any further, even if base current is increased, and V_{CE} is at its minimum value. The analogous states in a FET are called *fully on* and *fully off*. The voltage and current waveforms below the circuit show how the load current reacts to V_{IN}.

Since the FET uses voltage to control its drain current, forward transconductance, g_{fs} measures the effect of the control signal.

$$g_{fs} = \Delta I_D / \Delta V_{GS} \qquad [1]$$

This parameter has the same units (Siemens, S) as conductance, which is the reciprocal of resistance (1/R). One can think of the FET acting as a voltage-controlled resistor, with g_{fs} showing how much the resistance value changes in response to changes in the gate voltage.

Designing Driver Circuits

First, select a transistor that can handle the load current and dissipate whatever power is lost as heat. Second, be sure that the input signal source can supply an adequate input signal (drive). You must meet both of these conditions to ensure reliable driver operation.

To choose the proper transistor, the load current and supply voltage must both be known. The supply voltage often varies widely. For example, a car's 12 V dc power bus may vary from 9 to 18 V dc, depending on battery condition and the state of the vehicle's charging system. The transistor must withstand the maximum supply voltage, V_{MAX}, when it is off.

The load resistance, R_L, must also be known. The maximum current the switch must handle is:

$$I_{MAX} = V_{MAX} / R_L \qquad [2]$$

Beware of surge currents at turn-on. Loads with capacitors may temporarily act like short circuits at turn-on. Also beware of voltage transients or "spikes" during switching. Inductive loads will present high voltages during the switch period (Remember that, for an inductor, V = L di/dt—the faster we try to change current through it, the higher the voltage). Your driver will therefore have to handle any current surges or voltage spikes induced by the load. ("Snubber" circuits, consisting of a clamp diode and a resistor-capacitor network, are frequently used to protect the driver from the spikes of inductive loads.) If you are using a bipolar transistor, you now can calculate how much base current you must supply to the switch:

$$I_B = I_{MAX} / \beta$$

β changes with collector current (it usually decreases as I_C increases), so use a value for β with I_C near I_{MAX}. This is specified on the transistor's data sheet. Using the *minimum* value for the input voltage, calculate the value of R_B:

$$R_B = (V_{INmin} - V_{BE}) / I_B \qquad [3]$$

The minimum value of input voltage must be used to accommodate the *worst-case* combination of circuit voltages and currents.

Designing with an FET is a little easier because the manufacturer usually specifies what the value of V_{GS} must be for the transistor to be fully on. The FET's gate, being insulated from the conducting channel, acts like a small capacitor of a few hundred pF and draws very little dc current. R_G in Figure 1 is required if the input voltage source does not actually output 0 V when off, such as a switch connected to a positive voltage. The FET won't turn off reliably if its gate is allowed to "float." R_G pulls the gate voltage to zero if the input is open-circuited. The input source must be able to supply current of V_{GS}/R_G.

Power dissipation is the next design hurdle. Even if the transistors are turned completely on, they will still dissipate some heat. Just as for a resistor, the switch power dissipation is:

$$P_D = V_{CE} I_C = V_{CEsat} I_{MAX} \text{ (for a bipolar transistor)} \qquad [4]$$

and

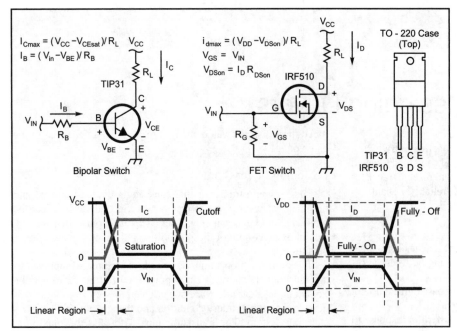

Figure 1—A pair of transistor driver circuits using a bipolar transistor and a MOSFET. The input and output signals show the linear, cutoff and saturation regions. The basing diagram for the TO-220 package is to the right.

Table 1

Comparison of Bipolar and MOSFET Power Transistors

Transistor Parameter (Typical Values)	TIP 31	IRF510
V_{CEsat}	1.2 V	N/A
R_{DSon}	N/A	0.4 Ω
V_{BE} or V_{GSon}	1.8 V	10 V
I_C or I_D	3.0 A	3.0 A
β or g_{fs}	25@I_C = 1 A	2 S (A/V)
P_{Dmax}	40 W	20 W

$$P_D = V_{DS} I_D = R_{DSon} I_{MAX}^2 \text{ (for a FET)} \quad [5]$$

R_{DSon} is the resistance of the channel from drain to source when the FET is on. Modern FETs have a very low on-resistance, but still dissipate power when driving a heavy load. Some FETs have gotten so good, however, that their on-resistance is now below 2 milliohms (that's 0.002 Ω!). To put this in perspective, some modern power MOSFETs can handle 20 A of current, dissipate less than 1 W and not require a heat sink under moderate ambient conditions! Look at the transistor's data sheet for the manufacturer's R_{DSon} specification.

Power dissipation is why a switching transistor needs to be kept out of its linear region. When it's turned off or fully on, either the current through the transistor or the voltage across it is low, thus keeping the product of voltage and current (dissipated power) low. As the waveforms in Figure 1 show, while in the linear region, both voltage and current have significant values and the transistor is generating heat. It's important to make the transition through the linear region quick enough to keep the transistor cool.

Once you have calculated the power dissipation the switch must handle, you must check to see whether the transistor can withstand it. The manufacturer of the transistor will specify a *free-air dissipation* that assumes no heat-sink and room-temperature (ambient) air circulating freely around the transistor. This should be at least 50 percent higher than your calculated power dissipation. If not, you must either use a larger

transistor or provide a heat sink. Let's make a driver!

Testing a Driver Circuit

• We're going to use a 25 Ω power resistor as a 0.5 A load, much like a heavy-duty solenoid or a small motor. Bipolar and MOSFET drivers will use a 12 V input signal. Table 1 shows the typical rating for two popular transistors.

• Solder the two 50 Ω resistors in parallel to create the load. Don't use your prototype board for this experiment due to the large currents—temporarily solder components together by their leads or use a terminal strip. The power supply should be able to deliver 12 V at 1 A.

• For the TIP31, if the collector current is to be 0.5 A and β is 25, base current must be at least 0.5/25 = 20 mA. From equation 3, the value of R_B = (12 – 1.8)/0.02 = 510 Ω.

• For the IRF510, since 10 V of gate drive is needed, the 12 V input signal can be used directly. Use a 4.7 kΩ resistor for R_G.

• Use equations 4 and 5 to calculate power dissipation for each transistor:
 TIP31: $P_D = 1.2 \times 0.5 = 0.6$ W
 IRF510: $P_D = 0.6 \times (0.5)^2 = 0.15$ W
 Load: $P_D = 25 \times (0.5)^2 = 6$ W — it will get warm, so keep it in the clear!

• Power up the circuit and use your voltmeter to check all of the transistor voltages. Load current can be calculated by measuring the voltage across the load and using Ohm's Law.

• Vary the amount of input current (TIP31) or voltage (IRF510) and observe the effect on the transistor's ability to drive the load. The base current can be varied by changing the value of R_B. The gate voltage can be varied by using a 20 kΩ potentiometer in series with R_G as a voltage divider.

• Place the transistor in its linear region for a short period by reducing the input signal and see how hot it gets—careful! You'll see why it's important to supply adequate drive.

Suggested Reading

Chapter 8 of *The 2004 ARRL Handbook* discusses both bipolar and MOSFET transistor construction. Chapter 3 of *The Art of Electronics*, by Horowitz and Hill, has a good section on power MOSFET switches and Chapter 6 reviews heat sinking. A list of Web links with technical tutorial information can be found on the Hands-On Radio Web site: **www.arrl.org/tis/info/html/hands-on-radio/**.

Shopping List

• TIP31 bipolar power transistor (RadioShack 276-2017), IRF510 MOSFET (RadioShack 276-2072)
• 1 package (2) of 50 Ω, 10 W resistors (RadioShack 271-133)
• 510 Ω, 4.7 kΩ ¼ W resistors
• 20 kΩ potentiometer

Next Month

As long as we're experimenting with power control, this would be a good opportunity to explore the SCR—a thyristor that acts like a switch and is widely used for ac power control and switching.

Experiment #10—Using SCRs

Thyristors—what a strange word! What do they do? Thyristors are common components found around the ham shack in power supplies and ac control circuits. They are solid-state replacements for *thyratrons*—tubes that act as current switches. Like transistors, a small current can switch a much larger current. In this experiment, we'll use the most common thyristor—a silicon-controlled rectifier or *SCR*—to control both ac and dc.

Terms to Learn

* *Breakover* and *breakdown voltage*—the voltages at which an SCR begins to conduct current without gate drive from anode-to-cathode (forward) and cathode-to-anode (reverse), respectively.
* *Conduction angle*—the number of degrees of an ac cycle during which the SCR is conducting forward current.
* *Holding current* (I_H)—the amount of forward current required to keep an SCR conducting.
* *Latch*—to change state and remain in that state.

How the SCR Works

The SCR has an NPN transistor's layered structure of N and P-type material but adds one additional P-type layer as shown in Figure 1. Starting at the cathode and moving left, you see what looks like the three layers of a regular NPN transistor. The extra P-type layer then creates a PN-diode at the anode. The SCR "looks like" a rectifier attached to an NPN transistor.

The SCR operates in just two states: ON and OFF. When OFF, the SCR acts like an open-circuit to voltages between the anode and cathode as long as the value is less than either the breakover or breakdown voltages. The SCR will remain OFF until gate-to-cathode current reaches the *gate trigger current*, I_{GT}, or *gate turn-on voltage*, V_{GTO}, at which point forward current flows from the anode to cathode and the SCR is ON.

It's important to understand that while the SCR is turned ON by gate current, it can't be turned OFF the same way. Once ON, the SCR is *latched* ON until forward current falls below the *holding current*, I_{HO}, when it resets to the OFF state. Forward current will fall below I_{HO} when the power source stops supplying or the load stops drawing current. In an ac circuit, the reversal of voltage across the SCR stops current flow.

Demonstrating SCR Functions

This is unfamiliar territory for many electronic designers, so let's start with a simple experiment that demonstrates the basic SCR functions to discharge a capacitor into a load.

* Construct the circuit of Figure 2. Don't use your prototype board; either solder the components together or use a terminal or barrier strip. A clip lead or jumper wire can be used for the switches.
* Open S2 then close S1. Connect the 12 V power supply. Monitor voltage across the capacitor to be sure it charges to 12 V. No voltage should appear across the 100 Ω load resistor.
* Open S1, leaving the charged capacitor connected to the SCR. Monitor voltage across the load resistor while *momentarily* closing S2. (If you leave S2 closed, gate current will continue to flow, overheating the 47 Ω resistor.) You will see a pulse of voltage across the load resistor as the capacitor discharges through it. The duration of the pulse will be approximately R × C = 100 × 9400 µF = 0.94 seconds.
* Observe the trailing edge of the pulse as the capacitor discharges. You will see load voltage abruptly drop to zero as current through the SCR falls below I_{HO}. This will happen with capacitor voltage around 2.2 V due to the 1.8 V forward voltage drop of the SCR, which leaves only 30-40 mA flowing in the load resistor. (This is clearest if you are able to monitor both capacitor and load voltage.)
* As soon as load voltage drops to zero, indicating that the SCR is reset, you can close S1 again to repeat the cycle.
* Experiment with the circuit by increasing the value of the gate resistor until the SCR no longer triggers. Similarly, if the load resistance is increased, maximum current will fall below I_{HO} and the capacitor will no longer discharge through the SCR.

Designing with SCRs

The circuit you just tested is similar to over-voltage protection circuits found in dc power supplies, called *crowbars*. A heavy-duty SCR is connected directly across the power supply output and triggered to act as a short circuit if the output voltage gets too high. SCRs can handle a large surge current, so this either trips the supply's current limit circuit or blows a fuse. Either way, equipment connected to the supply is not subjected to excessive voltage.

Another popular use of SCRs is in ac circuits that control power to a load such as a light bulb dimmer or motor speed control. The circuit of Figure 3A shows a simple dimmer circuit. Starting with the gate control potentiometer set to a high value, the SCR remains OFF over the entire ac cycle. As the control resistance is reduced,

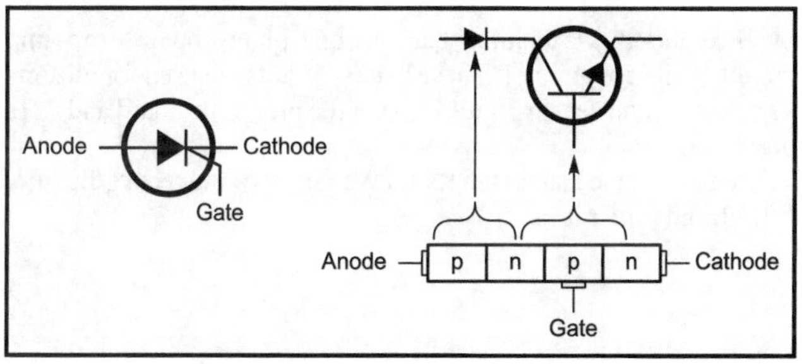

Figure 1—The internal construction shows that the SCR may be thought of as a rectifier in series with an NPN transistor.

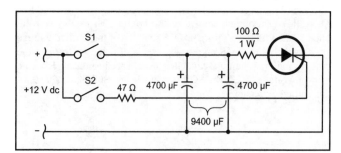

Figure 2—A simple charge-dumping circuit. The capacitor discharges through the load resistor and the SCR when a current pulse through the gate turns the SCR ON.

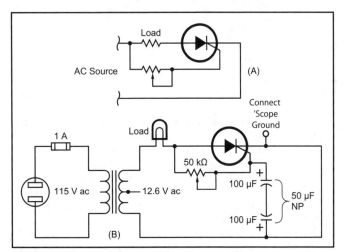

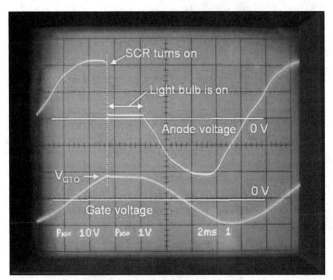

Figure 3—An RC-controlled dimmer circuit. To run this circuit at 115 V ac, the capacitor value can be reduced by a factor of 10 or more.

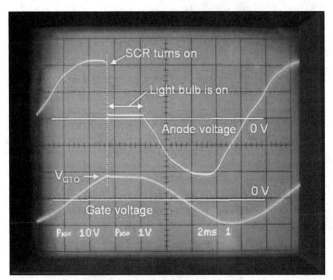

Figure 4—The SCR anode and gate voltages show a conduction angle of about 65°.

eventually enough current enters the SCR gate at the very peak of the ac cycle, turning it ON for the duration of the positive half-cycle. As the control's resistance is reduced further, the SCR turns ON at lower and lower voltages, conducting over more of the positive half-cycle and delivering more power to the load.

In Figure 3B, the load—a light bulb—has been moved to the supply side of the potentiometer and a gate capacitor has been added. This allows smoother control of the *conduction angle*. Starting once again with the SCR in the OFF state, all of the applied voltage appears across the SCR and the gate capacitor charges through the potentiometer. When the capacitor has charged to the SCR's gate turn-on voltage, V_{GTO}, the SCR turns ON. The SCR stays ON until the voltage reverses.

By choosing the right values for the potentiometer and capacitor, the SCR's conduction angle can be varied from about 30°, turning on near the end of the positive half-cycle, to almost 180°, conducting over the entire positive half-cycle. Ready to try it for real?

Testing a Dimmer Circuit

- Construct the circuit of Figure 3B taking special care with the ac supply. All 115 V_{rms} line circuits must be insulated and fused. Use a ground-fault interrupter (GFI) circuit, if possible. The gate capacitor must be nonpolarized and is constructed from two electrolytic caps connected back to back with opposing polarities.
- Set the potentiometer to its maximum value. Monitor SCR anode voltage and gate capacitor voltage with an oscilloscope. Connect a voltmeter across the light bulb set to measure ac voltage. Power up the circuit. The light bulb should be OFF. You will observe a small ac voltage across the gate capacitor. Connect the 'scope ground to the SCR cathode.
- Slowly reduce the potentiometer value until voltage across the light bulb begins to increase. You will see the gate capacitor voltage increasing to V_{GTO} (about 1 V) at which point the SCR turns ON. Continue decreasing the potentiometer resistance. The gate capacitor will charge to V_{GTO} faster and the SCR will conduct over more of the ac cycle, increasing bulb brightness and the voltage across it. Figure 4 shows one ac cycle of the SCR gate and anode voltage.
- Try to maximize the range of the SCR's conduction angle by changing the gate capacitor or control pot values. A 25 kΩ pot and 100 µF capacitors worked best for the SCR I used.

Suggested Reading

The amateur literature is sparse in the area of thyristors, but manufacturers offer detailed design and application information. The Teccor Electronics Web site has an excellent series of downloadable application notes on thyristors at **www.teccor.com/web/menuitems/downloads/appnotes.htm**. The classic, but old data book by RCA—the *Transistor, Thyristor and Diode Manual*—also has an excellent tutorial section on thyristor basics.

Shopping List

- SCR—RadioShack 276-1067, 267-1020 or similar.
- 115 V_{rms} to 12.6 V_{rms} power transformer—RadioShack 273-1365 or similar.
- Two 4700 µF @ 16 V or greater, two 100 µF @ 16 V or greater capacitors.
- 100 Ω-1 W, 47 Ω-¼ W resistors.
- 50 kΩ potentiometer—RadioShack 271-1716.
- 12 V incandescent lamp—RadioShack 900-2665 or similar.

Next Month

Next month we'll jump back to one of my favorite op-amp circuits—the comparator. These handy circuits are used for all sorts of detection and sensing duties, so get the prototype board and 741s dusted off!

Remember the Hands-On Radio Web site: **www.arrl.org/tis/info/html/hands-on-radio/**.

Experiment #12—Field Effect Transistors

Welcome to the second year of "Hands-On Radio." After an introduction and 11 experiments, we've covered a lot of ground but it seems like we've only scratched the surface! Radio electronics is a pretty broad field, so there are lots of experiment topics remaining.

The field effect transistor, or FET, is an attractive replacement for bipolar transistors in switches and amplifiers. Why? The FET offers high input impedance, excellent gain, and easy biasing. We'll revisit the first "Hands-On Radio" experiment and find out how these characteristics fit the common-emitter design.

Terms to Learn

- *Transconductance*—The measure of change in output current caused by a change in input voltage.
- *Channel*—The semiconductor material between an FET drain and source through which current flows.
- *Enhancement and depletion mode*—In enhancement-mode FETs, increasing gate voltage causes channel conductivity to increase. For depletion-mode FETs, the opposite is true.
- *On-resistance*—The drain-to-source resistance of an FET's channel at maximum conductivity.

Background

While you may know that John Bardeen, Walter Brattain and William Shockley constructed the first bipolar transistor in 1948, you may not know that the idea behind the FET was patented in 1926 by Julius Lilienfield. A working (but very slow) amplifier was made using salt by Robert Pohl in 1938. The FET is actually the oldest transistor and its operation is much closer to the vacuum tube than the bipolar transistor.

Figure 1 shows the rudimentary construction and symbols for the two primary types of FETs, the junction FET (JFET) and the metal-oxide-semiconductor FET (MOSFET), that we met in experiment #9. Metal electrodes attach leads to the semiconductor material. The junction in a JFET is formed by the different material types (P and N) of the gate and the channel. MOS describes the construction of the gate; a metal electrode coating an insulating layer of oxide (usually quartz, silicon dioxide or SiO_2) which, in turn, contacts the channel material directly. FET and bipolar transistors have terminals with similar functions—gate and base, collector and drain, and emitter and source.

Where the bipolar transistor uses input current to control output current, the FET uses input voltage. In place of the bipolar transistor's pair of P-N junctions placed back-to-back between collector and emitter, the FET has a *channel* of either P-type or N-type material. In the bipolar transistor, current flows from the base to emitter, controlling current flow through the two P-N junctions. In the FET, gate voltage changes the conductivity of the channel and so the current flowing between drain and source also changes. Very little current flows in the gate of an FET.

Like the bipolar transistor's NPN and PNP devices, the FET comes in different flavors, but it has *four* instead of two. Figure 1 shows N-channel devices, but the channels can be made of either N or P-type material and the device can be designed so that increasing gate voltage causes more or less current to flow in the channel. If more channel current flows with increasing gate voltage, it is an *enhancement-mode* device. Conversely, *depletion-mode* devices have less current with increasing gate voltage. The most widely used device is the N-channel enhancement-mode FET.

The change in output current caused by a change in input voltage is called *transconductance*. Analogous to a bipolar transistor's current gain or beta, its symbol is g_m and its units are siemens (S) because it measures the ratio of current to voltage.[1] The input voltage, V_{GS}, is measured between the FET gate and source. The output current, I_{DS}, flows from drain to source.

$$g_m = \Delta I_{DS} / \Delta V_{GS} \text{ and } \Delta I_{DS} = g_m \Delta V_{GS} \qquad [Eq 1]$$

The voltage gain of the FET amplifier in Figure 2 depends on the FET transconductance because varying the current in the FET drain causes a varying voltage across the drain resistance. The model for the FET is the variable resistive divider shown in Figure 2A, with V_{GS} controlling the value of R_{DS}. If V_O is measured at the drain terminal (just as the common-emitter output voltage is measured at the collector), then

$$\Delta V_O = -\Delta I_{DS} R1 = -g_m \Delta V_{GS} R1 \qquad [Eq 2]$$

Substituting this relationship gives voltage gain in terms of transconductance and the drain load:

$$A_V = \Delta V_O / \Delta V_{GS} = -g_m R1 \qquad [Eq 3]$$

[1]Siemens (pronounced "see-mins") is the international unit for conductance, formerly mhos. Its symbol is a capital "S" and 1 siemens = 1 A/V.

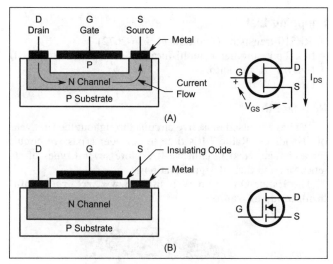

Figure 1—JFET (A) and MOSFET (B) construction are shown along with their symbols. N-channel, enhancement-mode devices are shown.

Figure 2—(A) A MOSFET common-source amplifier can be modeled as a variable voltage divider between the drain load and the FET. (B) A simple MOSFET amplifier with a voltage divider for supplying gate bias.

The minus sign results from the output voltage decreasing as drain current increases, just as with the common-emitter amplifier.

A key difference between the FET and bipolar transistor is that the channel of an FET acts like a variable resistance. That means that drain-to-source voltage can become quite low—lower than a completely saturated bipolar transistor's V_{CE}. Note that the *on-resistance* for power FETs can be very low—in the milliohm range. This allows them to switch heavy loads while dissipating little power. In amplifiers, this also allows more output voltage swing.

Another important parameter of FETs is the gate-to-source voltage at which no more current flows through the channel. This is called the *pinch-off voltage*, V_P. Imagine the gate voltage as a pair of fingers tightening or loosening around a hose carrying a stream of water and you'll have a pretty good idea of the mechanics involved. When V_{GS} reaches V_P, the area of the channel through which current flows is reduced to zero. Depending on the type of FET, V_P can be positive or negative. Switching MOSFETs are generally designed to have V_P greater than zero to make interfacing with digital logic easier. The voltage at which the MOSFET begins to conduct current is usually shown as $V_{GS(TH)}$, the *gate threshold voltage*.

Testing a MOSFET Common-Source Amplifier

This experiment will use a common switching MOSFET, the IRF510. This is a large transistor capable of handling several amps of drain current, but it demonstrates the mechanics of MOSFET amplifiers well. You may want to download the data sheet for the transistor.[2]

- When using a single power supply, it's necessary to bias the gate so that output voltage can both increase and decrease. Bias is supplied by R_a and R_b which act as a voltage divider—$V_{GS} = R_b / (R_a + R_b)$. For the divider, use a 10 kΩ potentiometer with the wiper connected to the FET gate and the remaining leads connected to V+ and ground. Start with the potentiometer set so that the wiper is nearly at ground voltage. Leave the input signal source disconnected.
- The IRF510 can handle a lot of current, but we'll limit drain current to 12 mA by using a 1 kΩ resistor for R1.
- Monitor the FET drain voltage and slowly adjust the bias pot so that gate voltage increases. When the gate threshold voltage is reached, the FET will start conducting and drain voltage will fall rapidly to zero. Record the gate threshold voltage as well as the voltage when the FET drain is 1 V below V+ and 1 V above ground.

[2]The IRF510 data sheet may be downloaded from **www.rigelcorp. com/__doc/8051/IRF510.pdf**. (Note: There are two consecutive underscores prior to "doc.")

- Set the signal generator to output a 0.1 V_{p-p} 1 kHz sine wave. Set the bias voltage halfway between $V_{GS(TH)}$ and V+. Connect the input signal. Observe the output voltage and experiment by adjusting the bias voltage to get the largest undistorted output.
- Calculate voltage gain, $A_v = -$ (drain voltage change) / (gate voltage change) and transconductance, $g_m = - A_v / R1$. My FET showed a voltage gain of -18 and a transconductance of 0.018 S.
- Experiment by varying R1 and observing the effect on voltage gain. Readjust the bias setting and input voltage to get the maximum undistorted output voltage for each value of R1.

You may be asking yourself why your measured transconductance is so low compared to the specified minimum of 1.3 S in the data sheet. The answer lies in the graph of transconductance versus drain current (Figure 12 in the data sheet). The IRF510 transconductance is optimized for drain currents of several amperes and it falls off drastically at low currents.

Suggested Reading

Begin by reading the ARRL *Handbook* sections on FETs, beginning on pages 8.23 and 10.32. *The Art of Electronics* devotes all of Chapter 3 to FETs, with sections 3.07 and 3.08 covering amplifier design.

Shopping List

- IRF510 transistor (RadioShack 276-2072)
- 10 kΩ potentiometer (multi-turn preferred, but not required)
- Two 0.1 μF capacitors
- 1 kΩ, 1/4 W resistor

Next Month

We have focused on active circuits throughout the first year of "Hands-On Radio." It's time to consider a passive circuit for a change. Next month, we'll explore several types of attenuators and their design equations.

The Hands-On Radio Web site is **www.arrl.org/tis/info/ html/hands-on-radio/**.

Experiment #19: Current Sources

You may be familiar with the voltage source—a power source that maintains a constant voltage regardless of the current drawn—but its cousin, the current source, is nearly unknown. The current source is a mighty handy tool to have in your designer's toolbox and can be constructed in a number of different ways.

Terms to Learn

- *Compliance*—the range of output voltages over which a current source can maintain constant current.
- *Current-voltage characteristics*—a graph showing all of the combinations of voltage and current a power source can produce.
- *Internal impedance*—the power consuming elements inside a power source, usually shown as a single, equivalent resistance.

Background

Voltage and current sources are the twin power sources of electronics. Batteries and power supplies do a credible imitation of an ideal voltage source. They deliver nearly constant voltage over a wide range of load currents. The current source that delivers a constant current independent of output voltage isn't used to power equipment but is, nevertheless, quite common. Current sources are found in battery chargers, transistor bias and load circuits, and resistance meters, to name just three uses. We'll learn how to make a current source with a transistor, an op-amp or a voltage regulator, and I'll explain one of my favorite circuits, the current mirror.

Current-Voltage Characteristics

Practical power sources have limits: They can only supply so many watts, volts or amps. Figure 1 shows the *current-voltage characteristics* of ideal (dashed line) and real (gray line) voltage (VS) and current sources (CS). An *ideal* voltage source's output voltage, V_S, is the same at any current, whereas a real source's internal impedance, Z_{INT}, causes a voltage drop that gets bigger with current ($V_O = V_S - I_O \times Z_{INT}$). The sloping gray line, shown in Figure 1, gets farther from V_S as current increases. Power supplies usually also have a maximum current, I_{LIMIT}, at which they either shut down or blow up!

The ideal current source's internal impedance is infinite—it pumps out the same current no matter what the resulting output voltage has to be. For a real current source, as output voltage rises, more and more current flows through Z_{INT}, as shown by the sloping gray line of Figure 1 labeled CSREAL, leaving less for the load until the voltage limit is reached.

You'll never see the most common use for current sources—biasing transistors in analog ICs. This is an important function, as we saw in Experiments #1 and #2. You might use a current source every time you sit down at your workbench. Voltmeters send a known current through an unknown resistance and measure the resulting voltage, using Ohm's Law to calculate the resistance. Current sources are also used for battery charging where a constant current is required for trickle charging. Current sources—they're everywhere!

A Single Transistor Current Source

Figure 2A shows how a single PNP transistor can be wired to provide a relatively constant current. Because collector current (the load current) equals $I_B \times \beta$, the load current can be set with a single resistor, R. Base voltage equals $V_{CC} - V_{EB}$ (assumed to be 0.7 V), so $I_B = (V_{CC} - 0.7) / R$. Load current is also dependent

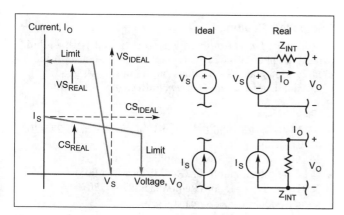

Figure 1—The current-voltage characteristics of ideal (dashed) and practical (gray) voltage and current sources. The symbols and equivalent circuits for the sources are shown to the right.

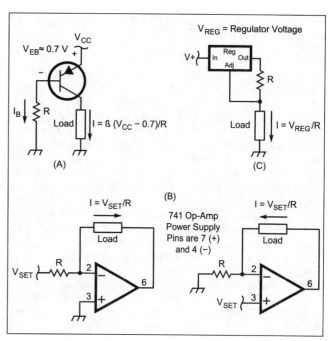

Figure 2—Three current source circuits. A single resistor sets the current for all three circuits. The circuit in A is quite dependent on V_{cc}, but those in B and C offer excellent current regulation.

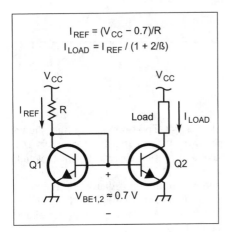

$$I_{REF} = (V_{CC} - 0.7)/R$$
$$I_{LOAD} = I_{REF} / (1 + 2/\beta)$$

Figure 3—The current mirror's collector currents are matched by making V_{BE} the same value in both transistors.

on V_{CC}, so a well-regulated supply must be used for this circuit.

Measure your transistor's beta if you can; otherwise, assume a value of 200 and we'll recalculate it. Let's design for a load current of 5 mA using a 12 V power supply. From the equation for I_B,

$$R = \beta (V_{CC} - 0.7) / 5 \text{ mA} = 452 \text{ k}\Omega \text{ (for } \beta = 200)$$

Use a value of 470 kΩ and build the circuit with a 1 kΩ load resistor. Measure current through the load resistor by either connecting your meter in series with it (remember to switch the leads to the current terminals) or by measuring voltage across it and using Ohm's Law.

If you assumed a value of 200 for β, load current is probably not exactly 5 mA. The actual value of beta can be calculated, using your measured base resistance and load current:

$$\beta = I_{LOAD} R / (V_{CC} - 0.7)$$

Vary the load resistance and make a graph of load current and voltage. Raise the load resistance until the voltage across it limits near V_{CC}. You can even short-circuit the load and the transistor will still put out only 5 mA!

Building a Floating Current Source

Sometimes, the load may not be grounded and that's when a *floating* current source is required, such as for a voltmeter. Figure 2B shows how to make such a current source by using an op-amp. The key is to remember that the high-gain of the op-amp forces the voltage at both the non-inverting (+) and inverting (−) terminals to be almost exactly the same, while allowing very little current to flow into its input pins.

In the right-hand circuit, the op-amp forces the voltage at pin 2 to V_{SET}. By Ohm's Law, the current through R must be V_{SET} / R. Because no current flows into the op-amp's inverting input, the same current must flow in the load. The op-amp raises its output voltage until load current just balances the current through R. Both terminals of the load are thus above ground potential.

In the left-hand circuit, current is balanced through the load in the other direction. The input current is V_{SET} / R. The op-amp lowers its output voltage until the load current balances the input current. This leaves one terminal of the load at ground potential (not grounded, just kept equal to ground) and the other at a negative voltage, requiring a ±12 V supply for this circuit.

When you build these circuits, V_{SET} can be generated by a second power supply (be sure to connect the power supply common connections together) or by a battery. Aim, once again, for 5 mA of load current. Measure V_{SET} and divide by 5 mA to get R, using the closest standard value. Confirm that both op-amp inputs are at the same voltage. Measure load current with a meter in series with the load or by measuring the load voltage and us-

ing Ohm's Law. If you can vary V_{SET} or R, observe the effect on load current. Don't reduce R so much that it or the load dissipate too much power: $P = V_{SET}^2 / R$. Vary the load resistance, including an open and a short circuit, to see what happens.

Using a Voltage Regulator

A common three-terminal regulator can be tricked into putting out constant current instead of constant voltage! The regulator does its best to maintain a fixed voltage between its output and ground terminals. When a fixed-value resistor is connected between them, the current through the resistor is constant, as shown in Figure 2C. The regulator's ground terminal draws little current, so the current flows through the load, regardless of what the load voltage is.

The 7805 is a good choice for regulator-based current sources; it handles high current and is easy to attach to a heat sink. The only caveat is that the current set resistor, R, must be able to dissipate $(I_{LOAD}^2 R)$ W. If 5 mA is the desired load current, R must be 5 V / 5 mA = 1 kΩ. The regulator will dissipate power equal to the load current times the voltage between its input and output pins. If you are using a 12 V supply, at 5 mA load current, the regulator dissipates $(12 - 5) \times 5$ mA = 35 mW. Try various values of R and load resistance, again trying the open and short circuits.

The Current Mirror

The circuit in Figure 3 can throw you for a loop with Q1's base and collector shorted together. This is the current mirror, so named because the collector current of Q2 mirrors that in Q1. The current mirror is used when the reference current must be kept separate from the load current or when more than one load current must be controlled by a single reference current.

Current mirrors work because of the bipolar transistor's property that matched transistors with the same base-to-emitter voltage will have the same collector currents. Since the bases and emitters are connected together, V_{BE} must be the same. Matching two transistors means that they usually are made of the same materials, have equal current gains (β) and operate at the same temperature. This is the usual case inside an IC or in a multiple-transistor package such as the MPQ2222—four 2N2222 transistors in a 16 pin DIP package.

Build the current mirror by using a pair of 2N3904 transistors (or an MPQ2222). If you can measure β, pick a pair of transistors with β within a few percent of each other. Set I_{REF} to 5 mA by calculating the value for $R = (V_{CC} - 0.7) / 5$ mA. With a 1 kΩ load, verify that I_{LOAD} is close to 5 mA. Vary R to change I_{REF} while observing load current, and vary the load resistance while monitoring I_{LOAD}.

Suggested Reading

The Art of Electronics, by Horowitz and Hill, includes extensive material on current sources and current mirrors, including a number of variations on the mirror. A good on-line discussion can be found at **www.4qdtec.com/csm.html**.

Shopping List

- MPS2907 or 2N3906 PNP transistor (RadioShack 276-2023 or 276-1604).
- 2N3904 NPN transistor (RadioShack 276-2016).
- 741 operational amplifier (RadioShack 276-007).
- 7805 voltage regulator (RadioShack 276-1770).
- Various values of ¼ W resistors.

Next Month

In September, we're going to meet the DA. Not the district attorney—the differential amplifier—a key element of the op-amp. You'll also learn about common-mode signals and the DA's ability to reject them. See you next month!

Experiment #20: The Differential Amplifier

In all of our operational amplifier experiments, a *differential amplifier* (DA) was lurking behind the op-amp's input terminals. Sporting high gain and high input impedance, the DA applied its gain to only the *difference* in voltage at its inputs; ignoring any voltage that those inputs had in common. All this from just a pair of transistors and four resistors!

Terms to Learn

Common-mode—a signal that appears equally at both inputs of a differential amplifier or on both connections to a signal source.

Common-mode rejection ratio (CMRR)—the ratio of differential-mode gain to common-mode gain, usually expressed in dB.

Differential-mode—a signal that appears as a difference in voltage between the inputs of a differential amplifier or between connections to a signal source, also called *normal mode*.

Background

In many applications, it's useful to measure or amplify just the difference in voltage between two points, ignoring any voltage that is present at both points. For example, a low-level microphone signal with a dc offset or carrying ac hum needs to be amplified, while the offset or hum is ignored. For this job, a difference or differential amplifier is used. The ideal DA has high-gain, infinite input impedance, and only amplifies the difference in voltage at its inputs. This can be approximated with the simple circuit of Figure 1. This is an emitter-coupled DA, a pair of common-emitter (CE) amplifiers that share a path for their emitter currents. The output of the DA can remain differential (taken between the transistor collectors) or be converted to *single-ended* (referenced to ground) by only using one collector output.

Let's refresh our understanding of the CE amplifier circuit before proceeding. From our first experiment, the gain of the CE amplifier is $A_V \approx R_C/R_E$ and the transistor collector current is $I_C = \beta I_B$. This is true for each of the amplifiers, even if they share most of their emitter resistance in R_1. The sharing of R_1 is important.

Returning to Figure 1, consider what happens when the voltage at the base of transistor 1 goes up slightly and drops the same amount at the base of transistor 2. This is just what happens when a small differential signal is applied. I_{C1} goes up and I_{C2} goes down—the same amount. This leaves the voltage at point A (where the two currents combine) unchanged. That means we can treat point A as an ac ground, as long as both transistors aren't driven into cutoff or saturation and remain in their active regions. Thus R_1 doesn't affect gain, only collector current. The only difference in the CE amplifier's gain is that the input signal is actually twice the input at either transistor, so the differential gain, A_{DM} is:

$$A_{DM} \approx R_C/2R_e \qquad [1]$$

How do we calculate transistor collector current? The quiescent current (with no signal applied) can be determined by using Kirchhoff's Voltage Law (KVL)—the sum of voltages around any current path is zero. Let's do a KVL from the transistor base, through R_E and R_1, through the negative supply V_{EE}, and back to the base.

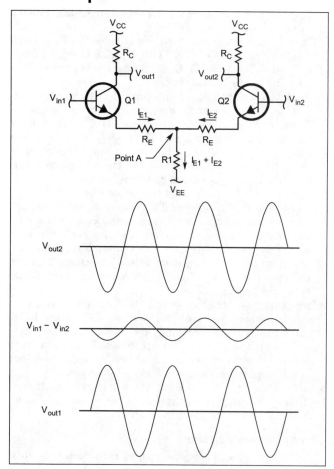

Figure 1—The basic emitter-coupled differential amplifier circuit. The outputs from the collectors are equal and out of phase for an input signal appearing between the transistor bases.

$$V_B + V_{BE} + R_E I_E + 2(R_1 I_E) - V_{EE} = 0$$

The base is at zero volts, so $V_B = 0$. If the transistor is in its active region, $V_{BE} \approx 0.7$ V. The voltage drop across R_E from the emitter current follows. The next term accounts for the sharing of R_1, in which emitter current from both transistors flows. If the transistors and resistors are matched, the current will be the same in each transistor and so each contributes half of the voltage across R_1. Making these substitutions and solving:

$$I_E = (V_{EE} - 0.7) / (R_E + 2R_1) \qquad [2]$$

If the β of the transistors is large (>100), we can make the simplifying assumption that $I_C=I_E$. Because we want high gain, equation 1 says that R_E must be small, so a further simplification results in:

$$I_C = (V_{EE} - 0.7) / (2R_1) \qquad [3]$$

We can now design a DA with a specific gain and collector current.

Design and Build a Differential Amplifier

• Start by selecting the power supply voltages. This experiment requires both positive and negative voltages. The usual case is that the voltages are balanced—I used ±12 V, but that's not required. If you are using a +12 V supply, you can create a negative supply with batteries. Make V_{EE} at least –6 V to keep the resistor values reasonable.

- Choose a collector current—2 mA is a reasonable value. Find R_1 by using Equation 3. 2 mA = (12 – 0.7) / (2R_1) so R_1= 2.98 kΩ. Use a standard value from 2.7 to 3.3 kΩ. I used a value of 3 kΩ.
- Choose a gain—let's try for 30. We assumed that R_E is small compared to R_1, so use 100 Ω (or 0.1 kΩ). Using Equation 1, R_C=2(0.1)30 = 6 kΩ. Use a standard value from 5.6 to 6.8 kΩ. I used a 6.2 kΩ resistor.
- Check your circuit's dc performance to be sure your calculations are okay. Ground the base of each transistor so that no signal is applied. Be sure V_{BE} is close to 0.7 V. Check I_C by measuring the voltage across R_C: I_C=V_{RC}/R_C. In my case I_C=11.2/6.2=1.8 mA. Also, measure the voltage at point A. Don't proceed unless your collector current and base current are close to your expected values.
- Apply a small 1 kHz signal of 100 mV or less to one transistor input as shown in Figure 2A. Observe the output voltage at each transistor collector with an oscilloscope. You should observe that the collectors have identical waveforms, 180° out of phase. Be sure that the output waveforms are undistorted, reducing the input signal if necessary. Measure the input voltage, V_{IN}. Check point A to observe that the dc voltage is unchanged.
- Even though we aren't applying a true differential signal (one transistor base is still grounded), we can still measure differential gain, A_{DM}, by measuring the output between the two collector outputs. Use a voltmeter to measure the ac voltage between the two collectors or use the ADD function of your oscilloscope. I measured A_{DM} = (V_{C1}–V_{C2})/V_{IN} = 32.
- Measure the ac voltage at point A. It will be very small, confirming that point A is effectively an ac ground due to the balancing act of the two transistors.

Common Mode Rejection

Gain is one thing, but rejecting unwanted signals is another. A common-mode signal is one that is present at both inputs in the same amount. Good examples of common-mode signals include 60 Hz ac hum, dc offset, or noise picked up by a long input cable. In any case, it's important to keep those signals from contaminating the amplifier output.

Let's return to the description of how the DA amplifies differential input signals a few paragraphs ago. Remember that it was important that the symmetry of the emitter current changes kept point A at a fixed voltage. For common-mode signals, both emitter currents change in the *same* direction and point A changes, too. This means that the circuit's common-mode gain formula must include R_1.

$$A_{CM} = R_C / (2R_1+R_E)$$

If we ignore R_E because it is small compared to R_1,

$$A_{CM} \approx R_C / (2R_1) \qquad [4]$$

For the circuit we constructed, A_{CM} should be about 6/(2×3)=1—much smaller than the differential gain of 30.

The ratio of differential to common-mode gain is called the *common-mode rejection ratio* or CMRR and is typically measured in dB. Larger values are better.

$$CMRR = 20 \log (A_{DM}/A_{CM}) \qquad [5]$$

Measuring CMRR

- IConnect your input signal to the bases of *both* transistors as shown in Figure 2B.
- Increase the input voltage to 0.5 V (check to be sure the collector voltage of each transistor is undistorted).

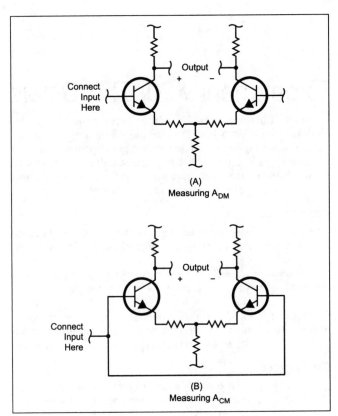

Figure 2—The two methods of connecting the circuit to measure differential gain (A) and common-mode gain (B).

- Measure the voltage between the collectors using a voltmeter or the oscilloscope's ADD feature. Calculate A_{CM}. My measured common mode gain was 0.6.
- Calculate CMRR in dB. My CMRR was 20 log (32/0.6)= 34.5 dB. This is pretty good for a simple circuit with unmatched resistors and transistors! It says that common mode signals are rejected by a factor of 50.

A circuit with better selection of transistor gains and resistor matching can have even better performance. Experiment with different transistors or match the pairs of resistors for R_C and R_E to see what effect this has on A_{CM}.

Improving CMRR

Last month, we created a current source and I mentioned that they were used in op-amps. In fact, they are often used in place of R_1, creating a very high effective resistance due to their very low compliance. That means the common-mode gain of the circuit will be very low, as shown by Equation 4.

Suggested Reading

Chapter 2 of *The Art of Electronics*, by Horowitz and Hill, has a very good discussion of differential amplifiers, including the use of current sources. Section 2.5 of *Experimental Methods in RF Design*, by Hayward, Campbell and Larkin also illustrates the differential amplifier.

Shopping List

- Two 2N3904 NPN transistors (RadioShack 276-2016).
- Miscellaneous 1/4 W resistors.

Next Month

Now it's time to extend our experiments beyond low-frequency signals to RF and the simplest impedance matching method—the L network. For this experiment, you'll need to have access to an antenna analyzer, such as the MFJ-259, that can display SWR in the 10 meter band.

Experiment #28: The Common Base Amplifier

Even though it looks "funny," the common base amplifier and the FET common gate amplifier perform some pretty useful tricks. They're more common than you think!

Terms to Learn

- *Indirect Measurement*—calculating the value of a parameter from the measured values of other parameters
- *Isolation*—a lack of effects on one circuit from changes in another circuit
- *Self-biased*—a circuit that operates at a fixed bias point without a separate biasing circuit

Introduction

Common-base (CB) and common-gate (CG) amplifiers are the third form of single-transistor amplifier circuit topology. Their claim to fame is low input impedance, high voltage gain and high output resistance. This makes them a good choice for RF amplifiers. You may have already made use of the vacuum tube version of the CB circuit—a grounded-grid amplifier! As we discuss these amplifiers, I'll make reference to previous experiments that can be downloaded from the Hands-On Radio Web site, **www.arrl.org/tis/info/HTML/Hands-On-Radio/**.

CB and CG Circuits

Figure 1 shows the CB amplifier—the transistor is turned on its side, with the emitter facing the input. How can that possibly amplify anything? Understanding, as it often does, comes from changing one's view of a problem. Figure 1 redraws the odd-looking regular CB circuit in the more familiar common-emitter style. The input is just moved from the base circuit to the emitter circuit.

Remember—the input signal only needs to cause changes in the transistor base-emitter current. Placing the input in the emitter circuit does exactly that, except that a positive change in input amplitude *reduces* base current by lowering V_{BE}, thus raising V_C. As a result, the CB amplifier is *non-inverting* with

output and input signals in-phase.

Practical circuits for the CB and the JFET CG circuit are shown in Figure 2. Looking at the CB amplifier from a dc point of view (replace the capacitors with open circuits), all of the same resistors are there as in the good old common-emitter amplifier we learned about in Experiment #1. The input capacitors, C_{IN}, allow the dc emitter (or source) current to flow "around" the ac input signal source.

Let's analyze the CB amplifier first. Since the input signal is also the ac emitter current, i_e, the ac collector current must be:

$$i_c = i_e \, [\beta/(\beta+1)] \text{ so, current gain } A_I = i_c/i_e = [\beta/(b+1)] \quad [1]$$

Current gain is always just below unity, just as voltage gain for the EF amp is just below unity. The neat thing about the CB amplifier is that you can hang just about any load resistance on the output and current gain is unchanged. This configuration has excellent *isolation* between output and input, meaning changes in load don't affect the input impedance—a good thing for RF systems that require stable impedances.

By making the load resistance greater than the input resistance while keeping current constant, you get voltage gain. To calculate the input resistance of the CB amp, we encounter a new transistor parameter, h_{ie}, representing the resistance between the base and emitter. Following reasoning similar to that for the emitter follower (EF) amplifier (see Experiment #2), explaining why current gain multiplied the effect of R_E at the input, we find that input resistance for the CB amp is:

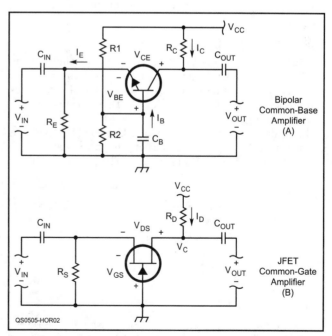

Figure 2—The Common Base and Common Gate amplifiers are great wide-bandwidth amplifiers, with low input impedance and good voltage gain.

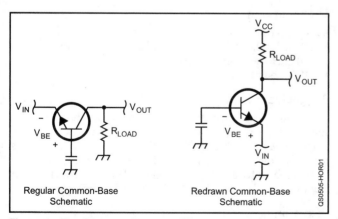

Figure 1—The Common Base amplifier can be redrawn to show its similarity to the better-known Common Emitter amplifier.

$$R_{in} = h_{ie}/(1 + \beta) \text{ and } v_{in} = R_{in} \, i_e \qquad [2]$$

For a 2N3904 transistor, h_{ie} averages about 1 kΩ between 1 and 10 mA of collector current and β is about 150 over the same range. That means the input resistance will be about 6 Ω. A more sophisticated analysis will come up with a somewhat higher figure—around 20 Ω—but the CB input resistance is still quite low and can be controlled by changing the bias current. Transistors used as preamplifiers are designed with h_{ie} to result in a 50 Ω input resistance for reasonable values of collector current.

To figure voltage gain, A_V, start with $v_o = i_c R_L$ and make substitutions from equations 1 and 2. R_L is the parallel combination of R_C and whatever load is attached at V_{OUT}.

$$A_V \approx \beta(R_L/h_{ie}) \qquad [3]$$

It doesn't take a big load resistance to create a substantial voltage gain. Using the 2N3904 again, a 500 Ω load results in $A_V = 150 (500/1000) = 75$. This is why the CB and CG amplifiers are often used as preamplifiers.

Setting the operating or Q point of the CB amplifier starts with selecting A_V and calculating the required R_L—the parallel combination of R_C and whatever load is connected at V_{OUT}. Determine R_C and proceed to determine R_E, R_1 and R_2, as in the CE amplifier.

In the JFET common-gate amplifier circuit one of the bias resistors is missing. What's up with that? This is called a *source self-biased* circuit. For a depletion-mode JFET, V_{GS} needs to be somewhere between 0 V and V_P, the pinch-off voltage. One way to make V_{GS} negative would be to use a negative supply, but it's easiest to hold V_G at 0 V (by grounding it) and raise V_S instead. With $V_G = 0$:

$$V_{GS} = -I_{DS}R_S \qquad [4]$$

Since V_{GS} and I_{DS} are predetermined as the selected Q point, you can easily solve for R_S.

The JFET CG performance equations are:

$R_{IN} \approx 1/g_m$, where g_m is the JFET transconductance
$A_V = g_m R_D$

Input and Output Resistance

Much is made of the input and output resistances of the CB/CG amplifier. Can they be measured? Not directly, such as with a VOM, but indirectly, by adding external resistances and observing the effect on the circuit. These methods are illustrated in Figure 3.

Let's start with input resistance. When combined with an external resistor, R_{ADJ}, the amplifier's input resistance, R_{IN}, forms a voltage divider. If I know V_{IN} and V_E, and I can mea-

sure R_{ADJ}, I can calculate R_{IN}. Input a known voltage V_{IN} and adjust R_{ADJ} until V_E (measured across R_E) is $1/2 V_{IN}$. At this point, the resistances in the divider are equal, so $R_{IN} = R_{ADJ}$.

Measuring output resistance is a two-step process. First, disconnect the load resistor, R_L, entirely, and measure the open-circuit voltage, V_{OC}. Then connect a load resistor between one-half and twice the expected value of R_{OUT}. Measure the output voltage, V_L. Once again, you have a voltage divider and, with a little math:

$$R_{OUT} = R_L (V_{OC} - V_L) / V_L \qquad [5]$$

For most transistors in this circuit, R_{OUT} will be approximately the same as R_C. Ready to try it out? Let's go!

Building and Testing a CB Amplifier

In this experiment, you'll build a CB amplifier, measure the voltage gain, and then measure the input and output resistance. Start by constructing the amplifier circuit of Figure 2A using resistor values from Experiment #1 (R1 = 39 kΩ, R2 = 6.8 kΩ, R_C = 1.5 kΩ, R_E = 270 Ω), C_{IN} = C_B = C_{OUT} = 10 μF (connect + leads to transistor) and V_{CC} = 12 V. Use equation 3 to calculate the expected value of A_V with R_C as the load. Assume that β=150 and h_{ie} = 1000 Ω. Use equation 2 to calculate the expected value of R_{IN}.

- Confirm that the circuit is operating at its Q point: $V_{CEQ} \approx 5$ V and $I_{CQ} \approx 4$ mA.
- Apply a 10 kHz sine wave to the input at a voltage small enough so that the output is not distorted. (You may have to use a voltmeter to accurately measure the voltage.) Measure the output voltage (which is V_{OC}) and calculate the gain. I obtained a gain of 150. Measured gain will be somewhat lower than the calculations because our equation is somewhat oversimplified. (Voltmeter users—confirm distortionless operation by making sure that changes in the input cause a proportional change in the output.)
- Measure input resistance by placing a 100 Ω potentiometer in series with the input signal and adjusting it until the ac value of $V_E = 1/2 \, V_{IN}$. Remove the potentiometer and measure its value—mine was 10.2 Ω.
- Reconnect the input signal directly to C_{IN}. Add a load resistor, R_L = 1 kΩ by connecting it from the OUTPUT side of C_{OUT} to ground, *not* from the collector to ground—that would change the dc biasing. Calculate R_{OUT} by using equation 5. R_{OUT} should be almost the same as R_C—mine was 1.59 kΩ.
- Experiment with different values of load resistance to see what happens to gain.

Shopping List

- 2N3904 transistor
- 270 Ω, 1 kΩ, 1.5 kΩ, 6.8 kΩ, 39 kΩ ¼ W resistors
- 3—10 μF electrolytic capacitors
- 100 Ω potentiometer

Suggested Reading

Common-base amplifiers are not often covered in detail, since they are not common. Chapter 6 of TAB Books' *Guide to Understanding Electricity and Electronics*, 2nd edition, has broad coverage of all three types of amplifier circuits. A simple UHF preamplifier project using a JFET is available at **www.dxzone.com/cgi-bin/dir/jump2.cgi?ID=9258**.

Next Month

Who is this Kirchhoff guy and what are his laws that electrical engineers keep referring to? Tune in next month and learn about two fundamentals of all circuit analysis and design—Kirchhoff's Voltage and Current Laws.

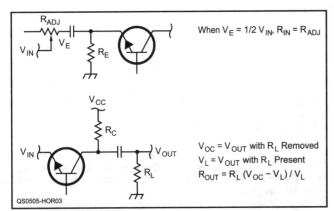

When $V_E = 1/2 V_{IN}$, $R_{IN} = R_{ADJ}$

$V_{OC} = V_{OUT}$ with R_L Removed
$V_L = V_{OUT}$ with R_L Present
$R_{OUT} = R_L (V_{OC} - V_L) / V_L$

QS0505-HOR03

Figure 3—Input and output impedance of amplifier circuits must be measured indirectly.

Building Block Circuits

Experiment #3—Basic Operational Amplifiers

Let's give transistors a rest this month and take a look at one of the most popular components in electronics—the op-amp. The most widely used circuits are two simple amplifiers and an adder circuit.

Background

Op-amp is an abbreviation for *operational amplifier*, a term coined 70 years ago. Complicated mathematical equations were then solved by analog computers. Amplifiers were used to add, multiply, integrate, or perform other "operations" on signals. Originally made with vacuum tubes, integrated circuit op amps—such as the 741—started a revolution in electronics.

Op-amps generally have a high voltage gain, a high input impedance and a low output impedance. These properties make designing op-amp circuits easy because they simplify the design equations, as we'll see.

Terms to Learn

Inverting (–) and non-inverting (+)—signals at the inverting input cause the op-amp output to respond in the opposite "direction" and, for signals at the non-inverting input, in the same direction.

Negative feedback—routing some of a circuit's output back to the input in such a way as to oppose the effect of the input signal.

The Operational Amplifier

Figure 1 shows the basic op-amp symbol, including the inverting and non-inverting inputs. *The 2003 ARRL Handbook* incorrectly shows the pin-outs for several popular op-amps on page 24.27—the inverting and non-inverting input connections are *reversed*. The industry standard for single op-amp ICs is that pin 2 is the inverting input (–) and pin 3 the non-inverting input (+).

The bypass or decoupling capacitors (C1, C2) shown in Figure 1 keep the power bus clean and help prevent feedback paths that might cause the op-amp circuit to oscillate. They bypass the power connections to ground, hence "decoupling" ac signals from the circuit.

An op-amp has a huge capacity to amplify—80 dB or more of voltage gain at dc! Most of the time that's far too much gain, but so-called "negative feedback" can control that gain, creating useful behavior. Consider that the op-amp's gain is acting solely on the voltage differential between its two inputs. The trick is to connect components from the output to the inputs so that when the output is doing what we want, the voltages at both input pins are balanced. This is a "correction" or "feedback" signal. It stabilizes the op-amp output by correcting its input. If the input changes—even a little bit—the high gain immediately causes the op-amp to react, changing its output and the feedback signal until its inputs are balanced once again. When feedback is used we refer to the circuit being "closed-loop."

The Non-Inverting Amplifier

Figure 2A shows a non-inverting amplifier. The input signal, V_I, is connected directly to the non-inverting (+) input, while resistors R_f and R form a feedback network. Remember that the op-amp has a very high input impedance, so we can treat the series

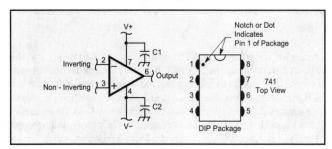

Figure 1—The operational-amplifier schematic symbol and typical package details.

combination of R and R_f as a voltage divider connected between the output pin and ground. The voltage at the inverting (–) input of the op-amp, V_i, must be:

$$V_i = V_{out} \, R \, / \, (R + R_f)$$

Since the op-amp's inputs must balance, $V_i = V_I$ and the circuit's gain, A_v must be:

$$A_v = V_{out} / V_I = (R + R_f) / R = 1 + R_f / R \qquad [1]$$

The non-inverting amplifier's gain is always greater than 1 and is determined only by the ratio of R_f and R. There's no magic—the op-amp is just connected so that when its output is the correct amount larger than the input signal, both inputs balance.

Testing the Non-Inverting Amplifier

• Design the amplifier to have a gain of 2. That requires $R_f = R$. Use a value of 1 kΩ for this first circuit. Your power supply should be set to at least ±12 V (+12 V if you are using a single-polarity supply). Caution—do not apply signals above or below the power supply to the op-amp inputs or you may damage the IC.

• Build the circuit as shown in Figure 2A, including a 10 µF bypass capacitor to ground at each power supply pin. The 1 kΩ potentiometer will serve as an adjustable voltage source for V_I. Set the potentiometer so that the resistance from the wiper to ground is about 100 Ω. After checking all your connections, apply power and measure V_I and V_{out}. V_I should be approximately 1.2 V (one-tenth of V+) and V_{out} should be close to twice the value of V_I.

• The voltage at the inverting input, V_i should follow V_I very closely.

• Adjust the potentiometer output voltage up and down while measuring both V_I and V_{out}.

• You need a ±12 V power supply for this step. Replace the potentiometer with a function generator supplying a 1 V_{p-p}, 1 kHz sine wave. Use the oscilloscope to measure the output—it should be just like the input, but with twice the voltage.

• Experiment by changing the ratio of R and R_f to obtain different gains. (Keep resistor values above 100Ω.)

• Make a unity-gain voltage follower by removing R and replacing R_f with a direct connection as shown in Figure 2B. This circuit is frequently used to isolate a sensitive input or drive a heavy load.

The Inverting Amplifier

The high-impedance of the op-amp input can be used to

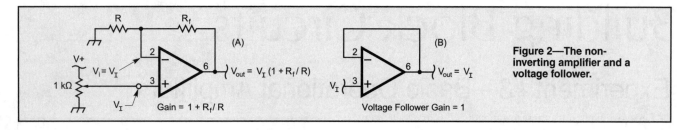

Figure 2—The non-inverting amplifier and a voltage follower.

create an inverting amplifier whose gain is also set by the ratio of two resistors. In Figure 3, R and R_f are again connected to the inverting input, but the input signal is connected to the free end of R and the non-inverting input is grounded. How does this work? Remember that the op-amp inputs are balanced, so the inverting input must also be at ground potential. It's not grounded, it's just at ground potential. This is called a "virtual ground."

With the inverting input at 0 V, the current through R must be $I_I = V_I / R$. Remember, too, that the op-amp input impedance is very high, so the input current must be balanced by the op-amp's output removing just as much current through Rf as flows through R. By Ohm's Law, the output voltage is then:

$$V_{out} = 0 - (I_I) R_f = -(V_I / R) R_f = -V_I R_f / R$$

and the gain must be:

$$A_v = V_{out} / V_I = -(V_I R_f / R)/V_I = -R_f / R \qquad [2]$$

Testing the Inverting Amplifier

• Design the amplifier to have a gain of –4. Select a value for R of 1 kΩ. This requires R_f to be 4 kΩ. The closest standard value is 3.9 kΩ. You will need a ±12 V power supply to test this amplifier configuration.

• Build the amplifier as shown in Figure 3 and connect a 1 V_{p-p}, 1 kHz sine wave to the input. You should see a 3.9 V_{p-p} sine wave at the output, but inverted with respect to the input. Look at the inverting input to verify that it is at ground potential.

• Use different resistor ratios to change the gain. (Keep resistor values above 100 Ω to limit how much power the op-amp must supply.) Input a dc voltage by using the 1 kΩ potentiometer as before and see if the circuit output is of the opposite polarity.

The Summing Amplifier

The circuit of Figure 4 shows how more than one signal can be combined and amplified by a summing amplifier. As for the inverting amplifier, the op-amp must balance all of the currents at the inverting input—even if current comes from more than one source!

The current from each input signal equals V_{in} / R, so the total current in R_f must be their sum:

$$I_f = V_{in1} / R_1 + V_{in2} / R_2$$

Using the same reasoning as before, the output voltage must be:

$$V_{out} = -(V_{in1} / R_1 + V_{in2} / R_2)R_f \qquad [3]$$

The gain for either input signal is still the ratio, $-R_f / R$.

Testing the Summing Amplifier

• Design the amplifier to have a gain of –1 for each input by setting all three resistors (R_1, R_2 and R_f) to 10 kΩ. You will need a ±12 V power supply to test this amplifier configuration.

• Build the circuit and input the 1 V_{p-p}, 1 kHz sine wave to input 1. Use the 1 kΩ potentiometer as before to supply input 2.

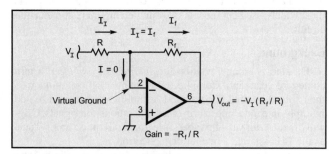

Figure 3—The inverting amplifier.

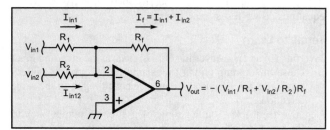

Figure 4—A summing amplifier.

• Vary the potentiometer while watching the output on your oscilloscope. You will see the inverted sine wave from input 1 shifted up and down as the dc level at input 2 changes.

• Experiment by altering the ratio of either input resistor and R_f to observe the effect on the addition of signals. Replace R_1 or R_2 (or both) with a 10 kΩ potentiometer and vary the channel ratios independently. Congratulations—you've just built a 2-channel mixer!

Suggested Reading

The 2003 ARRL Handbook, pp 8.32-8.35; Horowitz and Hill, *The Art of Electronics*, chapter 4, sections 4.01-4.08; Ian Poole, G3YWX, "An Introduction to Op Amps," *QST*, Feb 1999, pp 55-56. The ARRL Web site for this series is **www.arrl.org/tis/info/html/hands-on-radio/**. Use it!

Shopping List

You'll need the following components:

• 741 op-amp—The part may be labeled as an LM741CN, MC1741CP1, µA741C, etc. The prefixes and suffixes identify the manufacturer, package style and temperature grade. RadioShack part number 276-007 will fill the bill.

• ¼ W resistors of the following values: 1 kΩ (2 ea), 3.9 kΩ, 10 kΩ (4 ea) and miscellaneous values between 1 kΩ and 10 kΩ.

• 1 kΩ and 10 kΩ potentiometer (single or multi-turn).

• 2—10 µF capacitors with a voltage rating of 25 V dc or more.

Next Month

Op-amps are frequently used as the engine driving an active filter. Sprinkle on a few capacitors and resistors and next month we'll see just how easy creating an audio filter can be.

Experiment #11—Comparators

The *comparator* made an appearance in Hands-On Radio experiment #5 on timers. As a crucial part of the type 555 integrated circuit (IC), it made the decision about when it was time to change the timer's operation from one state to another. We'll now delve deeply into comparator functions including the mysterious property called *hysteresis*.

Terms to Learn

- *Hysteresis*—a shift in the switching threshold of a comparator purposely caused by positive feedback.
- *Chatter*—oscillations of a comparator output when the input signal is near the threshold.
- *Open-collector output*—an IC output consisting of the isolated collector of a bipolar transistor or FET drain.
- *Threshold*—the voltage at which a comparator circuit switches states.

Background

The basic function of a comparator is, surprisingly (!), to compare the magnitudes of two inputs and indicate which is greater. The comparator is found in many places around the shack—battery chargers, power supplies, antenna tuners and switches, just to name a few.

While there are lots of circuits that can compare voltages, the most common is a high-gain amplifier with two high-impedance inputs. If this sounds like an op-amp, it should—the comparator is basically an op-amp with an *open-collector output*. This is an NPN transistor with its collector connected to the OUTPUT pin, but nothing else. It allows the comparator to interface to digital circuits and drive switched loads better than an op-amp. It also supports a neat noise-control design trick, as we'll see later.

Figure 1 shows a comparator in a simple temperature control circuit. No feedback is used, so its full voltage gain (in the thousands at dc and low frequencies) turns the output transistor OFF if the + input voltage is greater than that of the – input (by even a few millivolts) and vice versa. The point at which the comparator changes state is called the *threshold*. The output states can be reversed by switching the input connections.

In this circuit, the negative input (–) voltage is fixed at a value representing the desired temperature (the system setpoint), V_{SP}. If the sensor's output voltage is lower than V_{SP}, the comparator's output transistor will be turned ON and the heater will be ON, raising the temperature. When the sensor is hotter than the desired temperature, the output transistor is turned OFF, turning the heater OFF. The system cycles between a little too hot and a little too cold.

Testing a Simple Comparator

Let's start with the simple voltage detector circuit of Figure 2, such as might be used in a power supply to detect overvoltage. We want the LED to turn ON whenever the variable input voltage is higher than the fixed input voltage (setpoint). Fixed resistors R1 and R2 form a resistive divider that creates the setpoint voltage, V_{SP}.

Use an LM311 with its V+ power sup-

ply pin connected to +12 V and its V– pin connected to ground. Be sure to connect pins 1 and 4 together so the emitter of the output transistor is grounded.

To keep current through the resistive divider small, assume R1 + R2 = 50 kΩ, and R1 = 50 kΩ – R2.

- Create a setpoint of V_{SP} = 5 V. Use the voltage divider equation: $V_{SP} = V+ \times [R2/(R1+R2)] = 12\ V \times [R2/(50\ k\Omega)]$. So R2 = 5 V × 50 kΩ/12 V = 20.8 kΩ. Use 22 kΩ for R2. R1 = 50 kΩ – 22 kΩ = 28 kΩ, so use a 27 kΩ resistor.
- Build the circuit and vary the potentiometer while watching the LED. Measure the setpoint and variable voltages at threshold to be sure they agree with the calculated values. Redesign the resistive divider for different setpoint values or use a 10 kΩ potentiometer to change the setpoint.
- Adjust the variable input slowly through the setpoint value. Do you see the LED flicker or light dimly before staying ON or OFF? If you are using an oscilloscope, watch the LM311 output voltage as the setpoint is passed for rapid changes between ON to OFF before settling at the final value.
- Measure the comparator's output voltage, V_{OH}, with the LED turned OFF for use in the next part of the experiment. The forward voltage drop across the LED, even when OFF, will make V_{OH} about 1.5 V lower than V+.

Hysteresis

Comparators are often used to drive relays. The audible noise of the relay contacts rapidly opening and closing as the comparator output switches states is called *chatter* and it is damaging to the

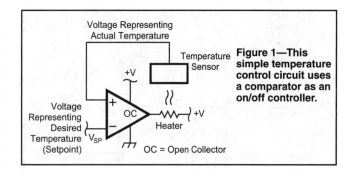

Figure 1—This simple temperature control circuit uses a comparator as an on/off controller.

OC = Open Collector

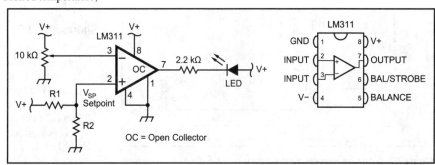

Figure 2—This voltage detector uses a resistive divider to create a fixed setpoint. Note that the input connections for the LM311 are reversed from those of the 741 op-amp.

relay and to the circuit it controls. Chatter is caused by noise on either the setpoint or the input voltage. As shown in Figure 3A, even small noise peaks can cause a temporary crossing of the threshold. When the input voltage is close to the threshold, the effect of the noise is multiplied by the comparator's high gain. The noise from the load current switching can also feed back into the inputs and cause extended oscillations.

Filtering the input signal (as we did in experiment #8) by adding a capacitor to the setpoint divider to reduce noise, can reduce chatter. A more reliable way is to use the comparator output to shift the threshold. It can be shifted a bit in the *opposite* direction of the input signal when the threshold voltage is crossed. This is illustrated in Figure 3B. By moving the threshold, chatter is eliminated.

This is accomplished by adding positive feedback from the output to the setpoint as shown in Figure 4. When the variable input voltage is less than the setpoint, V_{SP}, the output transistor is OFF and the voltage at the comparator's output is close to V+. As the variable input voltage increases past the setpoint, the output transistor turns ON, turning the LED ON. This circuit is called a *Schmitt Trigger*.

When the transistor is ON it places R3 in parallel with R2, lowering the setpoint voltage to V_{TL} and moving it away from the variable input voltage shown in Figure 3B. The reverse occurs when the threshold is crossed in the opposite direction so that the threshold is raised to V_{TH} as R3 is placed in parallel with R1. This shift in the setpoint depending on whether the input is increasing or decreasing is called *hysteresis*. The amount of hysteresis, $V_H = V_{TH} - V_{TL}$.

In designing a circuit to use hysteresis with specific values for V_{TH} and V_{TL}, we can simplify the calculations considerably by making the following assumptions:

- V_{OL} (the comparator output with the output transistor ON) = 0

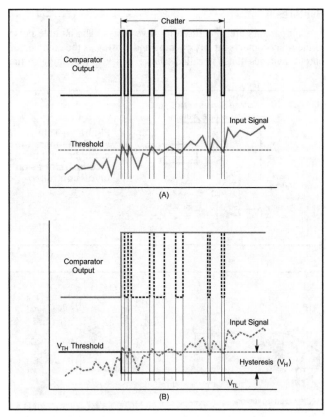

Figure 3—A shows chatter as the noisy input signal crosses and recrosses the comparator's switching threshold. B shows how moving the threshold after switching reduces chatter.

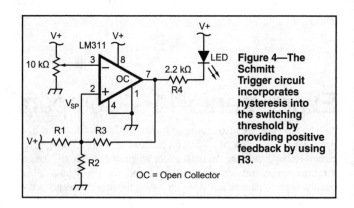

Figure 4—The Schmitt Trigger circuit incorporates hysteresis into the switching threshold by providing positive feedback by using R3.

- R3 is much larger than the combination of R1 in parallel with R2
- R4 is much smaller than R3

You can calculate the amount of hysteresis by assuming that R3 only adds current to R2 or removes a little current from R2, depending on whether the comparator output is ON or OFF.

$$V_H \approx (V_{OH}) (R1 \parallel R2)/[R3 + (R1 \parallel R2)] \qquad \text{[Eq 1]}$$

Solving for R3 if the other values are known:

$$R3 \approx [(V_{OH})(R1 \parallel R2)/V_H] - (R1 \parallel R2) \qquad \text{[Eq 2]}$$

Testing a Schmitt Trigger

Let's add 0.5 V of hysteresis to the voltage detector we just built, keeping the setpoint at 5 V, R1=28 kΩ, and R2=22 kΩ. Leave R4 at 2.2 kΩ, satisfying the assumption R4<<R3. I'll use V_{OH}=10.5 V, but you should use the value you measured earlier.

- Using Equation 2, R3 = [(10.5 V)(12 kΩ)/0.5 V]–12 kΩ = 240 kΩ. Use a 220 kΩ resistor. Remember to substitute your own value for V_{OH}.
- Monitor the variable input voltage as you slowly increase and decrease it through the 5 V setpoint. Record the point at which the LED turns ON and OFF. Subtract those two voltages to find the circuit's hysteresis voltage. For my circuit, I observed 400 mV (0.4 V) of hysteresis—pretty good for an approximate solution.
- Experiment with the circuit by increasing R3 to reduce hysteresis, and vice versa.

Suggested Reading

The Art of Electronics, by Horowitz and Hill, covers comparators in several sections, primarily 4.23 and 9.07. The National Semiconductor data sheet for the LM311 at **www.national.com/ds/LM/LM311.pdf** (and LP311 data sheet at **www.national.com/ds/LP/LP311.pdf**) includes numerous application hints and circuits.

Shopping List

- LM311 comparator (The LP311 comparator, RadioShack 900-6272, is available online only. An LM339, part number 276-1712, may be substituted using the pin connections at **www.national.com/ds/LM/LM339.pdf**. Note that V– and GND are connected together internally.)
- 2.2 kΩ, 22 kΩ, 27 kΩ, 220 kΩ $^1/_4$ W resistors
- 10 kΩ potentiometer
- Red LED, RadioShack 276-026 or equivalent

Hands-On Radio Web site: **www.arrl.org/tis/info/html/hands-on-radio/**.

Experiment #13—Attenuators

Thus far, we've concentrated on active circuits—those that use applied power to transform an input signal. There are other passive circuits out there that don't need a power supply, yet perform useful functions. Attenuators are an excellent example. This month we'll explore common types and you will have a couple of useful gadgets when we're through.

Terms to Learn

- *Minimum loss*—an attenuator designed to match two impedances while incurring the minimum amount of power loss.
- *Nepers (Np)*—a logarithmic ratio similar to the decibel, except that the Naperian or natural log (ln or $\log_e$, where e=2.71828...) is used. Np is often used to specify ratios of voltage or current.
- *Symmetrical*—an attenuator whose attenuation and impedance is the same in either direction.

Background

Attenuators are used in many different audio and radio applications. Your HF rig probably has an attenuator at the front end of its receiver and your signal generator might use one to switch output voltage ranges. Along with voltage reduction, attenuators are used for impedance matching and isolation. Most attenuators are made from fixed and variable resistors, but some RF attenuators are made from PIN diodes. Microwave attenuators may be made from material inserted into waveguide.

There are many types of attenuator circuits and Figure 1 shows the most common, the T, Pi, H, O and L. The T, Pi and L circuits are all *unbalanced*, meaning that all circuit voltages are referenced to the common ground. The H and O circuits are the *balanced* equivalents of the T and Pi, respectively. The balanced circuits do not have a common ground. The adjustable L attenuator is often found in audio systems, called an *L Pad*,

with the potentiometers mechanically linked or *ganged*. Attenuators are often referred to as *pads* and attenuation as *padding*.

Attenuators are designed to have specific input and output impedances because the source and load impedances affect how much voltage appears across the attenuator's resistors. The source and load often need to be connected to a specific impedance to operate properly.

Designing Attenuators

The equations for attenuator resistor values are complex[1] so tables for values of attenuation and impedance are widely available, as in *The ARRL Handbook*, and reproduced as Table 1 for symmetric attenuators. Since most ham equipment uses 50 Ω inputs and outputs, we'll use that as our design impedance. Let's design a 50 Ω, 10 dB attenuator.

Although you may use either the T or Pi circuit, I used the Pi because it requires no center connection. If you choose the Pi, Table 1 gives values of 96.2 and 71.2 Ω for R1 and R2. (R1 = R3 for symmetric attenuators.) I substituted 100 Ω and 75 Ω resistors, which keeps the ratio (and thus the attenuation) close to 10 dB, while raising the impedance to 52 Ω.

- Build this circuit and test it by connecting it to a function generator on one side and a 51 Ω resistor on the other. (It's symmetrical, so it doesn't matter which side you choose as input and output.)
- Input a 1 kHz waveform and measure the output voltage. Calculate the attenuation using the following equation:

$$\text{Attenuation (dB)} = 20 \times \log (V_{out}/V_{in}) \qquad \text{[Eq 1]}$$

- Measure the input resistance with the 51 Ω output resistor connected. It should be within a percent or two of 52 Ω.

[1]Attenuator design equations can be found in *Reference Data for Radio Engineers*, Howard W. Sams & Company / ITT, Indianapolis, 1979 or at **www.microwaves101.com/encyclopedia/attenuators.cfm**.

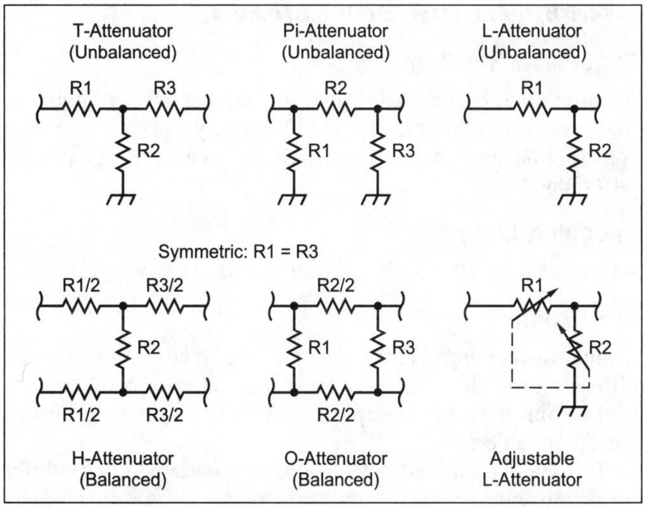

Figure 1—Several common attenuator circuits. To make the attenuators symmetric, make the values of R1 and R3 equal.

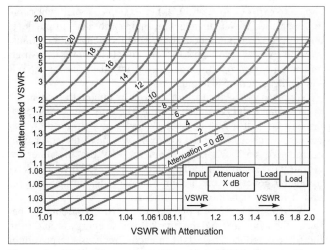

Figure 2—Attenuation can prevent a high SWR from upsetting a 50 Ω signal source. It can also mask an SWR problem at your antenna!

Table 1
Resistance Values for Symmetric T and Pi Resistive Attenuators

Pi-Network Attenuators (50 Ω)			T-Network Attenuators (50 Ω)		
Atten (dB)	R1, R3 (Ω)	R2 (Ω)	Atten (dB)	R1, R3 (Ω)	R2 (Ω)
1	870.0	5.8	1	2.9	433.3
2	436.0	11.6	2	5.7	215.2
3	292.0	17.6	3	8.5	141.9
4	221.0	23.8	4	11.3	104.8
5	178.6	30.4	5	14.0	82.2
6	150.5	37.3	6	16.6	66.9
7	130.7	44.8	7	19.0	55.8
8	116.0	52.8	8	21.5	47.3
9	105.0	61.6	9	23.8	40.6
10	96.2	71.2	10	26.0	35.0
11	89.2	81.6	11	28.0	30.6
12	83.5	93.2	12	30.0	26.8
13	78.8	106.0	13	31.7	23.5
14	74.9	120.3	14	33.3	20.8
15	71.6	136.1	15	35.0	18.4
16	68.8	153.8	16	36.3	16.2
17	66.4	173.4	17	37.6	14.4
18	64.4	195.4	18	38.8	12.8
19	62.6	220.0	19	40.0	11.4
20	61.0	247.5	20	41.0	10.0
21	59.7	278.2	21	41.8	9.0
22	58.6	312.7	22	42.6	8.0
23	57.6	351.9	23	43.4	7.1
24	56.7	394.6	24	44.0	6.3
25	56.0	443.1	25	44.7	5.6
30	53.2	789.7	30	47.0	3.2
35	51.8	1405.4	35	48.2	1.8
40	51.0	2500.0	40	49.0	1.0
45	50.5	4446.0	45	49.4	0.56
50	50.3	7905.6	50	49.7	0.32
55	50.2	14,058.0	55	49.8	0.18
60	50.1	25,000.0	60	49.9	0.10

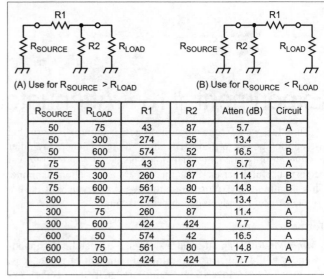

R$_{SOURCE}$	R$_{LOAD}$	R1	R2	Atten (dB)	Circuit
50	75	43	87	5.7	A
50	300	274	55	13.4	B
50	600	574	52	16.5	B
75	50	43	87	5.7	A
75	300	260	87	11.4	B
75	600	561	80	14.8	B
300	50	274	55	13.4	A
300	75	260	87	11.4	A
300	600	424	424	7.7	B
600	50	574	42	16.5	A
600	75	561	80	14.8	A
600	300	424	424	7.7	A

Figure 3—Minimum-loss attenuators match system impedances while exacting the least amount of signal energy.

- Try some of the other attenuations in the table. A 6 dB Pi-attenuator can be made from 150 Ω and 39 Ω resistors. Use 39 Ω and 10 Ω resistors for a 20 dB T-attenuator.

If you make the attenuator a permanent addition to your tool kit, you don't have to use a fancy enclosure. Find any metal enclosure that will seal tightly. (Some of the hallmarks of a good attenuator are insignificant leakage, constant impedance and accuracy.) Keep the leads short and straight so that the attenuator will work at high frequencies without looking like an inductor.

Using an Attenuator for Isolation

Attenuators can also provide isolation between two systems. This is useful at RF, where output amplifiers are usually designed to expect a load of 50 Ω. For example, signal generators expect a low VSWR to maintain their calibrated output level and purity. The input impedance of circuits such as filters, transmission lines and antennas is often not 50 Ω, however. An attenuator in front of the circuit being tested keeps the VSWR low at the generator's output.

Suppose you want to test a series-resonant trap to notch out a strong local broadcast station. The impedance of the filter will be just a few ohms, let's say 5 Ω at the notch frequency, and very high elsewhere. If you have the filter connected across a 50 Ω receiver input, the VSWR at the generator output will rise to 10:1 at the notch frequency. This will likely upset the generator calibration and degrade the accuracy of your filter attenuation measurements.

What happens if you put the 50 Ω, 10 dB attenuator between the generator and the filter? Because energy to and from the filter is reduced by 10 dB in each direction, the generator thinks the 10:1 SWR is much lower, 1.18:1. SWR is reduced because the attenuator reduces the reflected power from the mismatched load to a very small amount—0.7% of the generator's output power.[2] Figure 2 shows how much attenuation from a fixed attenuator or a feed line reduces VSWR.

- Put the 50 Ω, 10 dB attenuator back together and measure the resistance at the input with the output connected to a 51 Ω resistor, a 5 Ω resistor (two 10 Ω in parallel), an open-circuit and a short-circuit.
- Compute the VSWR for each with the following formula:
  $$VSWR = R_{meas}/50 \quad (if \ R_{meas} > 50 \ \Omega)$$
  $$VSWR = 50/R_{meas} \quad (if \ R_{meas} < 50 \ \Omega)$$
  The 10 dB pad is pretty effective at reducing SWR, isn't it?

Using an Attenuator for Impedance Matching

You might be more interested in making an attenuator match the impedance of two systems than in creating a fixed amount of loss. This can be done effectively with just a few resistors in an L configuration, similar to that shown in Figure 1. It is desired to match the impedances while creating as little extra loss as possible. These are called *minimum loss* attenuators.

Figure 3 shows the L attenuator circuits used for this application and several sets of values that make useful impedance-matching attenuators. If you have other impedances to match, an on-line calculator is available at **home.sandiego.edu/~ekim/ e194rfs01/minl_atten/minlosatten.html**.

Suggested Reading

Enter "audio attenuator" into an Internet search engine to find many different links. If you'd like to try a useful attenuator construction project, see the article at **www.arrl.org/tis/info/ pdf/9506033.pdf**.

Shopping List

- 10 (2 each)—10, 39, 51, 75 and 100 Ω, ¼ W resistors

Next Month

To transfer control and data signals between equipment with different grounds, engineers often use electro-optical components. Join in as we attempt to shed light on the workings of the optocoupler.

The Hands-On Radio Web site is **www.arrl.org/tis/info/ html/hands-on-radio/**.

[2]The attenuator reduces the power reaching the load by 10 dB. The reflected power is 1.7 dB below the forward power (return loss), which the attenuator reduces by another 10 dB for a total round trip loss of 21.7 dB. This corresponds to a VSWR of 1.18:1.

Experiment #14—Optocouplers

Trying to pass a signal between two circuits that don't share a common ground would be quite difficult but for the *optocoupler*. Also called an *optoisolator*, these handy devices use light to transfer a signal between circuits without using a direct connection. You'll find them used to isolate sensitive circuits, provide safety barrier between operators and high-voltage circuits and replace relays in low-power applications. Let's learn how they work.

Terms to Learn

• *Current-Transfer Ratio (CTR)*—the ratio of output current to the LED input current expressed as a percentage
• *Rise Time and Fall Time*—rise time refers to increasing signals and fall time to decreasing signals. Both refer to the time it takes for a circuit's output to reach 90% of the final output level after a sudden change at its input
• *Isolation Voltage*—the maximum rated voltage difference between an optoisolator's output and input

Background

The optocoupler was a serendipitous discovery. Early transistors were contained in metal cans with wire leads. Where they passed through the can, tiny glass beads around the wire kept them insulated. Troubleshooting a mysterious current leakage problem, technicians discovered that light entering through the beads caused the transistor to conduct slightly—transistor junctions were light sensitive! After the invention of the LED, the modern optocoupler was created.

One of the most popular IC optocouplers is the 4N35, one of a whole family of similar devices. Inside the IC, an infrared LED is positioned so that it shines on an exposed transistor junction. The photons of light take the place of base current, turning on the transistor. Optocouplers are available with SCRs, FETs, diodes, logic gates and driver amplifiers for outputs.

Central to design with optocouplers is the *current transfer ratio (CTR)*, a factor specified in percent. CTR is very similar to a transistor's current gain, or beta. As in a transistor, for a given input or *forward current*, I_f, through the LED, the output current, I_C, can only reach CTR × I_f.

$$CTR\ (\%) = [I_C / I_f] \times 100 \qquad [Eq\ 1]$$

CTR depends on the level of I_f and is usually specified as a maximum and minimum value for a given value of I_f and voltage across the output transistor. For example, the Agilent data sheet for the 4N35 (Figure 4, as shown in **literature.agilent.com/litweb/pdf/5988-4114EN.pdf**) has a graph of CTR versus I_f showing that CTR is optimum for a range in I_f of between 5 and 40 mA, dropping rapidly above and below that range.

Typical CTR values for optocouplers range from 50 to 300, with I_f in a range of 1 to 20 mA. The 4N35 is specified to have a minimum CTR of 100% with an I_f of 10 mA and a V_{CE} of 10 V across the output transistor. On Figure 4 of the data sheet, find I_f of 10 mA and trace upward to the curve on the graph labeled "$R_{BE} = \infty$." All are comfortably over 100%.

What's up with those curves labeled "$R_{BE} = \infty$, 500k and 100k?" Figure 1 shows the internal connections or *pin-outs* of the 4N35. You'll see that the base of the output transistor is connected to pin 6. CTR can be controlled by connecting the base to the emitter with a resistor, R_{BE}, so that some of the current created by the LED's light is diverted around the base-emitter junction. Conversely, the base pin can be used to bias the transistor on. For most designs, this connection is left open—do not ground it or tie it to a power supply voltage.

Optocouplers may be a great solution to isolating circuits from one another, but they are much slower than a transistor to turn on and off. This is because the photons that fall on the phototransistor take some time to diffuse into and out of the base—more time than with direct connections to the base. *rise time*, t_r, and *fall time*, t_f, are the parameters used to specify the switching speed of the output transistor. You'll find them in the data sheet's "Electrical Specifications" table. Data sheet Figures 9 and 10 show the effect of the load resistance on switching speed and frequency response. As R_L is reduced I_C increases, which means that the transistor reacts quicker to the incoming photons and when turning off, gets rids of them faster. Switching speed is particularly important when the optocoupler is being used to transmit digital data where signal edges need to be clean and fast.

To design an optocoupler circuit, you need to know the output load and power supply voltage. For example, if you are going to drive a reed relay, the coil resistance, say 500 Ω, is R_L. If the power supply is 12 V, the optocoupler's output will have to sink 24 mA. For a CTR of 100%, that requires I_f = 24 mA. Assuming an input voltage of 5 V and the typical forward voltage drop of the LED, 1.2 V:

$$R_{in} = (V_{in}-V_f) / I_f \text{ and } I_f = (V_{in}-V_f) / R_{in} \qquad [Eq\ 2]$$
$$= (5-1.2) / 24 = 158\ \Omega\text{—use a 150 }\Omega\text{ resistor}$$

The speed of the optocoupler is often a concern, as well. If you are going to use it to transmit digital data (a common application) the sum of rise and fall times should be less than 10% of the duration of the fastest bit you will send. For ex-

---

Maximum, Minimum and Typical—The Data Sheet Specifications

Properly interpreting these figures from a data sheet can be crucial to a successful design, particularly if a run of several circuits will be built. Maximum and Minimum are *guaranteed values*. All parts will fall between these two values. Depending on your design, either may be the *worst-case* that your circuit should be able to accommodate. A "typical" value is usually the most common or an average value (they're not always the same). If you're only building one circuit, using a typical value is probably okay, but you may have to test a few parts for getting one with "typical" performance.

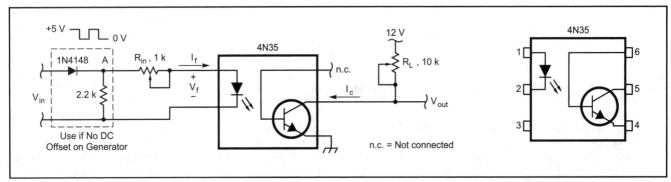

Figure 1—Adjust the input and output resistances to observe the effect of current levels on CTR and on switching speed.

ample, one bit of 9600 baud data is approximately 10 μs wide, so $t_r + t_f$ must be less than 1 μs. If you look at Figure 9 of the data sheet, you'll see that the 4N35 is not a good choice for 9600 baud data! For a load resistance of 1 kΩ, $t_r + t_f = 40$ μs, so the narrowest data pulse would be 400 μs—about 240 baud.

Working with Optocouplers

The first set of tests we'll do illustrate the effect of CTR and load resistance, R_L, on the ability of the optocoupler to transfer a signal.

Start by connecting the circuit shown in Figure 1. If your signal generator can add a dc offset to its output signal, you don't need the diode and 2.2 kΩ resistor. Set the signal generator to output a 3 kHz square wave and adjust the voltage so that the waveform at point A alternates between 5 V and ground. Set R_{in} to 1 kΩ and R_L to 5 kΩ. Use Eq 2 to calculate I_f.

Connect the oscilloscope to point A and to the output. You should see complementary waveforms with the output low with the input high, and vice versa. Once you have the circuit working, zoom in as shown in Figure 2. Notice that the rising edge of the output is rounded with respect to the falling edge. (Hint—trigger on the falling edge of the input signal and set the sweep speed to 20 μs/division.)

- Measure the delay from the falling edge of the input signal to where the output begins to rise. This is t_d. Estimate t_r and t_f. Reduce R_L to approximately 2.5 kΩ to see the effect of increasing I_C on t_r and t_f. Adjust R_{in} to 600 and 400 Ω and observe the effect of varying I_f. Return R_{in} to 500 Ω.
- Continue to reduce R_L. The minimum output voltage level will begin to rise above ground. Stop when it reaches 5 V and measure R_L. Calculate $I_C = (12\ V - 5\ V) / R_L$. Use the previously calculated value of I_f to calculate CTR using Eq 1. My 4N35 had a CTR of 113%, exceeding the specified minimum value.
- Return both potentiometers to their original values. Increase the frequency of the input signal to see what happens as t_r and t_f begin to eat up the signal.
- Experiment by changing input signal level and output voltage while observing the effect on output voltage levels. Try a design—pick a value of R_L, an input voltage, and a power supply voltage, then figure out R_{in} and try it!

Suggested Reading

Chapter 9 in *The Art of Electronics*, by Horowitz and Hill, discusses optocouplers as a means of interfacing with logic circuits. Agilent Technologies publishes a wide variety of excellent application notes and the *Optocoupler Designer's Guide* (Agilent part number 5988-4082EN) is worth the download at **literature.agilent.com/litweb/pdf/5988-4082EN.pdf**.

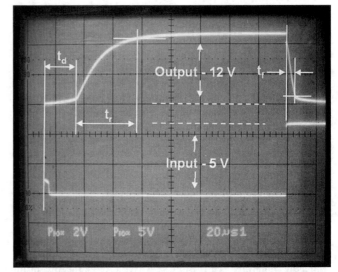

Figure 2—The upper trace shows the output waveform. Notice the significant rise and fall times of the output waveform.

Shopping List

- 4N35 optocoupler (available from many suppliers)
- 1N4148 diode
- 2.2 kΩ resistor, 1 kΩ and 10 kΩ potentiometers

Next Month

We return to power supply design with the first installment of a multipart experiment that will introduce you to switching power supply technology.

The Hands-On Radio Web site is **www.arrl.org/tis/info/html/hands-on-radio/**.

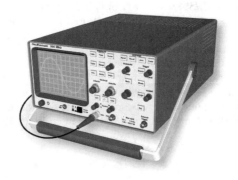

Experiment #25: Totem Pole Outputs

If you could look "under the hood" of ICs, the chances are good that you'd find a similar circuit at many of their output pins. With one transistor sitting atop another, the totem pole output does sort of look like its namesake. It's mighty handy, too, as you're about to find out!

Terms to Learn

- *Class A, AB, B operation*—an amplifier's operation with current flowing at all times (Class A), with a small current for zero input (Class AB) and with zero current at zero input (Class B).
- *Split Supply*—a power source with equal positive and negative voltages referenced to a common connection.

Introduction

Recently, I needed to adapt a small piece of consumer audio gadgetry to run on an ac supply (it was battery powered) for long-term use in the shack. Just get a wall-wart supply and add a connector…right? Wrong! The gadget used two batteries as a split supply; so the design search began. In the process, I crossed paths with the push-pull amplifier and the totem pole output circuit.

The Push-Pull Amplifier

The push-pull amplifier circuit shown in Figure 1A is a pair of emitter followers—one NPN and one PNP—connected as mirror images. Imagine removing the PNP transistor to see the upper emitter follower. Then imagine removing the NPN transistor to see the lower emitter follower.

Assuming V+ and V− are equal and opposite, as V_{IN} goes positive, Q1 is turned ON. Negative input signals turn Q2 ON. For zero input, both of the transistors are OFF. Finished? Not quite. To turn either transistor ON, its base-emitter voltage must exceed 0.7 V, creating crossover distortion as shown in the waveforms at the bottom of Figure 1A. Because each transis-

tor is completely OFF with zero input signal, this is Class B operation. If you need to hold the output voltage close to zero or make the signal go through zero volts smoothly, some improvements are required.

Figure 1B shows the circuit that forms the basis for many op-amp outputs. Resistors R1 and R2 bias the transistors to a small current, even for zero input, since the forward voltage drop across D1 and D2 is enough to turn the transistors on. This level of bias results in Class AB operation. The common-emitter and emitter-follower designs of earlier circuits (Experiments #1 and #2) used a large bias current that allowed the output current to make both positive and negative swings, or Class A operation.

The bias current lets both transistors work together to control the output when the input is between ±0.7 V. The penalty is that the constant current flow wastes some power. How much current flows when the input is zero? The bias current flows through R1, both transistor base-emitter junctions, and R2.

$$I_{bias} = ([(V+) + (V-)] - [V_{BE1} + V_{BE2}]) / (R1 + R2)$$

As the input signal becomes more positive, the additional current through D2 increases the voltage drop across R2, lowering V_{BE2} and turning off the lower transistor. All of the output current is supplied by Q1. The opposite occurs when the input signal is negative. This means that the output is in phase with the input.

I_{bias} has to be large enough so that either transistor can supply the maximum output current required by the load. If V+ and V− are balanced and equal to $\pm V_{PS}$ and, remembering that increasing the output voltage reduces the voltage across the biasing resistors, then:

$$I_{LOADmax} = V_{LOADmax} / R_{LOAD} = I_{bias} (\beta) \qquad [1]$$

$$R1, 2 = (V_{PS} - V_{BE} - V_{LOADmax}) / I_{bias} = (V_{PS} - 0.7) / \\ [(V_{LOADmax} / R_{LOAD}) / \beta] \qquad [2]$$

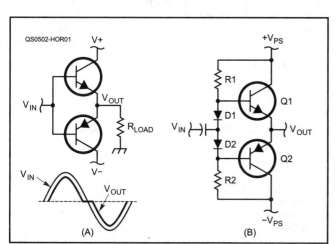

Figure 1—The push-pull amplifier in B uses bias and diodes to operate in Class AB, eliminating the crossover distortion shown in the waveform of A.

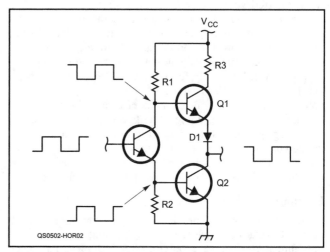

Figure 2—The totem pole circuit operates as an inverter on digital signals, driving the output high or low very quickly.

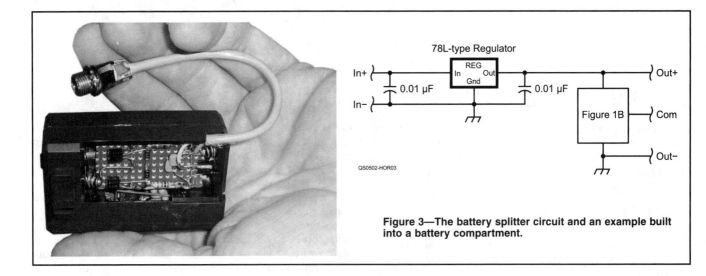

Figure 3—The battery splitter circuit and an example built into a battery compartment.

For example, if $R_{LOAD} = 100\ \Omega$, $V_{PS} = \pm6$ V, $V_{LOADmax} = \pm3$ V and each transistor has $\beta=125$, the bias resistors must be $(6 - 0.7 - 3) / [(3 / 100) / 125] = 9.6\ k\Omega$. If the transistors, bias resistors, and diodes are all perfectly matched (identical electrical characteristics), the output voltage will be exactly centered between $\pm V_{PS}$.

The Totem Pole Output

The true totem pole output circuit shown in Figure 2 is derived from the push-pull amplifier. The bottom transistor is now an NPN transistor, just like the top one. The totem pole adds an input transistor that acts as a phase splitter; inverting the output signals between its collector and emitter. The output of the totem pole is inverted from the input signal, as well.

When the input signal is low, Q3 is OFF, turning Q2 OFF—Q1 can then drive the output high. When the input signal is high, both Q3 and Q2 are ON—pulling the output low. But wait—what happens to Q1? Assuming that the input signal is large enough to drive Q3 and Q2 into saturation, V_{CE3} and V_{CE2} drop to about 0.3 V. That means the voltage at the base of Q1 (V_{BE1}) will be the sum of V_{CE3} and $V_{BE2} = 0.3 + 0.7 = 1$ V. With Q1's emitter connected to Q2's saturated collector voltage of 0.3 V, $V_{BE1} = 1 - 0.3 = 0.7$ V. That would leave Q1 turned ON, but D1 comes to the rescue. By removing 0.7 V from V_{BE1}, Q1 stays turned OFF when Q2 is ON.

All is well and good, except for the short period of time when the input signal is changing from low to high. During that transition, both Q1 and Q2 are ON to varying degrees, and that causes a big jump in the current drawn from the power supply. Granted, it's only for a short time in a digital signal, but those current spikes can cause drops in the power supply voltage, which results in problems elsewhere in the circuit. Having a lot of devices doing a lot of switching also increases the average power consumed. R3 (typically 100 Ω or less) limits the current spikes to a low value. The cost is that it takes longer for the output to change between high and low voltages and the high-level output voltage is lowered slightly.

Building a Battery Splitter

Back to my original problem—splitting the power supply output. Let's design a battery splitter. The end result is shown in Figure 3. You can see the circuit assembled on a small piece of perforated board cut to fit a 2-AAA battery compartment. The outputs are soldered directly to the battery contacts.

The battery splitter circuit is that of Figure 1B—omitting any input signal connection. We just want a constant output

equal to half the power supply voltage. The load is the common connection to the circuit you're powering. Here's how to design your own:

- Determine how much current your circuit draws. Calculate the value for R1 and R2 using equations 1 and 2. Leave plenty of margin when estimating the current requirements.
- Construct the circuit using the closest fixed values for the resistors. If you want to adjust your output voltage, substitute a potentiometer for R1 or R2 of about twice the value of the fixed resistor. For finer adjustments, use a fixed value resistor (of half the calculated value) in series with a potentiometer of close to the calculated value.
- I added a 3-terminal voltage regulator (see Experiment #8) to the input, because the wall-wart supply output had a lot of ripple that showed up as hum in the gadget's output audio. If the supply output is well filtered, you can omit the regulator. Depending on the voltage requirements, select a 78L05, -08, -12, or a 78L015.
- It's a good idea to build the circuit on your prototyping board first. Use resistors as closely matched as possible. Measure the output voltage—variations will be mostly due to mismatches in β. Substitute different transistors (if available), and vary one of the resistor values to observe the effect on the output voltage. Try different loads, as well.
- Once you build the splitter, be aware that you may need bypass capacitors at the input and output, if you are going to use it in the high RF fields that are possible in the ham shack.

Shopping List

- 2N3904 and 2N3906 transistors (or equivalent)
- 2 each, 1N4148 diodes (or equivalent)
- 78L-type voltage regulator
- 2 each, 0.01 μF, 16 V ceramic or disc capacitors
- Potentiometer and $^1/_4$ W resistors

Suggested Reading

The Art of Electronics, by Horowitz and Hill, has a lengthy discussion of the push-pull amplifier in its section on "Amplifier Building Blocks." For a more detailed description of the totem pole, try **www.digitallab.uni.cc/electronics-tutorials/logic-gates/The-not-gates3.php**.

Next Month

Routing ac signals with semiconductors eliminates clunky relays and manual switches. Next month, we'll explore the use of PIN diodes and some cool analog switch ICs!

Experiment #26: Solid-State RF Switches

PIN diodes and integrated-circuit CMOS switches have done away with the mechanical relay for many switching duties. This month, we learn how these devices work and experiment with a simple switch.

Terms to Learn

- *Compound Switches*—switching circuits made from several SPST switching elements
- *Doping*—impurities added to semiconductors to create P or N type material with extra or missing (holes) electrons, respectively
- *Intrinsic*—semiconductor material that does not have electron or hole donor impurities added. The material may be a pure semiconductor or doped with an impurity such as gold that does not affect the hole/electron balance.

Introduction

The PIN diode can act as either a switch or attenuator, controlled by a dc bias current. The integrated circuit CMOS switch uses MOSFETs to pass or block ac signals. Common in amateur equipment, these devices work at audio through microwaves with a fraction of the power requirement of relays and they are many times faster.

The PIN Diode

In the common PN junction diode, P and N type material are in direct contact. This creates a thin depletion region where holes and electrons quickly cancel each other out. The PIN diode, shown in Figure 1, adds a thick intrinsic or un-doped I layer between thin layers of highly doped P and N type material. The bias voltage applied from P to N creates a bias current of holes and electrons traveling across the I layer. They don't immediately combine with each other as they would in a regular PN diode. This *stored charge* makes the I layer a good conductor. Without the bias voltage, the resistance of the I layer is high and the PIN diode acts like a small capacitor.

When an ac voltage is added to the bias voltage across the diode, an ac current also flows. Surprisingly, the PIN diode can conduct an RF current larger than the bias current without rectifying it! The negative cycle of the RF current simply occurs too quickly for the stored charge in the I layer to be consumed, which would switch the diode OFF to a high resistance state. Diodes with thin I layers have faster switching times, while those with thicker I-layers can handle more current without distortion.

A PIN Diode Switch

Figure 1 shows two simple examples of switching circuits using PIN diodes. Each acts as an SPST switch in a different way. The diode in the series switch presents a high or low resistance in series with the RF signal path. Applying bias voltage and current causes the diode to change to its low-resistance state, allowing RF to flow to the load, R_L.

The shunt switch acts in a way dc switches aren't allowed—to prevent RF power from reaching the load, the diode shorts the signal to ground! The result is the same as the series switch—no RF voltage at the load. The shunt switch is usually used to protect an input or to present a high SWR, reflecting RF signals in a transmission line.

In both cases, extra components are required to keep the bias and RF signals apart. The dc blocking capacitors, C_{BL}, keep the bias current from flowing in the RF source or the load. The inductor, L_{BIAS}, presents a high impedance to the RF signal—typically at least 10 times the load impedance. R_{BIAS} sets the level of bias current in the diode. Sometimes, bias current is allowed to flow in the load, which eliminates one of the blocking capacitors. If the bias voltage source is also adjustable, the load can also serve as R_{BIAS}, eliminating one more component.

From these simple circuits, all manner of switches can be constructed. An SPDT switch is made from two series SPST switches connected to a single RF source. Remember the open-shorted quarter-wave stub from Experiment #22? Instead of a mechanical switch at the end of the stub, a PIN diode switch could be used instead. Combinations of series and shunt switches make up *compound switches* that provide much better performance than a single diode.

A compound switch found in transceivers is the Transmit-Receive switch shown in Figure 2. By alternating the diode bias voltages between ON and OFF, either the transmitter or the receiver is connected to the antenna (in the middle). Both diodes share a common bias resistor. The three RF chokes (RFC), isolate the bias voltage supply from the RF signals.

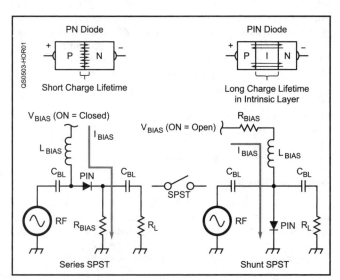

Figure 1—The PIN diode uses a wide intrinsic layer between P and N to create a controllable resistance. The PIN diode's variable resistance then creates simple switches.

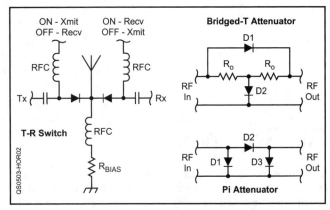

Figure 2—A T-R switch is a common application of PIN diode switches. When the full range of the PIN diode resistance is used, a continuously variable attenuator can be built. These are common in receiver gain control circuits.

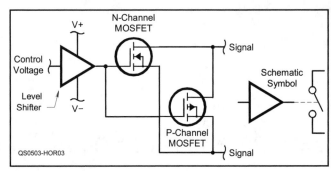

Figure 3—Parallel P and N channel MOSFETs are used to construct a solid state SPST switch.

PIN Diode Attenuators

In a switch, the PIN diode's resistance is changed between its extreme high and low values. It's also possible to create a variable resistance by controlling the amount of bias current flowing through the diode. PIN attenuators are often used in receiver AGC circuits. The most popular attenuator circuits are the bridged-T and pi circuits shown in Figure 2. (The biasing components are omitted for clarity.)

For the least attenuation in the bridged-T circuit, current through D1 is high, so it has the lowest resistance. Low bias current through D2 gives it a high resistance. To increase attenuation, bias current through D1 is lowered (increasing its resistance) and the bias current through D2 is raised (decreasing its resistance). At maximum attenuation, D2 looks like a short so that both the source and load "see" their matched resistance, R_o.

The pi attenuator works similarly. Shunt diodes D1 and D3 are turned OFF and the series diode D2 is turned ON for minimum attenuation and the opposite for maximum attention. In both circuits, the diode's resistance versus bias current characteristics must be well known and carefully matched.

Building a Diode Switch

PIN diodes are not that common, so we're going to practice diode switching using a 1N4148, an ordinary PN diode. This diode doesn't have a controllable ON resistance like a real PIN diode, but it can act as a good switch.

- Build the series SPST circuit of Figure 1 using a 1 mH choke, a 51 Ω load resistor, and 0.1 μF blocking capacitors.
- Assuming that you will be using a 12 V dc power supply, calculate the value for R_{BIAS} required for 10 mA of bias current, assuming that the forward voltage drop of a PIN diode is 1.0 V: $R_{BIAS} = (12\ V - V_F) / I_{BIAS} = 1.1\ k\Omega$ (use 1 kΩ).
- Connect a 100 kHz, 0.3 V_{P-P} sine wave to the input. (This level is small enough to prevent turning off the diode on negative peaks.) Connect an oscilloscope across the 51 Ω resistor. (A DVM may be used, but may not be accurate at this frequency.)
- With the bias voltage at 12 V dc, you should see a replica of the input waveform across the output resistor. Turn the bias voltage off and the output will go to zero.
- Experiment with gradually reducing the bias voltage below 3 V to see the diode act as an attenuator. Note that for very low bias voltages, the output becomes distorted as the diode begins to rectify the input.

- If you do have access to PIN diodes, such as an MPN3404, substitute one for the 1N4148 and repeat the experiment.

Integrated CMOS Switches

To switch audio and low-frequency RF signals, such as video, the integrated CMOS switch, shown in Figure 3, is used instead of the PIN diode, which works best at higher frequencies. Usually packaged as four or more switches in a single IC (such as the DG201BDJ), a logic-level input from TTL or CMOS circuits controls a solid-state SPST switch. The SPDT configuration is also available, so that the circuit builder can create very complicated switching circuits.

The switch itself is comprised of a pair of P and N channel MOSFETs, connected in parallel, to conduct either positive or negative signal voltages. When their gates are driven high, the source-drain channels create a low resistance path between the two signal pins. Because the switch is completely solid-state, it can turn on and off in a few hundred nanoseconds.

Using these switches in a circuit is a breeze, but you must keep their limitations in mind. To avoid distortion, the signals must be no greater than the IC's power supply voltages. The on-resistance (R_{DS}) of the switch (typically about 100 Ω) is much greater than that of a manual switch and must be accounted for in your circuit design. Maximum current for the switch is a few tens of mA and they do not withstand significant overloads very well. Using a single-supply polarity, such as +12 V dc, requires capacitive coupling of ac signals into and out of the switch and dc offset at the input to half the supply voltage. The signal bandwidth for most CMOS switches is a few MHz. Nevertheless, play within their rules and you can greatly simplify your signal switching!

Shopping List

- 1N4148 diode (or equivalent)
- 2 each, 0.1 μF, 16 V ceramic or disc capacitors
- 1 mH inductor
- 51 Ω and 1000 Ω, $^1/_4$ W resistors

Suggested Reading

For more information about PIN diodes, the Microsemi tutorial *PIN Diode Fundamentals* is available at **www. microsemi. com/micnotes/701.pdf** and the serious student will want to read Agilent's application note AN922, *Applications of PIN Diodes* at **cp.literature.agilent.com/litweb/pdf/5965-8666E.pdf.**

Next Month

If you've been doing these experiments with an oscilloscope, you are pretty familiar with the basic controls by now. Next month, we'll learn a few new tricks for the 'scope that may surprise you!

Experiment #36 — The Up-Down Counter

With so much of our analog hobby supported by digital electronics, counters are everywhere—timing, tallying, totaling. This month's experiment examines an inexpensive and versatile counter chip you'll be able to use in many designs.

Terms to Learn

Synchronous—all counter stages react simultaneously to the input

Ripple—each successive counter stage reacts to the input signal in a sequence

Introduction

Welcome to the start of *Hands-On Radio's* fourth year! The response of readers affirms that hams love to roll up their sleeves and dig deep into understanding of how electronics work. I'll do my best to help keep you shoveling!

If you open up a modern radio of reasonable sophistication you will find any number of black, multi-legged creatures—digital chips. They range from a few logic gates to full blown digital signal processors. In many cases, a significant portion of their duties involves handling pulses and clock signals from timing circuits, displays, annunciators, or user controls. These functions require the services of *counters*, whether implemented as discrete parts or buried in a complex integrated circuit (IC).

Counter Basics

The fundamental building block of counters is a digital logic *element* called a *flip-flop*. We met flip-flops in experiments 5 (Timers) and 31 (Multivibrators). ARRL members will find all previous experiments on the *Hands-On Radio* Web site at **www.arrl.org/tis/info/HTML/Hands-On-Radio**. The flip-flop responds to an input signal by toggling its outputs between two configurations or *states*. Since there are only two output states, each state is revisited at every other change.

Counters are really digital *dividers*. They don't divide numbers but rather frequencies. For example, if my input signal to a flip-flop is a train of pulses at a 100 Hz rate, the flip-flop's outputs will repeat in specific combinations of 1's and 0's at a frequency of 50 Hz, dividing the input frequency by two. By *cascading* the output of one flip-flop to another's input, I can make as many successive divisions by two as I need.

Figure 1 shows how two *D-type* flip-flops are connected together so that an input signal is divided by four. CLK represents the input to the flip-flop and Q the outputs. The overbar on $\overline{Q}$ shows that it is always in the opposite state to the pin labeled Q: if Q is a 1, then $\overline{Q}$ will be a 0 and vice versa. D represents an input to the flip-flop that controls how the outputs will respond to an input signal. (For a complete discussion of flip-flops and how they work, see the references in *Suggested Reading* below.) The Q signals form the counter circuit outputs.

The figure also includes a *truth table* and *state diagram*. The truth table is a description of how the counter outputs change in response to input pulse or *counts* (labeled CNT). Each successive

COUNT causes the Q outputs to advance to the next combination or state. After four changes, the outputs return to the same state. The change from both outputs being a 1 to a 0 is called *rollover*. The number of different states the counter outputs can have is called the counter's *modulus*. The state diagram at the right shows the counter advancing from state to state as each successive input pulse occurs. The number in each state bubble corresponds to one line in the truth table.

The truth table shows the combination of counter outputs forming a *binary* number. This counter can count a total of four input pulses, labeled 0 to 3. If I added a third flip-flop, then I would have one more output or *bit* in my binary number, so the circuit could then have a total of 8 different states (a modulus of 8) and the outputs would form a binary number from 0 to 7. Counters may be referred to by the number of output bits in the binary number they generate, so the counter in Figure 1 is a two-bit counter (nothing derogatory implied).

Staying in Sync

The counter in Figure 1 is an example of a *ripple counter*. The input at the left causes the first flip-flop to change, the output of which then causes the second to change. The changes in the outputs ripple through the counter. One problem—there's a short period of time when the outputs aren't in the right state! (This period of time is called the *propagation delay*.) For example, as the counter moves from state 1 to state 2, both outputs are 0 (state 0) until the second flip-flop reacts and catches up. Oops. This might not be a problem, but if the counter is being read by a microprocessor or controlling a switch, then that *transient* state or *glitch* can cause unexpected behavior.

The solution to the problem of transient states is to wire up all the flip-flops so that they change at the same time making it a *synchronous counter*. To make a synchronous counter requires a *J-K flip-flop* as shown in Figure 2. The two-bit synchronous

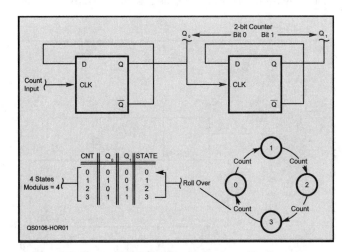

Figure 1—A two-bit ripple counter made from flip-flops can count from 0 to 3 in a continuous sequence.

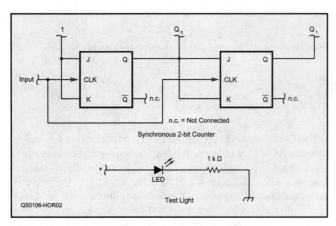

Figure 2—The synchronous counter uses J-K flip-flops and changes all of its outputs simultaneously. This prevents transient states due to propagation delay.

counter has exactly the same number and order of states as the two-bit ripple counter, but always proceeds from state to state in the correct order, without any transient states.

Practical Synchronous Counters

Counters such as the CD4029 are combined with additional support circuitry in one package to perform several useful functions. Officially, its title is "Presettable Binary/Decade Up/Down Counter." (Download the CD4029 data sheet from **jameco.com** by entering "CD4029" into the "Mfr Part # or Keyword" window and clicking "Go." The data sheet is available under "View Current Documents" in the part's description window.)

In its simplest configuration, the CD4029 is a four-bit synchronous counter that counts pulses at the CLOCK pin. The outputs (Q1, Q2, Q3 and Q4) form a *hexadecimal* number from 0 to 15 in 16 states. The CD4029 can also count from 0 to 9 in 10 states, if the BINARY/DECADE pin is grounded. This is a *decade counter*. In either binary or decimal modes, the CARRY OUT (or OUT) pin is grounded when the counter reaches its maximum count (9 or 15). The CARRY IN (or ENABLE) pin allows the counter to count when grounded.

The CD4029 can also count backwards, called *counting down* or *downcounting*. This is controlled by the UP/DOWN pin, which is grounded to cause the CD4029 to count down. In this mode the binary number formed by the outputs gets smaller with each count

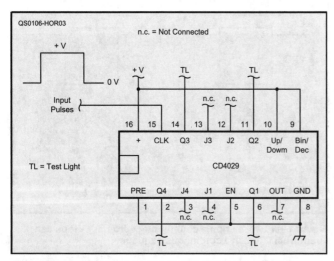

Figure 3—Begin your experiment with this basic CD4029 circuit. This circuit will count from 0 to 15.

and the rollover is from 0 to the maximum count of 9 or 15.

Even more interesting, the CD4029's internal flip-flops can be *preset* so that the counter outputs begin counting at a number other than 0 or the maximum count. This is used when counting a fixed number of pulses. For example, if you want to count six pulses and then generate a signal, configure the CD4029 to count down and preset the counter to 5 (remember that 0 counts as a separate state). As the pulses come in, the counter outputs read 4, 3, 2, 1, and then 0. The OUT pin will then change from 1 to 0 on the fifth pulse. To preset the counter, the *Jam* inputs (J1, J2, J3 and J4) are set to the desired value and a pulse applied to the PRESET ENABLE pin.

Experimenting with the CD4029

Before you rush off to the workbench, here are two basics of working with digital electronics. First, CMOS ICs such as the CD4000 series are very low-power devices and can't tolerate static at their inputs. Keep one finger on circuit ground when installing or removing any component on your breadboard. (Read the articles at **www.arrl.org/tis/info/eds.html** for a more complete discussion of this subject.)

Second, digital signals must be either close to the power supply voltage or close to circuit ground. If you use a 12 V supply, your input signals must also be 12 V or 0 V—a 5 V pulse won't work as an input signal. Check your function generator output and if you can't generate a 12 V signal, use a 7805-type voltage regulator to supply 5 V to your circuit. Similarly, be sure you can set your function generator to output pulses with a minimum voltage at or close to 0 V. Do not leave any input pins open—either ground them or tie them to the positive power supply (+) to prevent erratic operation.

Construct 5 LED "test lights" as shown in Figure 2. Connect a test light to each of the Q pins and to the OUT pin so that a positive voltage on the pin lights the LED.

Connect the CD4029 as shown in Figure 3 as a binary up counter. Apply a 1 Hz square wave to the INPUT and watch the LEDs "count" from 0 (all OFF) rolling over at 15 (all ON).

Move the wire on the UP/DOWN pin from + to ground and watch the LEDs "count backwards."

Move the wire on the BINARY/DECIMAL pin from + to ground and reconnect the UP/DOWN pin to +. The LEDs will now count to 9 (Q0 and Q3 ON, Q1 and Q2 OFF) before rolling over.

You can experiment with presetting the counter by connecting the Jam (J) inputs to + or ground, then temporarily connecting the PRESET ENABLE pin to +.

Shopping List

- CD4029 Up/Down counter.
- 5 ea LED, RadioShack 276-026 or similar.
- 5 ea 1 kΩ, ¼ W resistor.

Suggested Reading

To learn about basic digital circuits, the *ARRL Handbook* has a thorough chapter on Digital Electronics.[1] An excellent text and reference that you will keep for a long time is the *CMOS Cookbook* by Howard Berlin and Don Lancaster. It has numerous practical examples of useful digital circuits.

Next Month

Keep your prototype circuit hooked up because next month we're going to add a numeric display so you can really watch the numbers fly by!

[1]Available from your local dealer, or from the ARRL Bookstore, ARRL order number 9845. Telephone 860-594-0355 or, toll-free in the US 888-277-5289, fax 860-594-0303; **www.arrl.org/shop/; pubsales@arrl.org**.

Experiment #37 — Decoding for Display

Blinking lights are great, but they can be pretty hard to read as a number. This month, we'll update the counter you built in the previous experiment and give it a new way to display its total.

Terms to Learn

- Encoder—transforms data signals into a more compact form or to a coded format useful for a specific purpose.
- Decoder—translates data signals from a coded format to a form suitable for direct use by other circuits or by a display.
- Illegal Count or Input—combinations of inputs to encoders or decoders for which there is no defined output combination.

Introduction

Have you ever thought about how the bright red displays on the front panel of your radio change digital signals into human readable numbers? There are many ways of translating information from the electronic realm into something that makes sense to humans. This is such a common problem that catalogs are full of suitable devices—you'll find them labeled *decoders*.

The very simplest type of decoder is one that takes a binary number and turns on one of its outputs corresponding to the value of the number. For example, the counter in Experiment #36 (**www.arrl.org/tis/info/HTML/Hands-On-Radio**) generates a four bit binary number that counts from 0 to 15. We can determine the count by looking at the combinations of LEDs that are ON or OFF. If we were trying to turn on just one LED for each count, though, we

would have to build another circuit that translates or decodes the four bit number, activating just one output for each value.

The CD4028 BCD-to-decimal (or 1-of-10) decoder is just such a device. Before proceeding, download the CD4028 data sheet from **www.ee.washington.edu/stores** (click on "Library of Data Sheets," then "Logic CMOS - CD4xxx series," then "CD4028") or enter "CD4028 data sheet" into an Internet search engine. The data sheet will show the internal circuit that performs the translation magic. Imagine building all that from discrete ICs! This is why decoders are such useful parts.

The truth table on the data sheet shows just how the part performs. For any combination of inputs that form a number from 0 to 9, just one of the output pins is turned on, or HIGH, corresponding to a voltage close to the power supply voltage, V_{DD}. What about counts from 10 to 15? This is a binary coded decimal (BCD) decoder and it considers those to be illegal values and does not turn on any output. BCD refers to a decimal value from 0 to 9 in a binary format.

Let's give this a try to see how it works on our counter output. Build up another five LED test lights circuit as in Experiment #36 and connect the circuits as shown in Figure 1. There will be a lot of wires, so take your time and double check each connection.[1] Be sure to get the LEDs oriented properly so that the anode is connected to the CD4028 output and the LED only lights when the CD4028 output is HIGH. It will also be easier to see the decoding process working if the LEDs are lined up in order from 0 through 9.

Start with your counter configured to count UP in DECIMAL mode. You should see each LED winking ON and OFF as the counter progresses from 0 through 9 and then cycles back to the first LED. (Those of you with lots of LED test lights can even watch both the binary value and the CD4028 outputs changing.) Note that even though the signal is not symmetric, that is ON and OFF with a 50% duty cycle, the CD4028 outputs are all divided by 10 in frequency

[1]A good source of solid, insulated wire for prototype boards is discarded four conductor, round telephone cable (not the flat cable for handsets or receivers) with red, yellow, green and black wires.

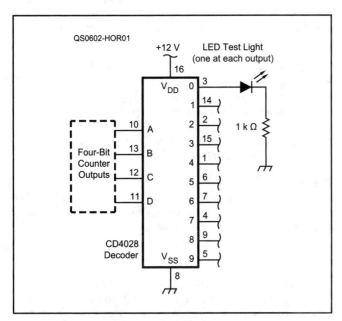

Figure 1—A 1-of-10 decoder circuit lights a single LED for each of the CD4028 counter output states, changing a binary number into a single output.

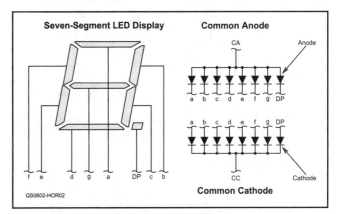

Figure 2—The seven-segment display has LEDs arranged in the shape of a simple digit and can form all decimal and hexadecimal numerals. They are available in both common-anode and common-cathode configurations.

from the counter input signal. Change the counter to count DOWN instead, and the output LED sequence will reverse.

Now change the counter to count UP in BINARY mode so that the output value goes from 0 to 15. Watch what happens when the decoder input reaches a value of 10—all of the output LEDs go out and stay out for six counts before the LED corresponding to 0 turns ON once again. These are the illegal counts that the decoder ignores. If you want a set of outputs that handle all 16 counts, you'll need to use a CD4514 or CD4515 1-of-16 decoder.

Seven-Segment Displays

What if you'd rather see the count displayed directly as a number, instead? This is where the LED display comes in, shown in Figure 2. These displays arrange seven individual bar shaped LEDs in one package. The bars are arranged so that they form the shape of an 8. From this shape all 10 numerals can be formed, as well as serviceable equivalents of the hexadecimal values A, b, C, d, E and F. Some displays also have an LED for a decimal point.

While this simplifies the task of a human reading the display, it complicates the electronics. The patterns that make up the numerals are "nonsense" as far as the orderly world of binary electronics is concerned. As with a 1-of-10 or 1-of-16 decoding circuit, building it up from discrete parts is very inefficient and so seven segment decoder ICs were created, such as the CD4511. Download a data sheet for the CD4511 (use the same technique as before) and look at the internal schematic. Even ignoring the flip-flop section at the left, you'll see a real rat's nest of connections that perform the translation to the seven output display segments.

Let's look at how the displays are constructed, as well. Download the Jameco 17187PS display datasheet from **jameco.com/ wcsstore/Jameco/Products/ProdDS/17187.pdf**. The display's segments are labeled A through G, not to be confused with the hexadecimal numerals A through F. There is also a single decimal point segment labeled DP that we will ignore for now. There are two configurations of pin connections—common anode and common cathode. To simplify the wiring of the displays, the assumption is made that the LEDs will share a common power supply or ground. This is a matter of convenience for the circuit designer. Common-anode displays have the shared pin (pins 3 and 8 on this part) connected to a positive supply. To turn on a segment, the A-G pin is connected to ground through a current-limiting resistor. Common-cathode displays connect the common pin to ground and drive current through the segment anodes and a current-limiting

resistor. Both types are common, so beware when purchasing them! We will use the common-cathode version in this experiment.

Now let's change those blinking LEDs into a number. Connect the circuit of Figure 3, replacing the CD4028 and LED test lights with a CD4511 and seven-segment display. Leave the DP segment disconnected.

Here's how to calculate the value of the current limiting resistors:

$$R = (V_{DD} - V_F) / I_{LED}$$

V_{DD} is the power supply voltage, V_F is the forward voltage drop of the segment LED, and I_{LED} is the current desired. If you want 20 mA through each display segment, are using a 12 V power supply, and the data sheet shows V_F is typically about 2 V, then R = 500 Ω (we'll use the standard value of 470 Ω). You must use a separate resistor for each segment.

Start with your counter configured to count UP in DECIMAL mode. You should see the display counting through the numbers from 0 to 9. Change the counter to count DOWN instead and watch the numbers reverse. What will happen if the counter is changed to BINARY? (Hint—look at the CD4511 truth table.) Try it out and see if the display really does go "dark" from counts 10 to 15. How fast can you run the counter before the numbers start to blur together?

The CD4511 has three control inputs common to display drivers—LATCH ENABLE/STROBE, Blanking Input ($\overline{BI}$), and Lamp Test ($\overline{LT}$). The LATCH ENABLE/STROBE pin allows a microprocessor to quickly write a digit's worth of data to the decoder without having to hold the value on the decoder's inputs forever. By keeping this input LOW, we enable the decoder's outputs continuously. Reconnect this input to the power supply pin to see the effect on the display. $\overline{BI}$ and $\overline{LT}$ are used to force all of the segments OFF or ON, respectively, when either of these inputs is grounded. You can test these functions, too.

One final trick to try is to substitute a single pulse for the counter's steady input stream. A push-button switch or wire jumper can be used to generate a pulse with the RC circuit shown in Figure 3. Any circuit that generates pulses can be used and your counter will keep a running total. If you have a lot of pulses to count, or want to extend your counter display to two digits, cascade a pair of CD4029's as we discussed in Experiment #36 and add a CD4511 to the output of each.

Shopping List

- CD4028—BCD to decimal decoder.
- CD4511—BCD to seven-segment decoder.
- Seven segment, common-cathode LED display, such as Jameco 17187PS or similar.
- LEDs—quantity five RadioShack 276-026 or similar.
- Resistors ¼ W—quantity five, 1 kΩ; quantity seven, 470 Ω.

Suggested Reading

If you have a copy of the *CMOS Cookbook*,[2] there is a whole chapter on digital displays. Even if they're quite complicated, most systems are built around the simple concepts of the basic seven-segment displays and decoders presented here.

Next Month

I purchased a small gel-cell battery to run my SWR analyzer and built a simple battery charger to keep it "topped off" between antenna projects. We'll start with the linear regulator circuit of Experiment #8 and add some useful controls to see how it works.

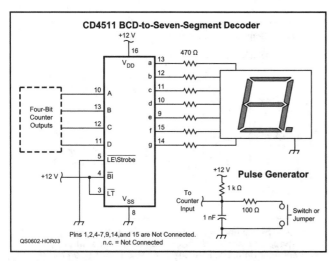

Figure 3—Adding a seven-segment display and a BCD-to-seven segment decoder converts the binary counter output to a human readable numeric digit. A simple pulse circuit can be substituted for counter input to observe pulse counting, as well.

[2]H. W. Silver, "Hands-on Radio, Experiment #34—Technical References," *QST*, Nov 2005, pp 64-65.

Experiment #40 — VOX

This month's column is another "under-the-hood" look at a circuit that many of us use every day — VOX, an abbreviation for *voice operated transmit*. The exact circuit I present is simpler than what you'll find in a commercial radio, but by building it, you'll have a much better grasp of what your radio is doing.

Terms to Learn

AC coupled — a circuit that passes ac voltage and current, but blocks dc.

Trip — activate a circuit with a sharp on-off behavior.

VOX

VOX refers to the function of using the audio signal from a microphone to switch a transceiver between receive and transmit. It's very handy for extended operating, contesting, and for times that your hands are busy doing something else.

Figure 1 shows a block diagram of a typical VOX circuit. Microphone audio is amplified and rectified by the VOX gain amplifier, creating a positive dc voltage. The anti-VOX rectifier creates a negative voltage from a sample of speaker audio. The summing circuit (Σ is the symbol for a summation) adds the two voltages together. A buffer amplifies the remaining voltage. The driver circuit actuates the radio's *transmit-receive* (TR) circuit or relay when there is sufficient output voltage from the buffer. The driver circuit also has an adjustable delay to prevent unnecessary switching between transmit and receive.

• VOX Gain sets the sensitivity of the VOX circuit to microphone audio. By increasing the gain of the VOX circuit's microphone amplifier, it takes less microphone audio to activate or trip the VOX. Controllable VOX gain allows operation in noisy or quiet areas.

• VOX Delay is the time it takes after microphone audio ceases for the output driver circuit to release the TR-switch or relay. The delay is adjustable to accommodate different styles of operating with long or short pauses between words.

• Anti-VOX uses the speaker audio to generate a "don't trip" signal, preventing speaker audio picked up by the mic from tripping the VOX. If the operator is not wearing headphones, audio from the speaker can trip the VOX, leading to a rhythmic "gulping" as the rig switches in and out of transmit.

• A radio's MIC GAIN control does not affect sensitivity of the

VOX circuit because microphone audio follows a separate path to the modulator circuits. This allows you to control modulation separately from the VOX functions.

The VOX microphone amplifier circuit will not be described in this article so that we can focus on the sections unique to VOX operation. If you would like to build your own microphone amplifier, *The 2006 ARRL Handbook* has a good circuit on page 14.44 or download the article "MikeMaster — A Microphone Preamplifier with Noise Gating and Compression" in March 1998 *QST* from the ARRL Technical Information Service at **www.arrl.org/tis/info/shakproj.html**.[1]

Audio Rectifier

Figure 2 shows the circuit for the two rectifiers that turn the ac audio signals from the microphone and speaker into dc voltages. Each rectifier is *ac-coupled* through 0.1 µF capacitors C1 and C3 so that any dc voltage present along with the audio signal does not affect the VOX circuit — it should react only to audio signals. Let's consider the microphone audio rectifier circuit first.

Microphone audio is turned into a positive dc voltage by D1 and D2. D1 passes current to the 0.1 µF charge storage capacitor C2 on positive half cycles. D2 allows current to discharge coupling capacitor C1 on the negative half cycle. In this way, each cycle of microphone audio charges C2 to the peak value of audio voltage minus the forward voltage drop of the diode. R1 is chosen to have a time constant with C2 of about 1 ms so that voice frequency audio can keep C2 charged but still provide enough current to turn on the buffer stage.

Anti-VOX

The anti-VOX rectifier works just like the microphone audio rectifier. D3 and D4 rectify speaker audio, but because they are oriented "backward" from D1 and D2, the voltage across C4 is negative. The sensitivity of the anti-VOX circuit is controlled by adjusting the speaker audio level. In an actual radio circuit a potentiometer is connected across the speaker output to act as a voltage divider and provide a small sample of the audio voltage — no amplifier is needed.

The output voltages from the two rectifier circuits work against

---

[1] *The ARRL Handbook of Radio Communications*. Available from your ARRL dealer or the ARRL Bookstore, ARRL order no. softcover — 9485, hardcover — 9493. Telephone 860-594-0355, or toll-free in the US 888-277-5289; **www.arrl.org/shop/**; **pubsales@arrl.org**.

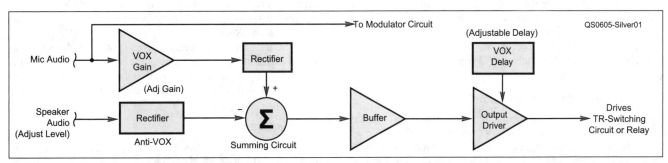

Figure 1 — **This block diagram of a VOX circuit shows how audio inputs from a microphone and speaker are rectified and combined to form a trigger signal. A buffer circuit and driver can operate a relay or control an electronic TR switch.**

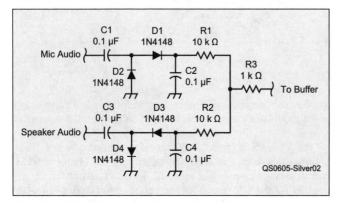

Figure 2 — Each audio input to the VOX circuit is rectified to form a control voltage. The resulting voltages are combined and drive a buffer circuit. Anti-VOX works against the microphone audio to prevent triggering on speaker audio.

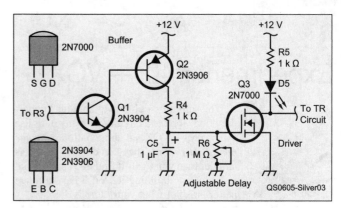

Figure 3 — Buffer, Q1 and Q2, and an adjustable delay circuit drive Q3, a MOSFET output transistor. A MOSFET is used because its high input impedance will not load the delay circuit. R5 and D5 provide a test indicator of the circuit's action.

each other. Microphone audio creates a positive voltage on C2 while speaker audio creates a negative voltage on C4. The resulting voltage at R3 is the sum of the two rectifier output voltages. The operator adjusts the anti-VOX level until the negative voltage on C4 is just enough to cancel the contribution of speaker audio picked up by the microphone.

Buffer

The buffer and driver circuits are shown in Figure 3. The buffer is formed by Q1 and Q2 which are connected to make a very high gain dc amplifier. The total current gain of the buffer equals $\beta Q1 \times \beta Q2$, approximately 10,000 for typical 2N3904 and 2N3906 transistors. As the voltage at the junction of R1, R2 and R3 exceeds 0.4 V, the small current through Q1 quickly turns Q2 ON as well.

When Q2 turns ON, the power supply quickly charges C5 to +12 V through R4. R4 limits the current to 12 V / 1 kΩ = 12 mA through Q2 when C5 is completely discharged, but C5 still charges in a few ms. When microphone input audio ceases, C2 rapidly discharges and Q1 turns OFF, turning OFF Q2 and any charging current into C5.

Driver and Adjustable VOX Delay

As soon as C5 charges to more than 2 to 3 volts, Q3 turns ON, grounding whatever is connected to its drain. This could turn on a relay or ground a signal line to a TR-switching circuit. (The 2N2700 data sheet parameter GATE THRESHOLD VOLTAGE, $V_{GS(th)}$, specifies at what level the 2N7000 will turn ON.) C5 stays charged as long as there is sufficient positive voltage at the junction of R1 and R2 to turn on Q1. A metal oxide semiconductor, field effect transistor (MOSFET) was used for Q3 because the high impedance of its gate would not drain current from C5.

When the buffer turns OFF, C5 begins to discharge through potentiometer R6. As Q3's gate voltage drops below $V_{GS(th)}$ Q3 turns OFF. This results in a *VOX delay* that holds Q3 ON (and the radio in transmit) for short periods when there is no microphone audio. High values of R6 discharge C5 more slowly and result in longer VOX delay times.

Building and Testing the VOX Circuit

For testing the VOX circuitry, one or two audio sources are needed. A function generator will work fine and so will a personal audio player that can supply a couple of volts or more. The VOX circuit will respond best to signals in the voice frequency range of 300 to 3000 Hz.

- Start by building the twin rectifier circuits shown in Figure 2. Test each separately with R1, R2 and R3 disconnected at their common junction. Confirm that audio input voltages

on either input measuring about 1 VRMS create output voltages at C2 or C4 of at least ± 1 V.

- Reconnect R1, R2 and R3, connecting the free end of R3 to ground. If you have two audio sources, connect one to each input and vary the levels to observe their effect on voltage at the resistor's junction.

- Add the buffer amplifier and adjustable delay circuit (C5 and R6), connecting R3 to the base of Q1. Set R6 to approximately 500 kΩ. With power ON and while applying audio only to the microphone input, measure the dc voltage on C5 as the input level increases from zero. Pay close attention to see the "snap action" as the input voltage is raised past the point at which the buffer amplifier turns ON, tripping the VOX.

- Complete the circuit with Q3. Add R5 and D5 to act as a VOX ON/OFF indicator. Q3 should turn ON and OFF as microphone audio input level is changed. Change the value of R6 and observe the change in delay as Q3 turns OFF after microphone audio is removed. With R6 at maximum value, the delay should be on the order of 1s.

- Vary the levels of audio on both inputs to observe the effect of anti-VOX on normal operation. See if you can completely inhibit normal VOX action by increasing anti-VOX audio input.

Recommended Reading

Data sheets for all three transistors are available at **www. ee.washington.edu/stores/**. Click on LIBRARY OF DATA SHEETS, then TRANSISTORS (2N3904 or 2N3906) or FET (2N7000).

Two good *QST* articles present complete VOX circuits suitable for use with transceivers in your shack. A recent article by KB6BT in December 2005 *QST* called "A VOX Circuit for PSK31" is suited for the new digital modes. The classic VOX circuit is presented in March 1976 *QST* by W1KLK, "A VOX For A Very Small Box." For some background, see "Getting to Know Your Radio, Over to You — Transmit/Receive Switching" in February 2006 *QST*.

Log on to the Google search engine (**www.google.com**) and enter an equation such as *2*pi* into the search window and hit RETURN. You might be surprised! Click on MORE ABOUT CALCULATOR under the answer to learn more about this little-known tool.

Next Month

What makes a filter or an amplifier "ring"? To answer that question, you have to understand damping factor — an important part of filter and amplifier design. Next month, you'll see the effects of damping factor on a simple low-pass filter.

For additional notes, check the FAQ section of the Hands-On Radio Web site at **www.arrl.org/tis**.

Experiment #53 — RF Peak Detector

This experiment is really a "three-fer." Not only do you get the peak detector, but also a dummy load! And wait, there's more — measuring RF power with an oscilloscope! You'll have a useful instrument and a new shack accessory, and you'll learn some valuable techniques by the time the dust clears.

Term to Learn

Detect — Recover modulating information from a waveform.

The Envelope Detector

A detector is a circuit that recovers information from any type of modulated waveform. Different types of detectors are used for AM, FM, PM, SSB and other modes. Most hams use the term to mean *envelope detector*, a circuit whose output is the envelope of an AM signal. A typical envelope detector is shown in Figure 1.

This envelope detector is basically a half-wave rectifier. The input signal source develops a voltage across R1. (R1 can also be the output impedance of the signal source.) If the voltage is greater than that across C1, current flows through diode D1 increasing the voltage across C1 until the voltages are equal. Once C1 is charged, it discharges through R2, which can be the input impedance of a following circuit, such as an audio amplifier. The voltage drop across D1 depends on both the semiconductor material and the current when the diode is conducting. The forward voltage of a silicon diode such as a 1N4148 is close to 0.6 V when fully on, while a germanium diode, such as a 1N34A will have a lower drop, typically 0.3 V.

The input signal to a typical envelope detector is an AM waveform whose carrier, f_C, is many hundreds of times higher in frequency than the highest modulating signal frequency, f_{Max}. For example, the carrier of an AM broadcast station on 1000 kHz is 200 times higher than a 5 kHz modulating frequency. This means C1 has to charge very quickly and discharge very slowly to separate the RF and AF components of the AM signal.

The discharge time constant $\tau2 = C1 \times R2$ should be chosen so that C1 discharges just slowly enough to reproduce the highest modulating frequency, f_{Max}. An ap-

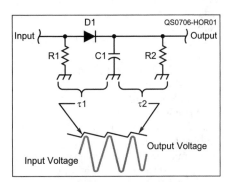

Figure 1 — The basic envelope detector circuit filters out the carrier signal and outputs only the modulating signal that creates the envelope. The time constant of C1 and R2 must be low enough to track the highest modulating frequency.

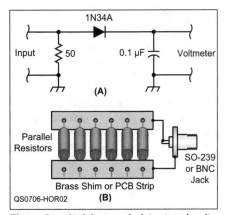

Figure 2 — At A is a peak detector circuit that uses an external voltmeter in place of R2. The input resistor is 50 Ω to present a good match to most generators and transmitters. At B is one way to construct a dummy load out of multiple low-power resistors in parallel.

proximation for the minimum value of $\tau2 = 1 / (4 \times f_{Max})$. To recover human voice audio (f_{Max} of 3 kHz), $\tau2 = 83$ μs. If R2 = 10 kΩ, then C1 = 83 μs / 10 kΩ = 0.00833 μF and a 0.01 μF capacitor will do nicely.

The combination of R1, R_D and C1 form a low-pass filter with $f_C = 1 / [2\pi \times C1 \times (R1+R_D)]$. This removes the carrier component from the output. R_D is the forward resistance of D1 and depends on the amount of current flowing through the diode. R_D can be estimated as $\Delta V_f / \Delta I_f$, for values of I_f that will be encountered in operation. For example,

from a 1N4152 data sheet (enter 1N4152 DATA SHEET into an Internet search engine), V_f for the 1N4152 is about 0.52 V for $I_f = 0.1$ mA and 0.62 V for $I_f = 1.0$ mA so $R_D = 0.1$ V / 0.9 mA = 111 Ω. If R1 = 50 Ω, $R_D = 100$ Ω, and C1 = 0.01 μF, the low-pass filter's cutoff frequency is approximately 106 kHz, attenuating carrier components above that frequency.

The Peak Detector

An envelope detector does not make a very good power measuring device because its output changes too quickly. What's needed is a *peak detector* whose output corresponds to the peak value of the envelope instead of individual modulating waveform cycles.

There's no need to change the input time constant, $\tau1$. The carrier, after all, still has to be removed. What's needed is to lengthen $\tau2$ so that the output stays at or near the peak value of the envelope long enough to be measured. If R2 is removed completely, then C1 will discharge only through its own and D1's leakage current. The voltage across C1 can be read by either a built-in voltmeter or by an external voltmeter such as a DVM or VOM.

Figure 2A shows a workbench peak detector for low-power signals up to 10 W or so. D1 is a 1N34A germanium diode to increase the sensitivity of the detector and R1 is 50 Ω to present a standard load to the circuit under test. R2 is replaced by the very high impedance of an external voltmeter. C2 is increased to 0.1 μF to increase $\tau2$ and hold the peak voltage steady for a stable reading. If the voltmeter has a 10 MΩ input impedance, $\tau2 = 0.1$ μF × 10 MΩ = 1 s. (Remember — megohms times microfarads equals seconds!)

Dummy Loads and Power Measurement

We'll use a transceiver as a signal source. To do so, you'll need a dummy load to which you can connect the peak detector circuit, so in the true ham spirit, we'll make our own. (Check your rig's manual for instructions on reducing output power below 5 W. You may have to use the ALC input.)

A good option for a single-resistor dummy load is an Ohmite TCH35P51R0J; a 51 Ω, 35 W resistor in a TO-220 transistor package, available from Mouser Electronics (**www.mouser.com/ohmite**) for less than $6. The

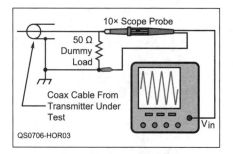

Figure 3 — Use a times 10 probe for power measurement directly at the dummy load. Do not use lengths of coaxial cable and T adapters because the mismatch between the coax and scope input can act as a stub, changing the impedance at the dummy load.

case of the resistor is electrically isolated so you can bolt it directly to a metal heat sink.

If your junk box is well stocked, you can construct a dummy load from multiple high value noninductive resistors whose combined resistance is 50 Ω. For example, 10 510 Ω, 2 W resistors in parallel can make a 51 Ω, 20 W resistor, if there's enough air between them. Be sure to use noninductive resistors — not wirewound or film resistors.

Use two strips of solderable metal such as brass or copper or PC board stock as shown in Figure 2B. Drill holes spaced to allow some airflow between the resistors and solder the resistors to the strips. Attach an SO-239 or BNC coaxial connector at one end as shown. Keep all leads short so that the impedance stays close to 50 Ω at high frequencies.

When you calibrate your peak detector, you'll need to measure the RF power from the transceiver accurately. This requires an oscilloscope. To avoid any impedance changes due to transmission line effects, use a 10× probe connected directly to the dummy load as shown in Figure 3.

Calculate peak envelope power from the voltage measurements as follows:

PEP (watts) $= V_{RMS}^2 / 50$
PEP (watts) $= V_{peak}^2 / (2 \times 50)$

$= V_{pk\text{-}pk}^2 / (8 \times 50)$

Building a Peak Detector

Start by building the peak detector circuit on a solderless prototyping board. Set your transceiver to output a low-power AM or SSB signal (5 W or less) at the bottom of the 160 meter band. Attach the oscilloscope probe directly to the dummy load at the coax connector. Use short wires to connect the dummy load to the detector circuit on the prototyping board.

Verify that the circuit works by measuring the output voltage at several different power levels. You'll notice that the output voltage falls rapidly once below 0.5 V. This is due to the 0.3 V forward drop of D1. If the input signal is not greater than 0.3 V_{pk}, the diode does not turn on very strongly and little current is available to charge C1. When you speak into the microphone, you should see the peak reading jump to a higher level as the waveform envelope tracks voice peaks. Change the value of C1 to higher (add more capacitors in parallel) and lower values and observe the effect on how the detector responds to your voice.

Once you've verified that the circuit works, build it permanently on a terminal strip with three to five terminals. Use the mounting lug as ground. A BNC connector is a good choice for the input. You can use binding posts, or just a pair of wires with tinned ends, as your contact points for the voltmeter — be creative and use whatever is handy to make the voltmeter connection. Now find a metal enclosure big enough for your peak detector, including the dummy load. (Hint — the enclosure can also act as a heat sink!) Assemble the dummy load and detector circuit inside the enclosure. You're ready to calibrate!

[1]W. Hayward, W7ZOI, R. Campbell, KK7B, and R. Larkin, W7PUA, *Experimental Methods in RF Design*. Available from your ARRL dealer or the ARRL Bookstore, ARRL order no. 8799. Telephone 860-594-0355, or toll-free in the US 888-277-5289; **www.arrl.org/shop/**; **pubsales@arrl.org**.

The 1N34A diode can withstand a maximum of 65 V_{pk} representing a power of 42.3 W and the absolute maximum your detector can withstand. Set your voltmeter to the 10 V scale and attach it to the detector. Attach the transceiver to the detector input and set power so that the voltmeter reads full-scale. (10 V_{pk} across 50 Ω is 1 W.) Record the oscilloscope's peak (or peak-to-peak) voltage reading and convert to watts. Reduce power and make another four readings approximately equally spaced throughout the voltmeter's range, recording output voltage and input power.

Repeat the calibration steps on 80, 40, 20, 15 and 10 meters. The detector is less sensitive at higher frequencies because the capacitance of the diode's junction (just a few pF) causes it to be a less effective rectifier. Attach the calibration table to the enclosure of the detector and you have a useful peak detecting power meter!

Shopping List

1N34A diode.
0.1 µF disc ceramic capacitor.
Resistors and metal or PCB strips for 50 Ω dummy load (see text).
3 to 5 position terminal strip.
SO-239 or BNC chassis connector.
Binding posts (optional).
Metal enclosure.

Recommended Reading

Chapter 7 of *Experimental Methods in RF Design* discusses the peak detector in detail and presents a wealth of options for increasing its sensitivity and power-handling capabilities.[1] There are also many other instruments and techniques discussed in the book.

Next Month

Let's return to some low-frequency analog circuitry and put the versatile op-amp to work once again. We'll take a look at precision rectifier circuits and rectifiers with gain! See the Hands-On Radio Web site at **www. arrl.org/tis/info/HTML/Hands-On-Radio** for a clarification of how Rd is calculated.

Experiment #54 — Precision Rectifiers

Last month, we explored an RF application of a simple half-wave rectifier called a peak detector. Sometimes much more accurate rectification is required and here's how to get it.

Terms to Learn

Ideal diode — a diode with zero forward voltage drop and zero reverse current.

Linearize — change a nonlinear characteristic to a linear characteristic.

Voltage-current characteristic — the graph of voltage (X axis) versus current (Y axis) between two terminals of a device.

A Basic Op-Amp Rectifier

Passive rectifiers — those that use diodes in half or full wave configurations — are fine for rectifying large signals if the circuit is forgiving of the diode's forward voltage drop, V_F. For small signals, meaning those much smaller than V_F, passive rectifiers don't work well at all. Wouldn't it be nice if we could order an *ideal diode*? Vendors are often out of stock of ideal diodes, but we can make one by using the analog designer's favorite tool, an op-amp.

Semiconductor diodes "turn on" a little slowly before reaching a relatively constant voltage drop of 0.6 to 0.7 V (silicon) or 0.3 V (germanium). In a full wave circuit, this causes *crossover distortion* in the region the signal changes from forward to reverse current. Signals much smaller than V_F are attenuated as well, in both full and half wave circuits. By using feedback in an active circuit as shown in Figure 1, we can use the op-amp's high gain to *linearize* the non-

linear *voltage-current (V-I) characteristics* of a diode's PN junction. (A resistor's V-I characteristic is a straight line with a slope of A/V equal to its resistance in ohms.)

Figure 1 shows the basic half wave active rectifier circuit. Note the feedback connection between the cathode of D1 and the op-amp's inverting (–) input. When the input signal is positive, the op-amp's high gain causes its output to increase until the voltage at the (–) terminal (also the voltage at the diode's cathode) equals the input voltage at the non-inverting (+) terminal. If you measure the op-amp's output at pin 6 you'll find it is V_F above the diode's cathode. This is true for all positive input voltages, so V_F of the whole circuit is zero!

Let's test the circuit to see the effect of feedback and gain. Connect a 1N4148 silicon diode and 10 kΩ potentiometer in series across a 12 V power supply after setting the potentiometer to full resistance. (The diode's anode should be connected to the supply's positive terminal and the cathode to the pot's adjustable terminal.) Measure voltage across the diode and current through it as the pot's resistance is reduced to 500 Ω ($I_{DIODE} = V_{SUPPLY} / R_{POT}$). You should see voltage increase slowly with current until at a few mA, V_F becomes almost constant, regardless of current. Take care not to reduce the pot's resistance much below 500 Ω to keep diode current below 25 mA.

Build the circuit of Figure 1, paying attention to op-amp pin numbers and the feedback connection. (If you connect the inverting terminal directly to the op-amp output instead

of the diode's cathode, you'll just have a passive rectifier with a buffer amp driving it.) The power supply must output both +12 and –12 V so that the op-amp can operate properly with very small input signals. Connect V_{IN} to the supply's positive output and make the same plot as before. You should see that V_F (the voltage between the supply output and D1's cathode) is approximately zero for all currents through R2. (R1 provides a path for the op-amp's very small input bias current.) This circuit emulates an ideal diode and is called a *precision rectifier* because the error caused by V_F of real diodes is reduced nearly to zero. Even signals of a few mV peak-to-peak are rectified reasonably well by this circuit.

Fixing the Problems

Hold it — We're not quite finished yet! This circuit is pretty good, but it still has some shortcomings. It only has unity gain and it is just a half wave rectifier. Furthermore, when the input voltage to the circuit in Figure 1 is negative, what happens to the op-amp? It's still trying to create equal voltages at the inverting and noninverting terminals, but the diode isn't allowing any current to flow in the reverse direction, no matter how hard the op-amp tries. The op-amp output *saturates* at or near the negative supply voltage. (You can see this for yourself by connecting V_{IN} to a small negative voltage, such as from a 1.5 V battery, and measuring the op-amp output voltage.) Saturation makes the op-amp slow to recover from having all of its circuitry forced to one extreme, reducing high-frequency response of the circuit.

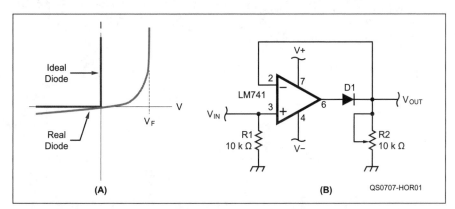

(A) (B) QS0707-HOR01

Figure 1 — The V-I characteristic curves for ideal and real diodes, showing V_F for real diodes. At B, a simple half-wave rectifier circuit with an adjustable load for measurements.

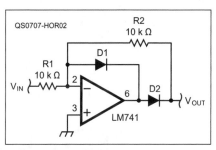

Figure 2 — A precision half-wave rectifier with adjustable gain controlled by the ratio of R1 and R2 with a diode clamp (D1) to prevent op-amp saturation.

Variable gain is added in Figure 2, but the input signal is inverted. If D1 is removed and D2 replaced by a short circuit, the circuit becomes the standard inverting amplifier. (This circuit is described in Figure 3 of Hands-On Radio Experiment #3.[1]) For this circuit, an ac signal will be rectified such that negative inputs cause a positive output and positive inputs cause zero output. To understand the op-amp circuits in this experiment, keep in mind that the + and − inputs have a very high input impedance so that very little current flows into or out of them.

D1 solves the op-amp saturation problem. With a positive input signal, current flows from the circuit input to the inverting input of the op-amp. The op-amp balances this current with a negative output that draws current through D1 and keeps the op-amp's + and − inputs at zero volts. The op-amp output only needs to reach $-V_F$ of D1.

D2 works just as in the circuit of Figure 1. When the op-amp output goes positive (the input signal is negative), D2 conducts and supplies current to the output. The op-amp increases output voltage until the current flowing through R2 to the − input balances the current flowing to V_{IN} input through R1. The ratio of R2:R1 sets the gain of the rectifier as described in Experiment #3.

Build the circuit of Figure 2. A +12 and −12 V dc supply is required. Use 10 kΩ resistors for R1 and R2 and 1N4148 diodes for D1 and D2. If you have a signal generator and oscilloscope apply a 1 V_{PP} sine wave to the input or plot the V-I graph for both positive and negative input voltages. Confirm that the circuit half-wave rectifies the input signal and that negative input voltage results in positive output voltage. Vary the ratio of R1 and R2 to see the effect on gain.

A Full-Wave Version

Figure 3 is a full-wave rectifier circuit, easiest understood by separately analyzing negative and positive input voltages. Note that the input op-amp U1 once again has its

[1]www.arrl.org/tis/info/HTML/Hands-On-Radio/.

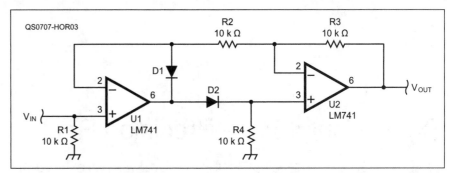

Figure 3 — Full-wave precision rectifier circuit with unity gain. D1 and D2 switch the feedback path between U2 and U1 so that the circuit alternates between inverting and noninverting gain to perform the rectification.

+ input connected to the circuit input so that its output voltage will be the same polarity as the input voltage. R1 and R4 provide a path to ground for input bias currents as before.

For positive input voltages, U1's output is also positive. The output is connected through D2 to the noninverting input of U2. U2's output also rises until its + and − inputs are at the same voltage. At this point, the − inputs of U1 and U2 are at the same because very little current is flowing through R2 or D1. The output of U1 continues to rise until its + and − inputs are equal. The output of U2 follows the input signal, supplying the positive half-cycle to the circuit output.

For negative input voltages, U1's output is also negative, reverse biasing D2 so it acts as an open circuit. U1's negative output pulls current through D1 and R2. U2's output rises until the current flowing in R3 exactly balances the current flowing in R2. If R2 and R3 are equal and their currents are equal, the voltage at the output of U2 will be equal and opposite polarity to the voltage at the − input of U1. U1's output raises the current through D1 and R2 until the voltage at its − input equals the input voltage. So the output of U2 is also positive for negative input signals as D1 and D2 switch the current paths.

Build the circuit of Figure 3 and confirm its positive output for both input polarities. What happens when you change the ratio of R2 and R3? Their ratio only affects the gain when the input is negative! Increase

the frequency of the input signal and determine the point at which the output is 3 dB (0.707 voltage ratio) below the input signal. This is rectifier's operating bandwidth and it is determined primarily by the speed of the op-amp. A more complex full-wave rectifier circuit with adjustable gain for both input polarities can be found at **sound.westhost.com/appnotes/an001.htm**.

Shopping List

- Four 10 kΩ, ¼ W resistors.
- Two LM741 op-amps, or equivalent (a single LM747 dual op-amp will also work).
- Two 1N4148 small signal diodes.
- 10 kΩ potentiometer.

Recommended Reading

The advanced reader will find a number of interesting rectifier circuits at **www.discover-circuits.com/R/rectifier.htm**. This circuit is also covered in detail in *The Art of Electronics* and the *Op-Amp Cookbook*.[2,3]

Next Month

Now that you have your op-amps all wired up, let's have some more fun with them by creating voltage-to-current and current-to-voltage converters!

[2]Horowitz and Hill, *The Art of Electronics*, Chapter 4, Cambridge University Press.
[3]W. Jung, *Op-Amp Cookbook*, Chapter 5, Prentice-Hall.

Experiment #55 — Current/Voltage Converters

Can the handy op-amp spin straw into gold? Not quite, but as the electronic equivalent of the *Philosopher's Stone* it can transmute current and voltage without much trouble at all!

Terms to Learn

Floating load — Load that has no ground connection.

High-side/low-side drive — Circuit that drives a load connected to ground (high-side) or to a power supply (low-side).

Transimpedance amplifier — Amplifier that acts an impedance to convert an input current to an output voltage.

Virtual ground — Point in a circuit that is maintained at ground potential, but is not actually connected to ground.

Introduction

Buried deep inside many electronic gadgets are circuits that output a voltage (or current) based on a current (or voltage) input signal. They are often used in radio for biasing, regulation, detection, and other functions. In fact, you use a current-to-voltage converter every time you change the TV channel with an infra-red remote control signal. The receiver's photodiode converts light pulses to a weak current that is then converted to a voltage signal by an op-amp circuit for the TV's digital electronics.

Voltage-to-Current Converters

Here's a secret — what's the simplest circuit that converts current to voltage and vice versa? It's a resistor! Ohm's law describes the process: $I = E / R$ and $E = I \times R$. If that's the only consideration you had in mind, you're done! In many circumstances, however, using a resistor is unsuitable. Inserting resistance into a current path may upset the operation of the circuit. The current may be too high (or too low) for realistic resistor values or power dissipation. In these cases, the op-amp converter can be used instead.

Figure 1 shows the simplest voltage-to-current converter. These are also called *current regulators* or *voltage-controlled current sources (VCCS)* in different texts and articles. A reference voltage, V_{REF}, is applied to the op-amp's non-inverting (+) input. Until the voltage at the inverting input (–) equals that

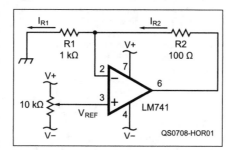

Figure 1 — The voltage-to-current circuit works by balancing voltages at its + and – terminals. The value of R1 sets the circuit's conversion sensitivity from voltage to current in the load resistor, R2.

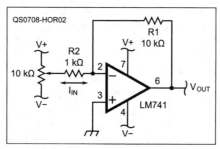

Figure 2 — The current-to-voltage converter is also known as a transimpedance amplifier. By requiring the current in R1 to equal that flowing into or out of the input, the circuit's output voltage is equal to $R1 \times I_{IN}$.

at the + input, the op-amp's output voltage increases, causing current to flow through R1 and R2 as shown.

With both op-amp inputs at the same voltage (V_{REF}), the current through R1 must be $I_{R1} = V_{REF} / R1$. Furthermore, the very high input impedance of the op-amp means that approximately no current flows into the – input. Therefore, I_{R1} must equal I_{R2} — otherwise, where would it go? If R2 is the load resistor, the current through it will *always* equal $V_{REF} / R1$. It doesn't matter what value of R2 is, even a short circuit, as long as the voltages at the output and the – input are within the op-amp's power supply limits. V_{REF} can be positive or negative — the current flow follows V_{REF}'s polarity.

The *conversion sensitivity* to input voltage is measured in amperes per volt (A/V) and is equal to $1 / R1$. For example, if $R1 = 10$ kΩ,

the conversion sensitivity is 0.1 mA / V, with V representing the input voltage. Let's build the circuit and test it. First, calculate the value of R1 for a conversion sensitivity of 2 mA / V. (500 Ω) If a standard value of 510 Ω is used, what is the actual conversion sensitivity? (1.96 mA/V.)

Build the circuit of Figure 1 using a 10 kΩ potentiometer ("pot" for short) to generate the variable reference voltage and a 100 Ω load resistor (R2). If you have two DVMs, use one to measure input voltage at the op-amp's + input and the other to measure current through R2. There are two ways to measure current in R2 — directly and indirectly. To use the direct method, connect the voltmeter (configured to measure current) in series with R2. Indirectly, measure the voltage across R2 and use Ohm's law to calculate the current.

Set the pot to approximately mid-travel and apply power. Adjust the pot for 0 V at the op-amp's + input. Confirm that current through R2 = 0, as well. Now adjust the pot for +1 V and measure the current through R2. It should be pretty close to $1 \times 1.96 = 1.96$ mA, with the direction from the op-amp's output toward R1. Now set the pot for –1 V and repeat the measurements. Current flow should be reversed, but of the same value.

Is the current flow really independent of the value of R2? Try different values of R2 below 100 Ω, including a short circuit. (Don't worry — you won't hurt the op-amp!) In each case, you should get the same value of current, unless R2 increases to the point at which the op-amp output voltage reaches its maximum limit. What value is that? If your power supply delivers ±12 V, the LM741 op-amp's output may be able to reach ±10.5 to 11 V. The op-amp's output voltage $V_{OUT} = V_{REF} + I_{R2} \times R2 = V_{REF} + (V_{REF} / R1) \times R2 = V_{REF} (1 + R2/R1)$. If V_{REF} is set to 1 V and $R1 = 510$ Ω, what value of R2 results in V_{OUT} reaching 10.5 V? (4.8 kΩ.) Try a 4.7 kΩ value for R2 and verify that V_{OUT} is close to 10.5 V. Then increase R2 to 6.2 kΩ without changing anything else. Can the op-amp supply the required amount of current? Continue to experiment by changing the conversion sensitivity (change R1) and the value of the load resistor (R2).

One drawback of this circuit is that neither

terminal of the load resistor can be grounded. This is called a *floating load*. There are a number of more complicated circuits that allow one end of the load to be grounded (*high-side drive*) or connected to the power supply (*low-side drive*). If an op-amp can't supply enough current through its output, there are also external circuits that can supply higher currents. These can be found in the references and in on-line Web sites.

Current-to-Voltage Converters

The complement to the previous circuits has a current signal for its input and produces an output voltage instead. Figure 2 shows the basic form of this circuit. At first glance, this circuit, known as a *transimpedance amplifier*, doesn't look like it should do much of anything. But it relies on the op-amp's high input impedance and the circuit's current balancing capabilities.

The current into the op-amp's – terminal must be balanced by an equal and opposite current through the feedback resistor, R1. (Remember to use the current-balance approach when figuring out op-amp circuits.) Since the op-amp's + terminal is grounded, the voltage at the – terminal will also be at ground potential, called a *virtual ground*. Given these two constraints, it's easy to figure out the output voltage: $V_{OUT} = -I_{IN} \times R1$. This balancing act is only limited by the power supply voltages and the op-amp's ability to supply or sink enough current.

This circuit also has a conversion sensitivity, measured in volts per ampere (V/A) and equal to the value of R1. This circuit is called a *transimpedance amplifier*, a fancy name for an "active resistor." An ordinary resistor would also act as a current to voltage converter, but the input source might not be able to supply enough voltage or power. The amplifier circuit of Figure 2 has a very high input impedance, so whatever is supplying the input current, such as a sensitive detector, is very lightly loaded. The high gain of the op-amp ensures that enough voltage is applied to R1 such that the currents balance at its – terminal.

Build the circuit of Figure 2, supplying input current through a 1 kΩ resistor (R2) connected to the same pot used in the previous part of the experiment. Use a 10 kΩ resistor for R1, giving a conversion sensitivity of 10,000 V/A or 10 V/mA. Set the pot to mid-scale and apply power. Measure both the input current (directly or indirectly) and the output voltage. Adjust the pot for $V_{OUT} = 0$ V and verify that input current is also very small.

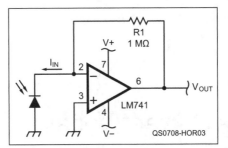

Figure 3 — All semiconductor PN junctions are sensitive to photons of light. The resulting current flow can be converted to a voltage signal by the transimpedance amplifier.

Adjust the pot for 1 mA into the circuit's input. Verify that 1 mA of input current causes –10 V of output voltage. This circuit is *inverting* — that is, a current into the circuit results in a negative output voltage and vice versa. Readjust the pot for 1 mA of current away from the – input and verify the output voltage inversion. The same limits on V_{OUT} with respect to power supply voltage apply to this circuit. What happens to V_{OUT} when the input current is increased to, say, 1.5 mA? Experiment by changing R1 for different conversion sensitivities.

A Light-Wave Receiver

The infrared detector circuit mentioned earlier is shown in a basic form in Figure 3. You can build a light detecting circuit by using photosensitive diodes. It's not necessary to use a special photodiode — all diodes are light sensitive to some degree. This was discovered in the early days of semiconductors when circuits behaved strangely and the effect was traced to light illuminating the junctions of transistors and diodes through their glass packages!

As is typical of the electronics industry, what was first considered a bug was quickly made into a feature. Each sufficiently energetic photon of light can cause an electron to cross the diode's depletion layer, creating a light-to-current converter. Thus was born a whole wave of light detection circuits and products.

Build the circuit of Figure 3, using an ordinary 1N4148 signal diode in place of the photodiode. Be sure that the 1N4148 is packaged in clear glass. A diode in an opaque, plastic package won't work. R1 is now 1 MΩ, so the conversion sensitivity of the circuit becomes 1 MV / A = 1 V / μA. Start with a piece of electrical tape around

the 1N4148 to prevent light from hitting the diode junction. Measure the circuit's output voltage and monitor it for a few minutes to get a feel for the drift and noise inherent in such sensitive dc circuits.

Now remove the tape and see if the output voltage changes somewhat. Dim the work-bench and room lights while shining a bright flashlight directly on the diode. This should cause a small increase in output voltage as the photons cause a current to flow from the diode's cathode to its anode. Try using other 1N4148 diodes to observe differences in sensitivity. Try 1N34 germanium diodes and clear LEDs, if you have some on hand. If you have an LED flashlight or laser pointer, try different colors of illumination to see if the diodes are more sensitive at different wavelengths of light.

If you have an oscilloscope, shine a remote control onto your most sensitive diode while watching the op-amp's output voltage. Can you see the pulses? Congratulations — you just constructed your first light-wave receiver!

Shopping List

- LM741 op-amp.
- 10 kΩ potentiometer.
- 1 ea 510 Ω, 1 kΩ, 4.7 kΩ, 6.2 kΩ, 1 MΩ ¼ W resistors.
- 1N4148 diode (use an assortment of diodes, if possible).

Recommended Reading

The *Op-Amp Cookbook* has a good section on voltage-to-current converters under "Current Regulators" with lots of variations to try.[1] You'll find more information on the voltage-to-current converter in the Wikipedia (**en.wikipedia.org/wiki/Current-to-voltage_converter**). Enter "current to voltage converter" or "voltage to current converter" into an Internet search engine for plenty of real-life circuit examples.

Next Month

Circuit designers know that the performance of components they buy may vary quite a bit from the values stated in the catalog. That's normal, but how does one take that into account when figuring out how your circuit will perform? Next month, we'll step from the bench to the calculator as we dive into the world of design variations and sensitivities.

[1]W. Jung, *Op-Amp Cookbook*, Sams Publishing, Chapter 4.

Power Supplies

Experiment #7—Voltage Multipliers

Background

This is the second of a three-part series of experiments on power supply circuits. Last month we studied the rectifier. This month we take the rectifier one step further to create output voltages higher than that of the power source…even of the opposite polarity!

Terms to Learn

• *Commutation*—periodic switching that is synchronized to a clock signal or a time reference

• *Floating*—a voltage source is floating if neither of its output connections are connected to ground

• *Ripple*—the regular (ac) variation of rectifier output voltage at the frequency at which the output capacitor (filter) is charged

• *Surge Current*—the large inrush of current into discharged capacitors when voltage is first applied

• *Voltage Regulation*—the change in output voltage with load current (usually expressed as a percentage change in voltage for a given change in output current)

The Voltage Multiplier

There are many instances where an ac power source is available but a dc voltage is needed by a circuit that can't be obtained by using a simple rectifier. Sometimes, a circuit just needs a "dab" of higher voltage…and it's not worth the expense of using a higher-voltage transformer or adding another secondary winding to get

it. For other applications, such as high-voltage supplies for amplifiers or other tube circuits, a full-voltage transformer may be too expensive (or too difficult to insulate for the high voltage needed). Voltage multiplier circuits are used to address both situations.

In the full-wave rectifiers of the previous experiment, we saw how diodes are used to route charging current into a storage capacitor. The diodes effectively double the frequency at which the capacitor can be charged. The doubling of the charge frequency also doubles the amount of current a rectifier can supply for a given voltage variation or ripple.

What if, instead of doubling the output current, there was a way to use the same diodes to double the output voltage? By arranging the diodes and capacitors properly, we can create a "bucket brigade" effect where the voltages of the capacitors can be added together.

Figure 1A shows the simplest voltage multiplier—a half-wave doubler—supplied from a source with an RMS voltage of V_{RMS} and whose peak voltage is 1.4 V_{RMS}. Starting with both capacitors discharged, a negative half-cycle from the voltage source charges C1 to 1.4 V_{RMS} through D1, as shown in Figure 1B. On the following half-cycle, in Figure 1C, the output capacitor C2 is charged through D2 but, like an acrobat springing onto another's shoulders, the voltage of C1 adds to the source voltage and C2 is charged to 2.8 V_{RMS}. Because one diode is always in the current path, the actual output voltage is less by one diode's forward voltage drop,

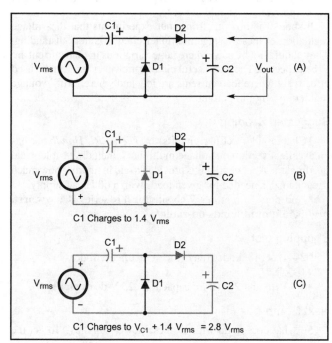

Figure 1—The half-wave voltage doubler circuit. Figures 1B and 1C show how the capacitors charge on alternating half-cycles. The voltages of C1 and C2 are added together as C2 is charged.

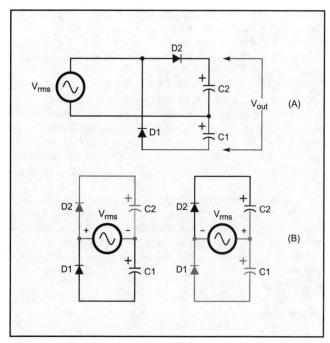

Figure 2—The full-wave voltage doubler. Figure 2A shows the usual schematic for the circuit. Figure 2B redraws the circuit for clarity and illustrates how the capacitors charge on alternate half-cycles.

V_f, of 0.7 V.

The half-wave doubler only charges the output capacitor once every other half-cycle, limiting the amount of current that can be drawn from the supply. Each diode and capacitor in the half-wave doubler must be rated to handle the full output voltage. These limitations can be a problem at high output voltages.

To increase the amount of output current and reduce the necessary ratings of individual components, the diodes and capacitors can be rearranged as shown in the full-wave doubler circuit of Figure 2. For the half-wave doubler, one side of the voltage source may be grounded, but for the full-wave doubler, the source must be floating.

Figure 2A shows the customary way of drawing the full-wave doubler circuit on a schematic, where the voltage source is usually a transformer secondary winding. However, it's a little easier to understand when redrawn as in Figure 2B. On alternate half-cycles, the source charges each capacitor to its peak voltage, 1.4 V_{RMS}. The output voltage is developed across C1 and C2 in series. This also means that the value of output capacitance that supplies current to the load is less than C1 or C2 by the equation:

$$C_{output} = (C1 \times C2) / (C1 + C2)$$

In addition, one diode drop is subtracted from the charging voltage of each capacitor, so the actual output voltage will be 2.8 V_{RMS} − [2×0.7 V].

Note that when using these voltage multiplier circuits for powering actual equipment at higher power, it is necessary to limit the surge current into the capacitors when the supply is first powered up. The discharged capacitors look like short circuits to the transformer secondary and diodes and can blow a fuse or damage components on those first few cycles of charging. That is why, in *The ARRL Handbook*, the discussion of voltage multipliers includes surge-limiting resistors. In our experiments, the surge currents are quite small and can be ignored.

Testing a Pair of Voltage Multipliers

Let's start with the half-wave doubler. As with last month's experiment, use your function generator as the voltage source. Construct the circuit as shown in Figure 1 taking care to observe the polarities of the capacitors.

• Set the function generator to output a 1 kHz sine wave at 5 V_{RMS}. Use your voltmeter to measure the dc voltage across C1 and C2. With no load to drain charge from either capacitor, you should measure nearly 2.8 × 5 V = 14 V dc across both C1 and C2.

• Connect a 10 kΩ load resistor across C2 and re-measure the capacitor voltages. You will see the voltage across C1 drop to just below 1.4 × 5 V = 7 V dc while the voltage across C2 stays about one diode forward voltage drop (0.7 V) below 14 V dc. If you are using an oscilloscope you should see waveforms like those of Figure 3.

• You can experiment with the doubler by varying the load resistance or capacitance values. Less load resistance (a heavier load) or less capacitance will drop the output voltage dramatically as C2 is discharged more during each half-cycle. Vary the frequency of the source. Raising the source frequency also charges the capacitors more frequently, so for a given load resistance, this will increase output voltage.

• Make a voltage inverter by switching the polarity of the diodes and capacitors.

• Construct a full-wave doubler, as in Figure 2, using the same diodes and capacitors as for the half-wave doubler. You won't be able to use the oscilloscope unless the function generator output is floating, so rely on your voltmeter.

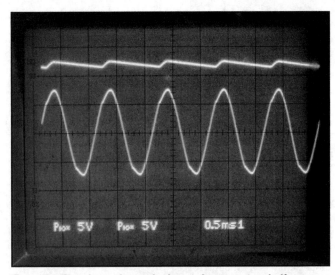

Figure 3—The photo shows the input sine wave to a half-wave voltage doubler and the output waveform across C2. Note that capacitor C2 is charged once every other half-cycle. Ground potential for both channels is at the center of the sine wave.

• With no load resistor connected, the output voltage will be close to 14 V dc, but with the 10 kΩ load, the output voltage will be lower than for the half-wave doubler because the effective output capacitance is less—C1 in series with C2—and there is an extra diode forward voltage drop. However, the *voltage regulation* of the full-wave doubler is better than the half-wave circuit because the output capacitors are charged more frequently, doubling the ripple frequency.

• If you add a 1 µF capacitor in parallel with both C1 and C2, the output voltage should increase.

It should be obvious from your experiments that the voltage regulation of these voltage multiplier circuits is not outstanding. They should not be used where large variations in load current are to be expected. They are useful circuits, however, and can be used effectively where load currents are low and where "stiff" voltage regulation is not important.

Suggested Reading

• Chapter 11 (rectifier circuits) of *The ARRL Handbook* has an excellent section on voltage multipliers, including triplers and quadruplers. A set of graphs is provided to aid in figuring how much capacitance is needed for given loads with a 60 Hz ac supply.

• And don't forget our Web site for this series is **www.arrl. org/tis/info/html/hands-on-radio/**.

Shopping List

• 2—1N4148 diodes (any silicon rectifier will do)
• 10 kΩ, $1/4$ W resistor
• 4—1 µF and 2—10 µF capacitors, 25 V dc or higher

Next Month

So what do you do with all these power supplies? To get the best results from most circuits, it's necessary to power them with a smooth, constant voltage. Next month, we'll design and build a voltage regulator to do just that.

Experiment #8—The Linear Regulator

Voltage regulators provide stable power for sensitive electronic circuits. In our final power supply experiment, we combine our experience with transistor amplifiers, op-amps and Zener diodes into a linear voltage regulator.

Terms to Learn

- *Linear*—a circuit in which the current and voltage can take on any value within a continuous range
- *Regulate*—to control a voltage or current such that it matches an established level
- *Setpoint*—the desired level at which the regulator output is to be maintained
- *Pass transistor*—the transistor in a regulator circuit through which current flows to the output circuit

The Linear Regulator

Figure 1A shows the block diagram of a *pass-type* voltage regulator. The *control element* is the decision-maker. It compares the output with its *setpoint* and varies the *control signal* to the *pass element* so that the output matches the setpoint. A simple example is squirting water from a hose with your thumb. The setpoint is where your eyes tell you the water is supposed to go. Your thumb is the pass element and your brain is the control element, constantly monitoring where your eyes say the water is actually going.

The control element in a linear regulator is a high-gain amplifier with one input connected to the setpoint and the other to the output. Any imbalance results in a strong response at the amplifier's output that causes the pass element to restore the output to the expected value. In our experiment, the control element will be an op-amp with the setpoint provided by a Zener diode. Figure 1B shows the complete circuit.

We can break this circuit down into three familiar parts—a Zener diode reference, an amplifier and an op-amp. The Zener diode that supplies the setpoint is the same one that we used in experiment #6 with an extra 0.1 μF capacitor to filter high-frequency noise. The pass transistor circuit is just an emitter-follower (EF) amplifier (Experiment #2) turned on its side! The EF's input is the control signal and its output is the load current. It is the job of the

op-amp to supply enough base current (I_b) to the pass transistor so that its emitter current (I_e) can drive the load to the desired voltage, balancing the output and setpoint voltages at its inputs.

Testing the Linear Regulator

- The object is to design a fixed-voltage regulator that supplies 10 mA to a 470 Ω load at 5.1 V dc.
- Using Experiment #6's Zener (1N4733A) circuit and assuming that the load current going into the op-amp is very small, we can use the same 330 Ω resistor for R_z to supply current to D_z, which then supplies a 5.1 V dc setpoint.
- How much base current is needed for the transistor to drive the load?

$$I_e = I_b (\beta+1), \text{ so } I_b = I_e / (\beta+1) \qquad \text{[Eq 1]}$$

The 2N4401 transistor's data sheet shows that its minimum dc current gain (β or h_{FE}) is 80 for an emitter current of 10 mA. That means I_b must be 125 μA or more to drive the transistor hard enough to allow I_e to reach 10 mA. This is well within the op-amp's capability.

- Take particular care to connect the op-amp's inverting (–) and noninverting (+) terminals correctly.
- Supply 12 V dc to the regulator's input—the Zener diode and output voltages should be almost identical and close to 5.1 V dc. The output of the op-amp should be about 0.7 V greater than the load voltage. How much power is the transistor dissipating?

$$P = I_e \times (V_{in} - V_{load}) \text{ and } I_e = V_{load} / 470 \ \Omega$$

- Vary the input voltage up and down by 3 V. What is the effect on load voltage? How low can the input go before the output voltage drops?

Variable Regulators

In many cases a variable output voltage is needed. Figure 2 shows two types of variable regulators that use a single reference Zener diode. The 0.1 μF capacitors remove high-frequency noise from the control voltages.

To regulate at load voltages greater than that of the Zener

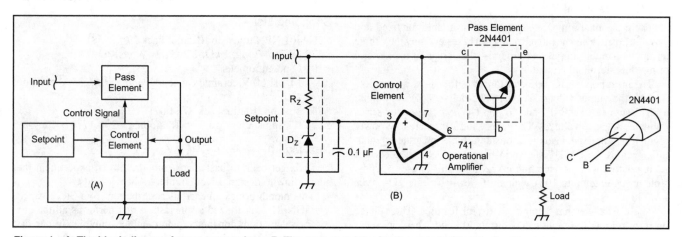

Figure 1—A: The block diagram for a pass regulator. B: The pass regulator implemented with actual components.

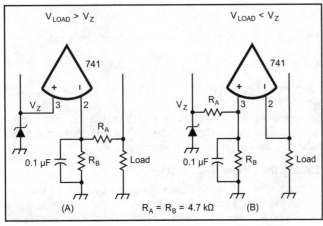

Figure 2—A: The voltage divider of R_A and R_B causes the op-amp to drive the pass transistor so that the load voltage is higher than the Zener voltage, V_Z. B: Performing the same trick for load voltages lower than V_Z.

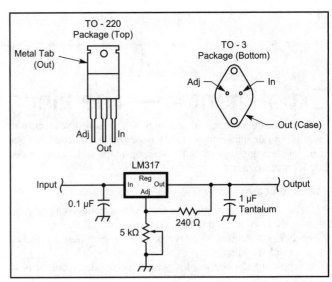

Figure 3—The LM317 adjustable three-terminal regulator is very versatile and rugged. The capacitors are required to ensure that the regulator's internal amplifiers remain stable under all conditions. The 240 Ω resistor limits the current through the 5 kΩ potentiometer. This regulator has an adjustable output from 1.2 V to a maximum that is about 3 V lower than the input voltage.

diode, a resistive voltage divider reduces the load voltage so that a fraction of the actual load voltage is supplied to the op-amp's inverting (–) terminal in Figure 2A.

$$V- = V_{load} (R_B / [R_A + R_B])$$

In order to balance its input voltages, the op-amp must drive the transistor until the load voltage is greater than the setpoint by the inverse of this fraction.

$$V_{load} = V_Z ([R_A + R_B] / R_B) \qquad [Eq\ 2]$$

To obtain load voltages less than the Zener's voltage, use the circuit of Figure 2B. The voltage divider to reduces the Zener voltage, causing the setpoint to be reduced.

$$V_{load} = V_Z (R_B / [R_A + R_B]) \qquad [Eq\ 3]$$

Testing a Variable Regulator

• Add two 4.7 kΩ resistors for R_A and R_B as shown in Figure 2A. The output voltage should change to nearly 10.2 V dc and the op-amp's output to around 10.9 V dc.
• Move the 4.7 kΩ resistors to divide the Zener voltage as in Figure 2B. Now the output voltage should be about 2.5 V dc and the op-amp's output about 3.2 V dc.
• Create an adjustable output regulator by replacing the two 4.7 kΩ resistors with a 10 kΩ potentiometer. Keep the 0.1 µF capacitor at the midpoint of the divider.

The Three-Terminal Regulator

There are many integrated regulators available for fixed and variable positive and negative voltages. These generally have three terminals—input, output and ground—thus creating the generic term "three-terminal regulator."

The most popular IC regulator family is the 78xx, where "xx" denotes the output voltage. A type 7805 delivers 5 V dc output, a 7812 supplies 12 V dc, and so on. The 79xx regulator series regulates negative voltages. The 78Lxx and 79Lxx are low-power regulators. There are also numerous adjustable integrated regulators, such as the LM317 shown in Figure 3. One of the earliest IC regulators was the Fairchild µA723; it's still in use. It's possible to regulate up to 10 A with an IC regulator (the TO-3 type LM396).

These packages have numerous useful features. The voltage drop from input to output can be up to 40 V dc. They can sense when they're getting too hot and shut themselves down. They're protected against short circuits. They have excellent regulation. You can see why they're so popular!

Two caveats, however. The regulators use high-gain amplifiers. These amplifiers can oscillate under some conditions and input and output capacitors are sometimes required, as shown in Figure 3. If overloaded, the regulators will temporarily shut themselves off until they cool, then turn back on. If the overload is persistent, this cycle can repeat as fast as tens of times per second. On a 'scope this appears as high-frequency "noise" from oscillation or a repeating "hiccup" as the chip switches between overheating and shutdown.

Try a 7805 or LM317 and learn how to use these valuable parts. Keep the current to 500 mA or less to avoid overheating the prototype board terminals.

Suggested Reading

Chapter 11 of *The ARRL Handbook* has a substantial discussion of power supply regulation. *The Art of Electronics*, by Horowitz and Hill, really shines, with page after page of Chapter 6 devoted to regulators and an excellent discussion of the 723 regulator IC.

Shopping List

• 2N4401 NPN transistor (RadioShack 276-2058)
• 470 Ω, 2 - 4.7 kΩ, 1 kΩ, 2.2 kΩ, ¼ W resistors
• 10 kΩ potentiometer
• 2 – 0.1 µF, 50 V ceramic capacitors and a 1 µF, 35 V tantalum capacitor
• 741 op-amp (RadioShack 276-007)
• LM317 adjustable regulator (RadioShack 276-1778)

Next Month

Let's get back to basics next month with an experiment that shows how to design driver circuits for heavy loads.

This month brings a generous contribution from Steve Alpert, W1GGN. He constructed a spreadsheet that performs all the necessary calculations for the common emitter amplifier in our first experiment. It also includes a nifty lookup table for standard resistor values. It's available on the Hands-On Radio Web site: **www.arrl. org/tis/info/html/hands-on-radio/**.

Experiment #15: Switchmode Regulators—*Part 1*

In case you hadn't noticed, the dc power supply has undergone a radical transformation. A 20 A, 12 V dc supply now weighs just a couple of pounds and is about the same size as a couple of good sized paperback novels. These are *switching* supplies that are much more efficient in delivering power. This month, you'll meet the *switchmode regulator*.

Terms to Learn

- *Buck* and *boost*—regulators that configure the inductor to subtract from and add to the input voltage, respectively
- *Commutating diode*—a diode that provides a path for inductor current to flow when the switch is turned off

Background

A power supply with a linear regulator (see Experiment #8)[1] acts like a smart resistor that constantly changes its value to drop the output voltage by just the right amount. This is inefficient, dissipating the unwanted power as heat. Neither can a linear regulator create an output voltage higher than its input.

The pass transistor in a linear regulator is operated in its *linear region* between cutoff (zero collector current, I_C) and saturation (minimum collector-to-emitter voltage, V_{CE}), and the power it dissipates is equal to $I_C \times V_{CE}$. For example, if I'm drawing 5 A at 12 V from the regulator output and the input voltage is 18 V, the pass transistor must dissipate $(18-12) \times 5 = 30$ W. No wonder such big heat sinks are required! 60 W ($12 V \times 5 A$) output for a total of 90 W supplied means only 67% efficiency.

Instead of using the pass transistor as a resistor, the switchmode regulator takes advantage of the fact that when either the current through or the voltage across a device is

[1]"Hands-On Radio," *QST*, Sep 2003, p 53.

low, power dissipation ($I \times V$) is also low. This allows the regulator to act more like a power bank, doling out power in small packets, through a switch, at low loss.

Switchmode regulators also make use of the relationship between inductor voltage and current shown in Equation 1:

$$V = L \, \Delta I / \Delta t = L \times \text{change in I per unit time} \qquad [Eq 1]$$

We can also turn Equation 1 around to find inductor current. For a constant applied voltage, current increases linearly with time according to this equation:

$$I = V \times t / L \qquad [Eq 2]$$

This is just what a switchmode supply does—apply voltage to an inductor for a fixed amount of time (a quantity measured in *volt-seconds*) in order to build up a certain amount of current. For example, 12 V applied for 10 µs to a 100 µH inductor results in a current that ramps up to 1.2 A. From the equation for energy stored in an inductor:

$$E = \frac{1}{2} (LI)^2 \qquad [Eq 3]$$

substitute Equation 2 for current into Equation 3 and come up with:

$$E = \frac{1}{2} L(V \times t / L)^2 = \frac{1}{2} (V \times t)^2 / L \qquad [Eq 4]$$

This means that for a specific value of inductor, the volt-seconds of the pulses determines the rate at which energy is delivered, which is power. With the pulse rate constant, you

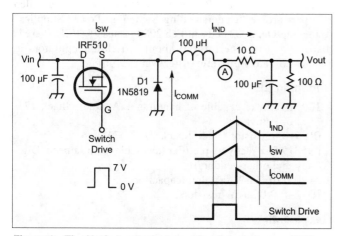

Figure 1—The basic buck regulator circuit including an FET as the switch. Note the commutating diode, D1, which keeps the inductor current flowing between switch drive pulses and avoids the voltage transient at the FET switch.

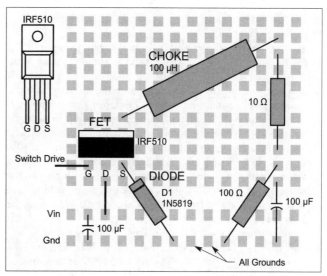

Figure 2—Recommended layout for the buck regulator of Figure 1 on a common prototyping board.

can vary power by controlling pulse width, and vice versa. Voilà! We have a power supply...almost. We still need a way of smoothing out the current, and we need to take care of one other problem.

The problem is that current through an inductor cannot change value instantaneously. Equation 1 says that if I try to change the current through an inductor, a voltage will be developed across the inductor that resists the change in current. For example, if I try to suddenly interrupt the current, a very large voltage will appear across the inductor. This is why *kick-back diodes* are required across relay coils.

To avoid having to deal with these high-voltage transients, it's better to figure out a way to let the inductor current keep flowing between pulses when the switch is off. The regulator in Figure 1 accomplishes this with a *commutating diode* (D1). The switch transistor applies voltage to the inductor for a fixed length of time. This causes the inductor current to "ramp up" until the transistor is turned off. A high voltage transient would then appear at the FET source because the output capacitor holds voltage on its end of the inductor constant. Instead, a diode is connected from ground to the inductor. When the transistor turns off, the inductor current just switches over to flow through the diode. The current doesn't change and so no big voltage transient is generated. Current continues to flow into the output capacitor, producing an easy-to-filter triangular current waveform as shown in Figure 1. The current in the diode is called *commutating current* because it switches with each cycle of operation. When the input switch is turned off, the inductor gradually "discharges" its current into the output capacitor and then waits for the next pulse. The 10 Ω resistor acts as a current sampling resistor so you can look at current with an oscilloscope.

This configuration is called a "buck" regulator because the inductor voltage will *oppose* or *buck* the power supply voltage when it is turned off. The output voltage of a buck regulator is simply:

$$V_{OUT} = V_{IN} \times \text{switch duty cycle} \qquad \text{[Eq 5]}$$

The output voltage of the buck regulator is less than that at the input.

Working with Switchmode Regulators

Let's build a buck regulator. You can reuse the power FET from Experiment #12.[2]
- Start by building the circuit of Figure 1 using Figure 2 as a layout guideline. Since we are talking about creating rapid current rise and fall times, it's a good idea to keep leads and connection lengths short. Be sure the inductor you use is adequately rated and not a low-power choke that will either saturate or burn out. The commutating diode must be a fast-recovery type so that it can switch current quickly.
- Set your generator to output pulses at 10 kHz with a 10% duty cycle by using the "symmetry" control on the square wave setting to skew the waveform to produce narrow pulses. If you can only generate a 50% duty cycle square wave, increase the frequency to around 50 kHz. See the previous experiment for a way to create a 0 to 7 V signal from a generator with no dc offset capability.
- Apply 3 V (you can also use a pair of D cells in series) to the input of the regulator. We're only using 3 V at the input in order to be able to apply sufficient voltage to the gate of the FET. 4 V between the gate and source is required.

[2]"Hands-On Radio," *QST*, Jan 2004, p 61.

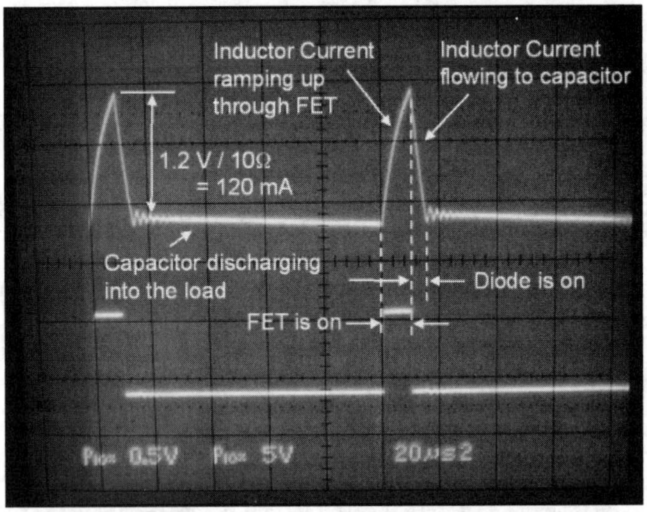

Figure 3—The top trace is the voltage at point A of Figure 1, showing current through the inductor. The bottom trace is the FET gate signal.

- Put one scope probe on the SWITCH DRIVE signal and one at point A. You should see waveforms like those in Figure 3. The current (top trace) through the inductor ramps up during the time that the switch is ON and back down when the switch is OFF. The peak current in my circuit is about 120 mA—or 1.2 V across the 10 Ω current sample resistor.
- Remove the output capacitor and measure the output voltage with a voltmeter. You should see a voltage that is close to 10% of the input voltage. Adjust the pulse duty cycle to see if you can verify Equation 5.
- Reconnect the output capacitor and experiment with the pulse duty cycle to see the effect on output voltage. Change the load resistor value to see how much load the regulator can supply without a big change in output voltage.

Suggested Reading

Not much information on switching supply operation is available in the ham radio press, which is surprising, considering their popularity. Ray Mack, WD5IFS, wrote a detailed two-part article "Understanding Switching Power Supplies" in the Sep/Oct 2002 and Jan/Feb 2003 issues of *QEX*. There is also a good on-line tutorial about switching regulators at **www.web-ee.com/primers/files/webex9.pdf**.

Shopping List

- 100 µH choke capable of handling 1 A, RadioShack 273-102 or equivalent
- IRF510 transistor (RadioShack 276-2072)
- 1N5819 fast-recovery rectifier (available from Jameco, Digi-Key and other vendors)
- 2—100 µF, 25 V tantalum capacitors
- 10 Ω, 100 Ω, ¼ W resistors

Next Month

Continuing with the switchmode theme, next month we'll investigate the boost converter that can create a higher output voltage than its input.

Hands-On Radio Web site: **www.arrl.org/tis/info/html/hands-on-radio/**.

Experiment #16: Switchmode Regulators—*Part 2*

Last month, we looked at the switchmode power converter. We constructed a *buck regulator* that outputs a voltage *lower* than its input. This month, the inductor in that circuit is used to create a *higher* output voltage. Let's examine the *boost regulator*.

Terms to Learn

- *Continuous and Discontinuous Mode*—In continuous mode, current flows in the inductor at all times. In discontinuous mode, inductor current only flows for part of the time.
- *Converter*—A circuit that transfers energy while converting it from one form to another, such as from a low voltage source to a high voltage load.
- *Saturated*—The state of an inductor core that cannot store any additional magnetic energy.

Background

Strictly speaking, our circuits are *converters* and not really regulators; they transfer energy from the power supply to a load and in the process change the voltage. Unlike our two circuits, *regulators* control the output so that it matches a desired set point. However, our buck and boost circuits are typical of the fundamental circuitry used in a true switchmode regulator.

The ability of the boost regulator to increase the output voltage over that at the input is very handy. Boost regulators are used in many types of battery-powered equipment, allowing one or two 1.5 V cells to power equipment that requires 5 V or more.

Figure 1 shows the boost regulator schematic. Like the buck regulator, the inductor carries all of the load current, but instead of being "downstream" from the switch transistor, it's now "upstream," with the switch connected between the inductor and ground. The commutating diode is now connected from the output of the inductor to the load capacitor.

At first, this looks funny—how can this possibly work? When the switch is ON, it's shorting the inductor to ground! The diode doesn't really look like it's doing anything at all, just passing current along to the output.

Let's start with the switch and the inductor. If the switch was never turned on at all, dc current would flow from the input source, through the inductor and diode, and on to the output capacitor. Output voltage would be less than the input voltage by the amount of forward voltage drop across the diode—about 0.7 V.

What does turning the switch ON and routing that current to ground accomplish? As with the buck configuration, the purpose of the switch is to "charge" the inductor with energy stored in a magnetic field by applying voltage to the inductor. When the switch is turned OFF, the inductor current is interrupted, causing the voltage across the inductor to rapidly change from positive to negative in the amount of $L \times (\Delta i / \Delta t)$. Since the input capacitor holds the inductor's input voltage constant during this period, the inductor's output voltage at the FET drain is forced to become greater than that of its input. This higher inductor output voltage forward biases D1 and allows the stored energy to be transferred to the output capacitor as current.

Inductor current gradually decreases until the inductor output voltage is insufficient to keep D1 forward biased. D1 then stops conducting with the output capacitor now charged to a higher voltage than at the power supply input. This is like pulling back a slingshot in order to release it and throw a weight to a higher level.

Figure 2 shows how inductor voltage changes when the switch is turned ON and OFF. Initially, the inductor voltage is at the full input voltage with the switch holding its output at ground potential. (The voltage "droop" observed is due to the relatively small input capacitor being discharged.) When the switch turns OFF, inductor voltage immediately reverses. With its input voltage constant, the output voltage rises to a higher voltage than the input. (Remember that it is the voltage across the inductor that becomes negative, not voltage with respect to ground.) The inductor output voltage gradually decays as the stored energy is

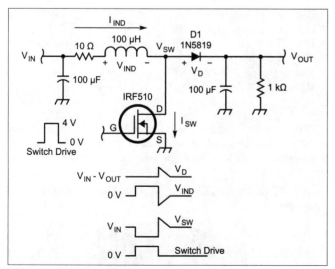

Figure 1—The basic boost regulator circuit using an FET as a switch.

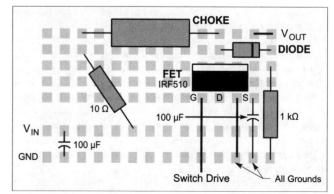

Figure 2—The recommended layout for the boost regulator of Figure 1. It is constructed on a common prototyping board.

transferred through D1 to the output capacitor. This relationship is shown in a simplified way in Figure 1.

If all components were lossless and the switch frequency is held constant, the output voltage would be:

$$V_{OUT} = V_{IN} / (1 - Duty\ Cycle) \qquad [Eq\ 1]$$

This is because the inductor voltage is added to the input voltage only during the period during which it is discharging—a time directly proportional to charging time. The commutating diode, D1, contributes more loss in this circuit because it is in series with the supply current at all times, not just during one-half of the inductor charge/discharge cycle. The diode's forward voltage drop is subtracted from the available output voltage.

Understanding how the inductor energy is stored and released is key to the operation of switchmode regulators. Just as important is the realization that the input and output capacitors temporarily hold voltage constant while the voltage across the inductor can change quickly. This constant voltage enables the changing inductor voltage to be either *added* to the input voltage (as in the *boost* configuration) or *subtracted* from the input voltage (as in the *buck* configuration).

Another important distinction between different types of switchmode designs is whether inductor current flows all the time or just some of the time. The former is called *continuous mode*. If current flows only part of the time, as in our buck and boost regulators, that is a *discontinuous mode* design. Inductors in a continuous mode circuit must be selected so that the energy in the core that is always present does not cause the core to *saturate*, like a bucket being overfilled with water.

Building a Boost Regulator

Since the switch drain is connected to the inductor and the source to ground, instead of in series with the inductor, the gate drive voltage can be reduced to 4 V. In addition, to more clearly observe the boost function, the output load resistor is increased to 1 kΩ.

- Build the circuit shown in Figure 1, and lay it out according to the general guidelines of Figure 3. As with the buck converter, keep leads short and direct, and use a common ground for the signal and oscilloscope leads.
- Set the function generator to supply 10 kHz pulses, with a duty cycle of approximately 10%, a minimum voltage of 0 V and a maximum of 4 V. Apply 3 V dc to the input (two D cells in series will work). If your function generator can't add a dc offset, see experiment #14 for a method of generating the proper waveform. If limited to a 50% duty cycle, increase the frequency to approximately 50 kHz.
- The output voltage measured on a voltmeter should be somewhat above 4 V dc, depending on the type of inductors and capacitors you use. My circuit's output was 4.7 V dc.
- If your oscilloscope has the ability to add two channels of input together on the screen, this would be an excellent time to learn how to use that facility. Typically, channel 1 is connected to the inductor input, channel 2 to the inductor output, and the two channels are added together, with channel 2 set to invert the input signal. Both channels must be set to the same vertical input sensitivity (volts/division) in order to perform the operation correctly. The result should look something like Figure 2 and is a display of channel 1 plus an inverted channel 2.
- Vary the switch drive duty cycle and see how the output compares to Equation 1. In my case, increasing the duty cycle to 50% resulted in an output voltage of 8.3 V dc.
- Set the duty cycle to obtain an output of 6 V dc. Experiment with different values of load resistance to see how that affects output voltage. *Caution*—removing the load

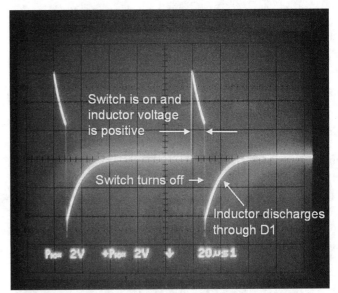

Figure 3—An oscilloscope photo of the inductor voltage. The droop on the top portion of the waveform is the input filter capacitor being partially discharged. Note how quickly the voltage reverses when the switch is turned OFF.

completely will result in a fairly large output voltage (possibly as high as 70 to 80 V dc) as the inductor discharges into the open circuit, pumping the capacitor full of charge. This can easily exceed the capacitor's working voltage rating and cause it to fail.

- As you change the load, readjust either duty cycle or frequency to return the output voltage to 6 V dc. This is just what a regulator circuit would do to control the output of a switching supply!

Suggested Reading

No additional reading material is suggested beyond that recommended last month.

Shopping List

There are no new parts from last month, but here is the list for those of you just starting:
- 100 µH choke capable of handling 1 A (RadioShack 273-102 or equivalent)
- IRF510 transistor (RadioShack 276-2072)
- 1N5819 fast-recovery rectifier (available from Jameco, Digi-Key and other vendors)
- Two 100 µF, 25 V dc tantalum capacitors
- 10 Ω and 100 Ω, ¼ W resistors

Next Month

Back into the realm of op-amps we will go for a quick spin cycle through the world of the oscillator. We'll investigate the phase shift oscillator—a simple source for sine waves in the audio region.

Hands-On Radio Web site: **www.arrl.org/tis/info/html/hands-on-radio/.**

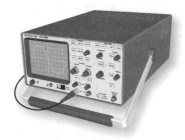

Experiment #30—The Charge Pump

The charge pump sounds like an exotic and mysterious circuit, but it's quite common and easy to use. Get a handle on an inexpensive and useful tool that should be in every experimenter's bucket of tricks.

Terms to Learn

- *Isolated*—the absence of a direct connection between two circuits
- *Synchronous*—activation of control circuits in a sequence determined by a master clock

The Charge Pump

We first met the charge pump as the "integrated voltage inverter," back in column #7 on "Voltage Multipliers." (You can review that column by downloading it from the ARRL Hands-On Radio Web site—**www.arrl.org/tis/info/HTML/Hands-On-Radio**.) In this column, we'll take a closer look at the charge pump and its workings.

The basic idea behind the charge pump is that you can put some charge in a capacitor, isolate the charge by disconnecting it from the charging circuit, and transfer that isolated charge by connecting the capacitor to another circuit. Think of the capacitor used to transfer the charge as an "electron bucket." Fill the bucket from one tank, close the tap, and dump it in another tank!

As you saw in ac power supply voltage multipliers, diodes can act as "check valves," allowing current to charge a capacitor, but not to discharge. The result was that capacitors could be effectively connected in series while being charged on alternate half-cycles of the power source. This doubled the output voltage, but because the capacitors were only charged every other half-cycle, half of the input current was available at the output. In the charge pump doubler, diodes are replaced with switches so that they can be turned on and off at any frequency.

Figure 1 shows how the process works. In step one, the input power source supplies I_{IN} through switches S1 and S2, charging the transfer capacitor, C_T. Switches S3 and S4 are open, so no charge can be transferred to the output. In step two, switches S1 and S2 are opened, disconnecting C_T entirely and trapping its charge. In step three, switches S3 and S4 are closed, connecting C_T to the output and allowing the trapped charge to flow as I_{OUT}. In practice, step two is very short—only long enough to ensure that S1 and S2 are open before S3 and S4 are closed. The orchestrated cycle of switching is called *synchronous switching* because the opening and closing happen in a specific sequence controlled by a single clock signal.

Note that it is not necessary to assume any voltage or current polarities or circuit ground connections for the input and output circuits. The output circuit can be completely *isolated* from the input circuit, as long as the circuits controlling the switches can handle any voltage differences between input and output.

Demonstration #1

You can do this yourself with a pair of DPST switches, a power supply and a 100 µF capacitor. Use a 12 V power supply to supply the input current. Connect a 10 kΩ resistor as the output circuit

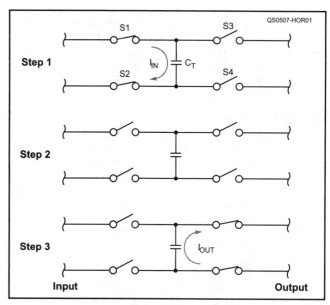

Figure 1—The basic charge pump uses four synchronous switches in a "charge—disconnect—transfer" cycle.

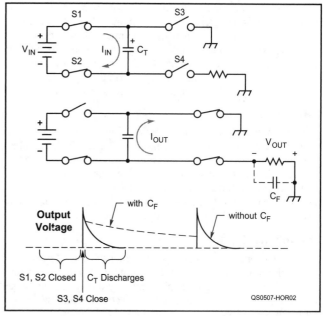

Figure 2—By connecting the positive terminal of the transfer capacitor to ground, the output voltage is inverted from the input.

and measure voltage across it with a voltmeter. One DPST switch is used for S1 and S2, the other for S3 and S4. Build the circuit of Figure 1 with S1 connected to the power supply's positive output. Manually follow steps one to three in a cycle. You have successfully "pumped charge"! Note that the faster you can switch, the higher the average voltage on the voltmeter.

The Charge Pump as Voltage Inverter

How can a positive voltage be turned into a negative voltage? The stored electrons in C_T don't know anything about circuit ground. If the positive terminal of C_T is connected to the output circuit ground when S3 and S4 are closed, the other terminal will be at a negative voltage in that circuit. This is illustrated in Figure 2.

If this was the whole circuit the output voltage would look like a sawtooth as C_T charges through S1 and S2, then discharges through S3 and S4. For that reason, a filter capacitor, C_F, is used to smooth the output voltage. If the switches are operated fast enough and the output load is not too big, the output voltage will be close to the same value as the input voltage, but negative.

Demonstration #2

In the circuit you built previously, connect the output of S3 to the input of S2 and to the voltmeter's negative lead. Manually operate the switches, taking care not to have both switches closed at the same time, which would short the supply. The output voltage will now be negative with respect to the power supply's negative terminal! Add another 100 µF capacitor as C_F. (Be sure to connect the positive terminal to ground.) The peak output voltage should be lower, but there will be less "ripple" if you switch fast enough.

The Charge Pump as a Voltage Multiplier

With the help of a pair of rectifiers and an output filter capacitor, C_T can be used to add voltage, as shown in Figure 3. Unlike the inverter circuit, where the output and input circuits can be isolated, the doubler circuit requires both circuits to share a common ground.

In step one, the negative terminal of C_T is connected to ground by S1 while it is being charged to V_{IN} through D1. S1 then opens and S2 closes, connecting the negative terminal of C_T to the power supply's positive terminal. This places C_T and the power supply in series, with their voltages adding. C_T then discharges through D2 into C_{OUT}. C_{OUT} can be charged to a maximum of $2V_{IN} - 1.4$ V, taking into account the forward voltage drops of D1 and D2.

Demonstration #3

Reconfigure your circuit to that of Figure 3, using just one pole of each of the DPST switches for S1 and S2. Remember that you still have to ensure that both switches aren't closed at the same time to avoid shorting the power supply. By manually operating the switches, you'll see voltages greater than V_{IN} on the output capacitor. Higher switching rates or lighter loads will result in higher and smoother output voltage.

The Voltage Divider

On occasion, it is necessary to generate a voltage lesser than that of the power source, such as to provide a mid-level reference voltage for a single-supply amplifier circuit. In that case the circuit of Figure 2 is used, but C_F is connected between the output of S3 and S4.

When S3 and S4 are closed, the two capacitors are connected in parallel and current flows from C_T into C_F until their voltages are equal. If $C_T = C_F$, then the output voltage is $\frac{1}{2} V_{IN}$ as long as the load current is small enough not to discharge C_F significantly between cycles. In general, $V_{OUT} = V_{IN} \times C_T / (C_T + C_F)$. The smaller C_F becomes, the closer V_{OUT} is to V_{IN}, although the available output current is reduced.

Current Considerations

The charge pump is limited in its ability to supply current

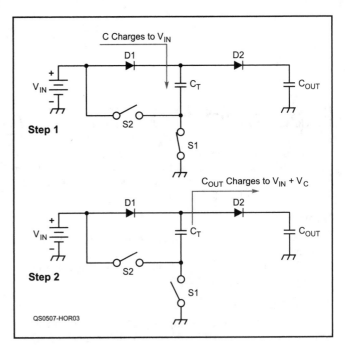

Figure 3—A voltage doubler is created by switching the transfer capacitor's negative terminal from ground to the power supply's positive terminal.

because it can only "fill and dump the bucket" at a finite rate and the bucket is only so big, making it act like a resistance! Consider that on each switching cycle C_T transfers a certain amount of charge between the input and the output, $\Delta Q = C_T (V_{IN} - V_{OUT})$, ignoring diode drops for the moment. Since this happens once every switching cycle, the current transferred by C_T is $I = f \times \Delta Q = f\, C_T(V_{IN} - V_{OUT})$. The effective resistance between V_{IN} and V_{OUT} is then,

$$R = V / I = (V_{IN} - V_{OUT}) / f\, C_T\, (V_{IN} - V_{OUT}) = 1/f\, C_T$$

R creates a voltage drop due to the charge pump's limited ability to keep up with the load, just as a water pump's output pressure drops if too much water is drawn. R can be reduced by increasing f or by increasing C_T. You can observe the effect of f and C on R in any of the demonstration circuits by increasing switching speed or by replacing C_T with a bigger capacitor.

Shopping List
- 2 ea DPST toggle switches
- 2 ea 100 µF, 35 V electrolytic capacitors
- 2 ea 1N4148 diodes
- 10 kΩ, 1/4 W resistor

Suggested Reading

The ICL7660 (Experiment #7) and the improved LTC1044 are industry-standard charge pump ICs widely available and with many variations. These two parts are described in their data sheet, **pdfserv.maxim-ic.com/en/ds/ICL7660-MAX1044.pdf**. The data sheet graph of output resistance versus frequency on page 4 and the application circuits make very interesting reading.

Next Month and an Error

Next month we'll visit another of the electronic world's fundamental circuits, the multivibrator. Also, Ralph, K1RD, alerted me to an error in Experiment #27 on 'Scope Tricks. The capacitor value in Figure 1 should have been 0.1 µF, not 0.01 µF—an early version of the circuit snuck in there.

Experiment #35—Power Supply Analysis

The past 34 experiments have tackled individual circuits in splendid isolation. Most electronic equipment consists of several circuits working together. This month, we'll take a common piece of equipment—the linear power supply—and find out why the whole is greater than the sum of the parts.

Introduction

When equipment needs troubleshooting, the schematic diagram for the equipment is opened up and the head scratching begins. While some schematics are a lot easier to read than others, you can tame even the most obtuse by breaking the overall circuit into its various subcircuits, each with a separate job to do.

Before we get started, I'd like to thank the Astron Corporation (**www.astroncorp.com**) for granting permission to reproduce a popular radio supply's schematic diagram, found at **www.repeater-builder.com/astron/astron-rs35m.pdf**. You should also review Experiments #6 (Rectifiers), #8 (Linear Regulator), and #10 (SCRs), all of which are available on the Hands-On Radio Web site, **www.arrl.org/tis/info/HTML/Hands-On-Radio**. A copy of the LM723 voltage regulator's data sheet can be had at **www.national.com/pf/LM/LM723.html#Datasheet**. Ready? Let's go!

Divide and Conquer

The first order of business is to understand the *big picture* by finding out where all of the inputs, outputs, power and controls are located. Most schematics have a flow of signals or power from left to right. A good schematic will also keep components that work together near each other and perhaps even labeled with their function. Before starting to trace a signal or troubleshoot a symptom, take a few minutes to understand how the schematic is organized. Remember the need for clarity the next time you draw a schematic yourself!

Figure 1 shows a schematic of one version of the popular Astron RS-35 power supply capable of supplying 12 V dc at 35 A. (If you have a linear Astron power supply, you might want to open up your unit and "follow along" as we go.) On the left you can see the ac input circuit, and on the right, the dc output terminals. As the power moves from input to output, it goes through a rectifier circuit and then pass transistors that are controlled by a regulator. There is also a mysterious circuit called a *crowbar* that protects equipment against excessive output voltage. I've drawn lines around some of the circuits, while the larger regulator circuit occupies everything in the middle. The numbers in hexagons are connections to the printed-circuit board. The two components labeled RX are only used for power supply testing at Astron.

Input and Rectifier

There's nothing fancy about the input circuit. The hot side of the ac line passes through an 8 A fuse—heavy enough to withstand the current surge at turn-on as the filter capacitors

COURTESY ASTRON

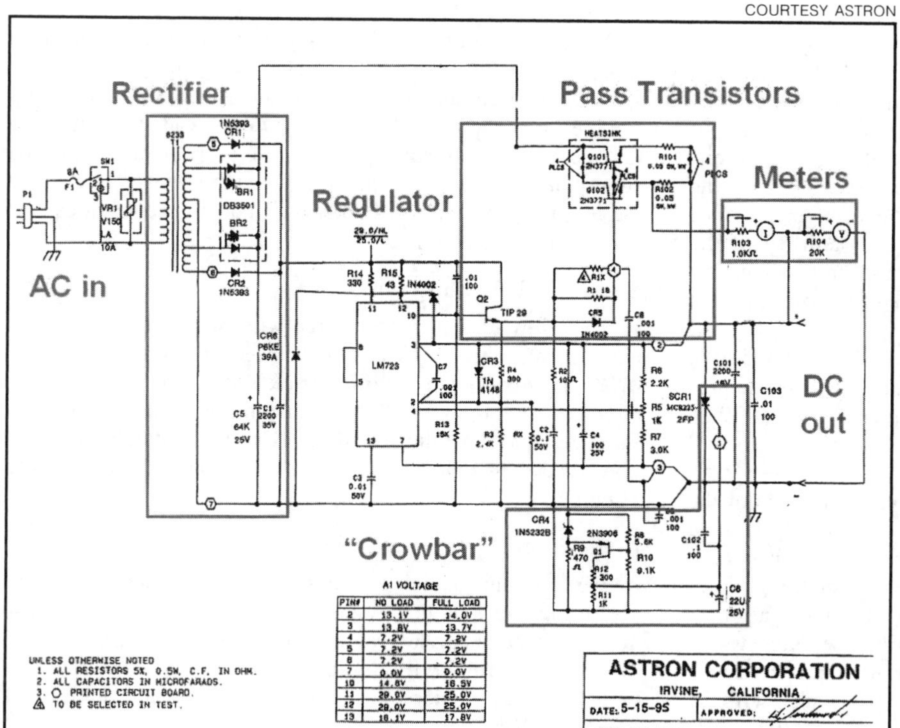

Figure 1—Power supply schematics are best understood with each "subcircuit" analyzed individually. The gray lines show the subcircuits. ←

Rectifier

Pass Transistors

Regulator

Meters

AC in

"Crowbar"

A1 VOLTAGE

PIN#	NO LOAD	FULL LOAD
2	13.1V	14.0V
3	13.8V	13.7V
4	7.2V	7.2V
5	7.2V	7.2V
6	7.2V	7.2V
7	0.0V	0.0V
10	14.0V	16.5V
11	29.0V	25.0V
12	29.0V	25.0V
13	18.1V	17.8V

UNLESS OTHERWISE NOTED
1. ALL RESISTORS 5%, 0.5W, C.F. IN OHM.
2. ALL CAPACITORS IN MICROFARADS.
3. ◯ PRINTED CIRCUIT BOARD.
△ TO BE SELECTED IN TEST.

ASTRON CORPORATION
IRVINE, CALIFORNIA
DATE: 5-15-95   APPROVED: _____
RS-35M/RS-35A

DC out

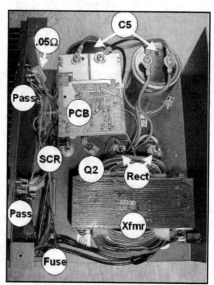

Figure 2—The major components of the power supply. Be careful to avoid contacting the ac line components when measuring voltages!

charge up. VR1 is a V150LA varistor that conducts at voltages above 150 V, protecting the supply against input voltage surges. (Note—you can usually find detailed information on components by entering their part number and *"data sheet"* with the quotes into an Internet search engine.)

The rectifier circuits look a little strange until you realize that there are two full-wave, center-tapped circuits nested one inside the other. The inner circuit supplies the high current output power. It uses a DB3501 full-wave bridge rectifier (**www.diotec-usa.com/35dbp.pdf**) with the diodes connected in parallel to share the current load. The dashed line around the diodes indicates that they're all in a single package. My model of the power supply in Figure 2 uses two separate diodes. The filter capacitor, C5, is a large 64,000 µF, 25 V electrolytic. My supply has two 32,000 µF caps in parallel. The outer circuit supplies power for the regulator circuitry at higher voltage and much lower current with 1N5393 rectifiers (CR1 and CR2) and C1, a 2200 µF, 35 V electrolytic.

Pass Transistors and Metering

Now follow the output of the high-current rectifier to the pass transistors. Here again, you encounter a dashed line as well as a cryptic notation, 4 PLCS, which means "four places" or "there are four of these." If you look at an actual supply, you'll see four 2N3771 transistor circuits all connected in parallel—that's what the dots mean on the connections between Q101 and Q102.

In order for the transistors to share current equally, 0.05 Ω, 5 W, wire-wound (WW) resistors are in series with the emitter of each transistor. If one transistor begins to hog all the current, the voltage across this resistor increases and lowers its base to emitter voltage, reducing drive and also emitter current. One resistor is used as a shunt, providing a voltage proportional to overall current so that a meter can display total current without having to pass all of it through the meter movement. The current meter, labeled I, conducts a few mA at full scale, as calibrated by R103. A voltage meter is connected directly across the output terminals.

Regulator

Look at the LM723 data sheet and find the equivalent circuit on page 2. This shows how the regulator works without including every transistor. Try to correlate the equivalent circuit with the linear regulator circuit of Experiment #8. In the LM723, the Zener diode is buffered by the voltage reference amplifier (output at pin 6) to improve the stability of the regulator's reference voltage. A "Current Limit" transistor (pins 10 and 11) works by diverting some of the output drive if the output current gets too high.

The LM723 uses a 29 V supply at pin 12, protected by a 1N4002 and CR6, a P6KE39A transient absorber. These protect the regulator IC and clamp any voltage spikes at 39 V. R15 acts to limit the current when a spike occurs, but is small enough not to upset regulator function.

The LM723 compares a fraction the output voltage of the supply (obtained through the voltage divider of R5, R6 and R7) at pin 4 to that of the voltage reference, which is connected to pin 5. If the output is too low the regulator supplies more output drive, and vice versa. Even with high-gain pass transistors, the LM723 can't drive them hard enough to get full output, so Q2, an intermediate driver transistor, is needed— a TIP129. The LM723's internal drive transistor with its collector connected to input power at pin 11 through R14, supplies base current to Q2 from pin 10. So, the LM723 drives Q2, which drives the 2N3771. Q2's output current passes through R1 (18 Ω) and CR5 (1N4002) that limit base drive current to the 2N3771's.

The current limiting transistor inside the LM723 (base connected to pin 2 and emitter to pin 3) is off unless the voltage at pin 2 rises to 0.7 V above the output voltage at pin 3, turning on the internal transistor and diverting drive current from Q2. The values of R3 and R4 set V_{PIN2} to $0.9 \times V_{Q2}$.

Working toward the output from Q2, there is a 0.7 V drop across CR5, another 0.7 V drop from the 2N3771's base to emitter, then $1/4$ of the output current times 0.05 W. So V_{PIN2} equals $0.9 \times (V_{OUT} + 0.7 + 0.7 + 0.05\ I_{OUT}/4)$. If the supply is set to the usual output voltage of 13.8 V, the current limiting transistor will turn on when the output current reaches about twice the rated steady state output current, or 70 A. (This is probably high because I assumed a low value of 0.7 V across the power transistors.) CR3 protects the current limit transistor from voltage spikes. There are a number of 0.1, 0.01 and 0.001 µF capacitors in the circuit—they filter out any RF that might upset regulator operation. C4 and C101 filter any sags or spikes at the output due to sudden changes in load.

Overvoltage Protection—The *Crowbar*

This leaves the odd circuit at the lower right, combining a Zener diode, a transistor and an SCR directly across the output of the supply. The function of this circuit is to protect external equipment against excessive voltage due to a supply failure. The remedy is a little extreme—the SCR is turned on, shorting out the supply (and hopefully blowing the input fuse)! It's just like dropping a crowbar across the output terminals and hence the name.

Q1 turns on whenever its emitter is 0.7 V above the base voltage, which is equal to $V_{OUT} \times R10 / (R8 + R10) = 0.62\ V_{OUT}$. Since Zener diode CR4 has a 5.6 V drop from V_{OUT}, Q1 will turn on when $V_{OUT} - 5.6$ V equals $0.62\ V_{OUT} + 0.7$ V, or when V_{OUT} equals 16.6 V. When Q1 turns on, C6 charges up through R12 and triggers the SCR, which dumps current to ground until the supply fuse blows or the filter caps are discharged. R9 keeps Q1 off until CR4 conducts and R11 keeps the SCR off until Q1 turns on.

We've covered the job done by every single component in this power supply! This won't make you a power supply designer, but it should make you a much better power supply troubleshooter! Using the table of voltages at the bottom of the schematic, you can rapidly isolate a problem and get the supply back on the job. Use these same techniques of carving the *big problem* into *little problems* and soon schematics will become much clearer.

Suggested Reading

To follow up on and reinforce what we've learned in this experiment, take a look at other power supply circuits in the *ARRL Handbook*,[1] magazine articles or schematics of other commercial equipment. See if you can break the circuit down into sections. For other regulator ICs, use a search engine to download their data sheets and see how they are used in the circuit.

Next Month

We're going to stick our toes in the deep waters of digital electronics next month by experimenting with an amazingly versatile counter/divider chip that can just about do it all. If you're not familiar with digital electronics, I suggest that you bone up on bit basics by reading the appropriate sections of the *ARRL Handbook*.[2]

[1,2]Available from your local ARRL dealer, or from the ARRL Bookstore, ARRL order number 9845. Telephone 860-594-0355 or, toll-free in the US 888-277-5289, fax 860-594-0303; **www.arrl.org/shop/**; **pubsales@arrl.org**.

Experiment #38 — Battery Charger

A trickle or a torrent? It's your choice as we design a dual-rate battery charger circuit!

Terms to Learn

Capacity — a battery's energy delivery capacity measured in ampere-hours (Ah).

Overcharge — charging a battery beyond its full-charge capacity.

Introduction

Rechargeable batteries are more popular than ever, but getting your money's worth from them requires careful charging. In this two-part experiment we'll explore battery charging by combining a comparator and a simple current source from Experiments 11 and 19. (ARRL members can download previous columns from **www.arrl.org/tis/info/HTML/Hands-On-Radio.**)

Battery Background

A battery's ability to supply energy is measured in ampere-hours (Ah). Multiplying amperes (coulombs per second) by time (hours) equals charge. For example, 1 A current flowing for 10 seconds results in 10 coulombs of charge. That means a battery's Ah rating is proportional to the total number of electrons it can supply. For this reason, a battery's capacity rating is often abbreviated C. The voltage across the battery terminals, V_{BATT}, is determined by the types of materials in the battery, such as nickel, zinc or lithium, that react to produce electrons. V_{BATT}, is independent of capacity, which is determined by the amount of reacting material or *reactants* in the battery. That generally translates to battery size or weight.

Why do total electrons equate to energy? The energy for each electron to be "pushed" through a circuit by the battery equals the charge of the electron times the voltage that pushes it. By counting electrons supplied and assuming that battery voltage, V_{BATT}, stays constant, the product is the total energy supplied to all the electrons: $V_{BATT} \times Ah$ = total battery energy.

V_{BATT} isn't constant, of course. It slowly drops as the battery's reactants are consumed, and then plummets when they are depleted. Similarly, the battery doesn't supply the rated current for one hour then turn off like a switch. The rating in Ah represents an effective amount of energy that can be delivered.

In non-rechargeable batteries, such as alkaline or zinc-air, the chemical reaction is one-way — once the reactants are used up, they're gone forever. Batteries that are rechargeable, such as nickel-cadmium (NiCd) or lithium-ion (Li-Ion), are made with materials whose reaction is reversible. That is, by using a charger to force electrons back into the battery, the chemical reaction can be made to run in reverse until a full charge is restored.

Battery Charging

Just as V_{BATT} falls as the battery is discharged, V_{BATT} rises as the battery is recharged. The simplest battery charger is a power supply that supplies current to the battery until the supply and battery voltages are equal. Because a discharged battery looks almost like a short circuit, using a power supply as a charger can result in very high current when the battery is fully discharged, possibly exceeding the supply's capability and blowing a fuse, or at worst, damaging the battery.

Battery manufacturers specify a maximum safe amount of charging current. This is called the *bulk-charge rate*. This current is generally around 0.1 C, where C is the battery energy capacity in Ah. For example, if I have an 1800 mAh battery, the bulk-charge current limit would be around 180 mA. Charging a fully discharged battery at 180 mA for 10 hours (without losses) would restore the battery to full charge.

It's possible to charge a battery more quickly with a fast-charge current of C/3. This can be harmful because of heat buildup. Over-heating a battery can cause it to vent, discharging gas and vapor through a safety port. This often damages the battery, but it does help prevent a cell from exploding! Fast-charging requires special chargers that can sense a battery's charge and discharge it to a safe level before charging it.

To control charging current, a current source (a transistor with a constant base current) is used. Figure 1 shows a circuit that supplies a controlled amount of current using a PNP pass transistor. The transistor's collector current, I_C, is equal to the base current, I_B, times the current gain, β. This is true even if the load is a short circuit, as you will see!

Testing the Current Source

- Configure your test meter to measure a current of up to 300 mA.
- Construct the circuit of Figure 1 using direct connections to the power supply for the leads shown in dark gray. (The current will be too high for a prototyping board.) Solder wires directly to the transistor leads as shown in Figure 2 and set the potentiometer to 100 kΩ.
- To provide a heat sink for the transistor, clamp the metal tab of the transistor flat against a piece of clean metal or grip it in a large pair of locking pliers. The tab and collector are connected, so prevent the heat sink from shorting to any other part of the circuit.
- Use a second voltmeter to measure V_B. If you don't have a second meter, alternate measurements between voltage and current, replacing the ammeter with a wire. Take care to reconfigure the meter before each measurement!
- Apply power and measure the output current directly. Measure

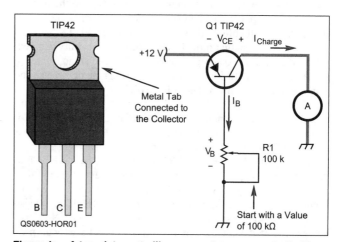

Figure 1 — A transistor acts like a current source controlled by the amount of base-emitter current. This current is independent of load impedance.

Figure 2 — The power transistor dissipates $I_C \times V_{CE}$ watts, so a heat sink is necessary. Locking pliers make a nice heat sink in a pinch!

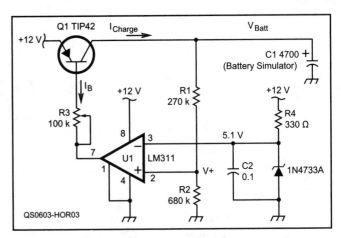

Figure 3 — The comparator circuit shuts off the charging current when the battery reaches full charge. Shut-off voltage is determined by R1 and R2.

base current by using Ohm's Law ($I_B = V_B / 100\ k\Omega$). Base current should be around 0.1 mA and output current from 5 to 20 mA. Compute the transistor's current gain $\beta = I_C / I_B$. Adjust potentiometer R1 until I_C is 10 mA and measure the potentiometer's resistance value.

* Decrease the potentiometer value until collector current reaches 100 mA then measure the potentiometer's resistance value. Measure the base current and calculate gain. Note that gain changes with current level.
* The transistor's power dissipation is $V_{CE} \times I = 12 \times 0.1 = 1.2$ W. It may get warm!

Charge Control

We can't just leave our simple current source connected to the battery. After the battery reached full charge, the charger would continue to force current into the battery, overcharging it. Even if it doesn't overheat and vent, high internal temperatures can severely reduce the battery's capacity. The charger must stop charging when full charge is reached.

Remember that battery voltage is an indicator of its state of charge. When battery voltage rises to the rated voltage for the battery, it should be considered a signal to the charger to turn off the charging circuit. That's just what the circuit of Figure 3 accomplishes by using a comparator to sense the battery voltage and switch off the pass transistor's base current.

The LM311 comparator has an open-circuit (OC) output that is an NPN transistor whose collector is connected to the output pin. (The emitter is connected to pin 1, which is grounded in our circuit.) When the output transistor is ON, current flows through the pass transistor's base, allowing charging current to flow to the battery. For R3, use the potentiometer from the first part of this experiment, set to the value that limited the output current to 10 mA.

To make our charger turn off when the battery is fully charged, we need to be able to compare battery voltage to some reference value or *setpoint*. In Figure 3, a 5.1 V Zener diode creates the setpoint of 5.1 V at pin 3. The voltage divider, R1 and R2, reduce the battery's voltage so that 5.1 V appears at pin 2 when the full charge voltage is reached. Thus, at full charge the pass transistor is turned off and charging is halted. (The 0.1 µF capacitor across the diode filters out any noise or transients.)

The combined resistance of R1 and R2 must be quite high to prevent the battery from discharging through them when the pass transistor is turned off. A few microamps of current is an acceptable drain, so let's pick 1 MΩ as the total resistance of R1+R2. We also need to know the full-charge voltage. If we are charging a NiCd battery pack of six AA cells in series, the full charge voltage for the pack will be $6 \times 1.2 = 7.2$ V. We can now determine R1 and R2:

$R1 + R2 = 1\ M\Omega$

$V+ = 5.1\ V = V_{BATT}\ (R2 / R1 + R2) = 7.2 \times (R2 / 1\ M)$

$R2 = 5.1 \times (1\ M\Omega) / 7.2 = 708.3\ k\Omega$ and $R1 = 1\ M\Omega - 708.3\ k\Omega = 291.7\ k\Omega$

The closest standard resistor values are 270 kΩ for R1 and 680 kΩ for R2. These values result in an acceptably close $V+ = 5.15$ V when $V_{BATT} = 7.2$ V.

Testing the Charger

* Build the circuit of Figure 3, replacing the battery with a short circuit. Measure the charging current as before and confirm that it is approximately 10 mA.
* Remove the short circuit and simulate the battery with a large capacitor, such as the 4700 µF unit in the Shopping List. Exact value is not important — a few thousand µF or more will do — but be sure the rated voltage is 16 V or greater.
* Re-energize the circuit and confirm that the capacitor is charged to approximately 7.2 V. (It will only take a second or two of charging.)
* Connect a load resistor of 1 kΩ across the capacitor and measure the output voltage of the comparator. You'll see it turn on for short periods when the capacitor discharges to less than 7.2 V.
* Change the values of R1 and R2 to create different full-charge voltages.
* Raise the value of R3 to lower the charging current and see how long it takes to charge the capacitor.

Don't start charging batteries quite yet — the charger needs a few more features that we'll add next month!

Recommended Reading

If you'd like to know a lot more about batteries, the Web site at **www.powerstream.com** is full of great reading. Click "Technical Resources" to find the list of tutorials and FAQ. To focus on lead-acid batteries, browse to **www.batterystuff.com/tutorial_battery.html**.

Shopping List

* TIP42 PNP transistor or equivalent, RadioShack 276-2016.
* 100 kΩ potentiometer.
* 1N4733A Zener diode, RadioShack 276-565.
* 330 Ω, 270 kΩ and 680 kΩ, ¼ W, 5% resistors.
* 4700 µF (or larger), 16 V electrolytic capacitor, RadioShack 272-1022 typical.

Next Month

Wouldn't it be nice if our charging circuit could switch from a high current to a low current when the battery is nearly charged? Next month, we'll see how that trick is done with the addition of just one resistor. We'll also make it possible to charge batteries of different voltages.

Experiment #39 — Battery Charger, Part 2

Complete last month's charger circuit — add dual current levels and a charge indicator.

Terms to Learn

• Absorption — applying a constant voltage slightly greater than the full-charge voltage to allow a battery to reach full charge.

• Trickle (or Float) — applying a small current to maintain a battery at full charge.

Last month we built a circuit that would apply a constant current to a battery. (Review the charger circuit design at **www.arrl.org/members-only/tis/info/pdf/0603052. pdf**.) The current was either fully on or fully off. This month, we extend our design so that the charger automatically reduces current as the battery reaches full charge.

Design Improvements

As it is currently designed, the charger won't quite fully recharge our battery. The circuit supplies current at the quick-charge level, then turns completely off. That leaves the battery short of full charge because it takes time for the battery to absorb all the charge in the charging current. If the charger switches to a lower current instead of turning off, that will gradually bring the battery to full charge and hold it there.

It would also be nice to be able to tell what the charger is doing. Is the battery charging or fully charged? With the current design, you have to use a voltmeter to tell. The new design adds LEDs to show which level of current the charger is supplying, high or low.

Finally, it would be nice to be able to use the circuit to charge different types of batteries without having to change components. We will make the full-charge voltage adjustable for flexibility.

Trickle and Float Charging

All batteries have a tendency to *self-discharge*. Either current leaks between the external terminals due to dampness or surface contamination or there is leakage across the battery's internal structure that keeps the reactants apart. Either way, once charging current is removed, the battery's voltage slowly declines.

The solution is to provide a small current that can more than make up for the leakage, but not so much as to heat and overcharge the battery. This level of current is called the *float* or *trickle charge* current. (There are slight differences between *float* and *trickle* based on

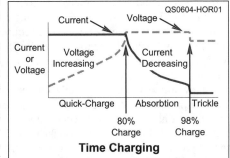

Figure 1 — A commercial lead-acid battery charger uses a three-step charging profile: constant-current, followed by constant-voltage (the absorption step), and trickle-charge to maintain the battery at full charge. The charger senses both battery voltage and current to change from one step to the next.

battery type, but for the purposes of this experiment they are equivalent.) Trickle charge currents are low enough that they can be applied to the battery indefinitely without damaging it. Applied to a battery long enough (after the quick-charge period) trickle charging will bring a battery to its full-charge state and hold it at full-charge.

Battery manufacturers have developed the three-step charging sequence or *profile* for lead-acid batteries shown in Figure 1. Initially, the charger operates in a *constant-current* quick-charge mode to apply the quick-charge current to the battery, rapidly bringing the battery to around 80% charge. During this phase you can see that current is constant while battery voltage slowly increases to the full-charge level.

The charger senses the rise in battery voltage and changes to the *constant voltage* or *absorption* mode in which the remaining charge is supplied and charging current gradually dwindles to a low level. When current is low enough, at a charge level of close to 100%, the charger switches to trickle-charge mode and supplies just enough current, typically 0.02 to 0.03 C (where C is the battery capacity, or Ah rating, as discussed in Experiment 38), to keep the battery at full charge.

Note and caution — different battery chemistries require different charging techniques to get the best performance out of a battery: number of recharges, time to charge, energy stored, etc. The charger circuit in this experiment will work with lead-acid batteries as a two-stage *taper charger* that applies fast charge current followed by a trickle charge current. NiCd and NiMH batteries require different techniques for best results. Use the appropriate charger for those types of batteries.

Changing Current Rates

Instead of turning current completely off when full-charge voltage is reached, we'd like the charger to switch to a lower trickle-charge current. Presently, all of the TIP42 base current goes through the output transistor of the LM311. By adding R4 to the circuit, some base current flows even when the LM311 output transistor is OFF, causing the TIP42 to supply the trickle charge current, I_{TC}. When the LM311 output transistor is ON, additional base current flows, charging the battery at the quick-charge rate, I_{FC}.

$$I_{TC} = \beta (12 - V_{EB}) / R4 = \beta (12 - 0.7) / R4 \qquad \text{[Eq 1a]}$$

$$I_{FC} = \beta (12 - 0.7) / (R4 // R3) \qquad \text{[Eq 1b]}$$

The // symbol stands for "in parallel with." β is the current gain of a transistor. Let's build the two-current charger!

Building the Two-Current Charger

First, check your circuit from last month as shown in Figure 2. (Don't connect R4 yet.) Reset the values of R1 and R2 for the original full-charge voltage of 7.2 V. Reset R3 for a fast-charge current of 100 mA. Power up the circuit with the battery replaced by a short circuit and be sure that it's working okay by measuring charging current.

Use equation 1a to calculate the value of R4 for a trickle charge current of 10 mA. Use the value of β you measured for the TIP42. Assuming your transistor has a β of 100, R4 = 100 (12 − 0.7) / 0.01 = 113 kΩ. Use the closest standard value, 120 kΩ in this case.

Connect R4 to your circuit as shown. Temporarily remove R3

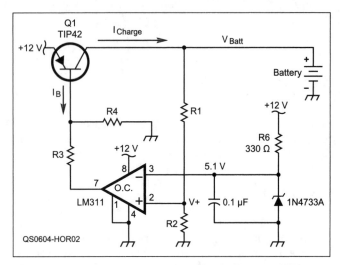

Figure 2 — Adding R4 to the charger circuit allows a small base current to flow at all times. This is the trickle-charge current.

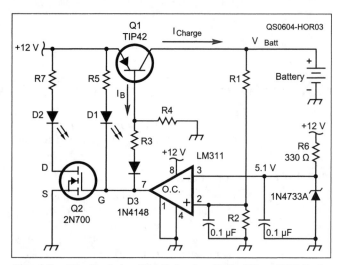

Figure 3 — The final circuit includes two LEDs (D1 and D2) that indicate whether the charger is in the quick-charge or trickle-charge mode. Changing R1 and R2 from fixed resistors to a potentiometer makes the full-charge voltage adjustable.

from the circuit and measure the output current, which should be close to 10 mA.

Reconnect R3. The output current will increase to approximately 110 mA resulting from the sum of base currents flowing through both R3 and R4. (Extra credit — use Equation 1b to find the value of R3 that will return fast-charge current to exactly 100 mA.)

Temporarily connect R6 to ground instead of +12 V. The output current should drop back to the trickle charge value because the – input of the LM311 is at ground instead of 5.1 V. With the + input at a higher voltage than the – input, the LM311 output transistor turns OFF and reduces TIP42 base current to the trickle-charge value. You have now demonstrated a dual-mode battery charger! When actually charging a battery, the voltage at the – input changes as the battery charges.

Getting an Indication

The next step is to add some visual indicators that will tell you at a glance whether the circuit is in fast-charge or trickle-charge mode. Adding a fast-charge indicator is relatively easy. Whenever the charger is in fast-charge mode, the output transistor of the LM311 is ON, and that means pin 7 of the LM311 is almost at ground. By connecting D1 and current-limiting resistor R5 to the LM311 as shown in Figure 3, D1 will light when the LM311 is ON. This is the fast-charge indicator.

But wait! If the LM311 is OFF, the current that flows through R5 and D1 will try to flow back through R3 and R4 to ground. This extra current in R4 will reduce the TIP42 base current. To prevent this from happening, D3 is added to block this backward current. D1 also changes the equation for fast-charge current because there are now two 0.7 V drops to account for.

$$I_{FC} = \beta \ (12 - 0.7 - 0.7) \ / \ (R3 \ // \ R4) \qquad [Eq\ 2]$$

The indicator for trickle charge is not as easy because there is no convenient signal strong enough to light an LED when the LM311 is OFF. That's where Q2 comes in. In trickle-charge mode the LM311 output transistor is OFF and pin 7 of the LM311 rises close to $12 - 0.7 - 0.7 = 10.6$ V. That's plenty to turn on Q2, whose gate (G) draws very little current. When Q2 turns ON, so does D2. This is the TIP42 base indicator. Only one indicator should light at a time.

Calculating the value for R5 and R7 requires that we know the LED current. Choosing 10 mA and assuming a 2 V drop across the LED,

$$R5 = R7 = (12 - 2) \ / \ 0.01 = 1 \ k\Omega$$

Add the indicators to the circuit and repeat the last step of the experiment above to confirm that the indicators light when they are supposed to. I suggest a green LED for trickle and red LED for fast charge.

Adjusting Full-Charge Voltage

The ratio of R1 and R2 sets the full-charge voltage, as we found last month. We can make the full-charge voltage adjustable by changing R1 and R2 from fixed resistors to a potentiometer, as shown in Figure 3. The sum of R1 and R2 is 1 MΩ to limit current drain from the battery, so the potentiometer should also have 1 MΩ of total resistance. By adjusting the potentiometer, the full-charge voltage is also varied. (Setting full-charge voltage is discussed in last month's experiment.) The 0.1 μF capacitor filters out noise at this sensitive spot in the circuit.

Using the Charger

Now that you have a battery charger circuit, it would be nice to charge some batteries, wouldn't it? Start with a small 6 V gel-cell (lead-acid) battery or a set of four rechargeable AA batteries. Determine the battery's Ah rating (C) and calculate the fast-charge current (0.1 C) and the trickle-charge current (0.03 C). Calculate the values of R3 and R4 to set the charging currents to the right value. Calculate the values of R1 and R2 required for a full-charge voltage of 6.9 V (full charge for a 6 V gel-cell) or 6 V (full charge for four NiMH batteries). Use an expendable battery or batteries for your experiment.

Follow the steps above to test the circuit and then give it a try. Monitor the voltage on the battery to be sure that you don't over-charge it during this initial test. After you've successfully charged a battery or two, you might want to make R3 and R4 adjustable, too, so that you can change the charging currents. This is a circuit that could even be built into a small enclosure to use on your workbench. If you do, remember to heat sink the main transistor!

Next Month

Hands-free operation, whether on a cell-phone or on ham radio requires a special voice-sensing circuit to operate the transmitter. This is a VOX (voice-operated transmit) circuit and it will be the subject of next month's column.

Filters

Experiment #4—Active Filters

Amplifiers are great, but where op-amps really prove their worth is in more advanced circuits that are difficult to execute with discrete transistors. A ham's radio shack is full of filters, many of which are based on the op-amp. This month, we'll take a look at two of the simplest filters and one that's a little more complex.

Terms to Learn

• *Cutoff Frequency*—The frequency, f_c, at which the filter output voltage falls to $1/\sqrt{2}$ or 70.7% of its peak output. At this frequency, the power of the output signal has been cut in half.

• *Low, High and Band-Pass Filters*—Low-pass filters attenuate signals with frequencies *above* the cutoff frequency. High-pass filters do the opposite (attenuate *below* cutoff). Band-pass filters pass a range of signal frequencies, but attenuate signals *outside* that range, called the passband.

• *Q*—The ratio of a filter's center frequency to the bandwidth of its passband. Higher-Q means a narrower passband for a given center frequency.

• *Roll-off*—The gradual reduction in signal amplitude beyond a filter's cutoff frequency.

The Low-Pass Filter

The amplifier circuits we built last month can amplify signals all the way from dc to the limits of the op-amp, more than 1 MHz. But what if we don't want to amplify all those frequencies—perhaps just those in the communication audio range below 3 kHz? That requires an amplifier whose gain changes with frequency, or a low-pass filter.

We'll start with the unity-gain amplifier (refer to Figure 3 in last month's column). Remember that the op-amp output must balance the input current (V_{in} / R_i) with an equal current through the feedback component, R_f. What if R_f was replaced with components whose impedance changed with frequency? Then the op-amp's output voltage would also have to change with frequency to keep the currents balanced.

That's just what is happening in Figure 1, where capacitor C_f has been placed across R_f. The reactance of C_f ($X = 1/2\pi f_c$) gets smaller with frequency. That means the impedance of the feedback path between the op-amp's inverting terminal and output also gets smaller with frequency. The lower impedance means that less output voltage is required to balance the input current and the circuit's output will decrease for high-frequency signals. This is a low-pass filter.

We only want to amplify communications audio, so the cutoff frequency, f_c, should be about 3 kHz. In this circuit, f_c is reached when the impedance in the feedback path (the parallel combination

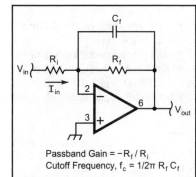

Figure 1—A low-pass filter.

Passband Gain = $-R_f / R_i$
Cutoff Frequency, $f_c = 1/2\pi\, R_f\, C_f$

of R_f and C_f) is one-half of the input resistance, R_i. This occurs when the reactance of C_f equals R_f. The design equations for our low-pass filter are:

$$C_f = 1/2\pi f_c R_f \text{ and } f_c = 1/2\pi C_f R_f \qquad [1]$$

Let's try it!

Testing the Low-Pass Filter

• Design the amplifier to have a passband gain of 1, so $R_f = R_{in}$. Use a value of 10 kΩ. For an f_c of 3 kHz, $C_f = 1/2\pi$ (3 kHz)(10 kΩ) = 5.3 nF. Use the closest standard value of 5.6 nF, which will result in an f_c of 2.8 kHz. (Don't forget the power supply bypass capacitors when building the circuit.)

• Confirm that the filter has unity-gain at dc by using a 1 kΩ potentiometer to apply a variable dc voltage as in the previous experiment. Use a ±12 V power supply across the potentiometer.

• Use the function generator to apply a 1 V_{p-p} sine wave at 10 Hz to the filter input. If you are using a DMM to measure signal voltage, this is 0.35 V_{RMS}. Measure the input and output voltage at 10, 20, 50, 100, 200, 500, 1000, 2000 and 5000 Hz.

• Find f_c by varying the signal frequency until output voltage is 0.7 V_{p-p} (or 0.25 V_{RMS}). It's unlikely that f_c will be exactly 2.8 kHz because the actual values of R_f and C_f are somewhat different than their labeled values.

• Change the filter's passband gain to 2.2 by increasing R_f to 22 kΩ. Measure the output voltage from 1000 to 5000 Hz. What happened to f_c? As R_f increases, the frequency at which the reactance of C_f balances R_c decreases. To restore f_c, C_f will have to be decreased by the same amount as R_f increased—to 5.6 nF / 2.2 = 2.5 nF. Replace C_f with the closest standard value of 2.7 nF and see if f_c is back where it belongs.

High-Pass Filters

You can also make gain "roll off" at low frequencies with components that cause the balancing function of the op-amp to reduce its output voltage below the cutoff frequency as shown in Figure 2. As frequency decreases, the reactance of Ci increases, reducing input current. Balancing current thus takes less output voltage and the filter's output will decrease along with input frequency. Following similar reasoning, the design equations for the high-pass filter are:

$$C_i = 1/2\pi f_c R_i \text{ and }$$
$$f_c = 1/2\pi C_i R_i \qquad [2]$$

Gain in the passband is still the same, $-R_f/R_i$.

Creating a Band-Pass Filter

Continuing with the communications audio theme, it's usually desired to attenuate frequencies below

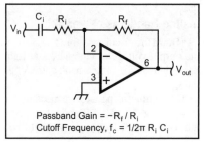

Figure 2—A high-pass filter.

Passband Gain = $-R_f / R_i$
Cutoff Frequency, $f_c = 1/2\pi\, R_i\, C_i$

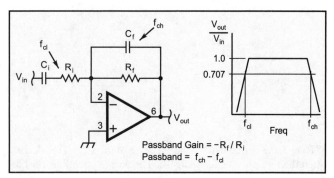

Figure 3—A band-pass filter.

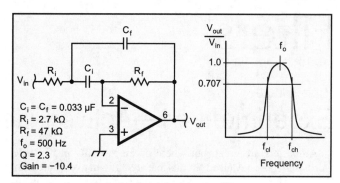

Figure 4—A multiple-feedback band-pass filter.

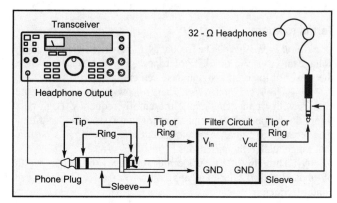

Figure 5—Listening to your filter circuit.

300 Hz. We can combine high-pass and low-pass functions as in Figure 3. This circuit has a cutoff frequency, f_{cl} and f_{ch}, at each end of the passband. We already have f_{ch} from our low-pass filter. For an f_{cl} of 300 Hz:

$$C_I = 1/2\pi(300 \text{ Hz})(10 \text{ k}\Omega) = 53 \text{ nF}$$

We'll use the closest standard value of 56 nF. Let's build it!

Testing Band-Pass Filter #1

• Restore the low-pass filter circuit to its original configuration with two 10 kΩ resistors. Add the 56 nF capacitor in series with R_{in}.

• Measure input and output voltage between 10 and 5000 Hz. Determine the lower cutoff frequency as before.

A Better Band-Pass Filter

More advanced designs have a much steeper rolloff above and below the cutoff frequencies. The passband can be narrowed, amplification can be combined with filtering functions. There are a number of filter types that achieve these goals.

Band-pass filters have two additional parameters that define how the filter affects the input signals. The first is the filter's frequency of peak response, also called the "center frequency," and abbreviated f_o. The second is a measure, called "Q" of the filter's passband relative to f_o. (The symbol Q is also used in other related measurements, but it only refers to the shape of the filter passband here.)

$$Q = f_o / (f_{ch} - f_{cl}) \qquad [3]$$

Higher values of Q mean that the filter's response is getting narrower or sharper. The quantity $f_{ch} - f_{cl}$ is the filter's bandwidth.

Figure 4 shows a "multiple feedback" band-pass filter, so-called because there are two feedback paths from the output through R_f and C_f. Although there are many methods of designing this circuit, we'll use the "Equal-C" method in which both C_i and C_f are given equal values. After f_o and Q are chosen, the resistor values are then calculated. The filter's gain is equal to $-2Q^2$. The circuit values shown set f_o to 500 Hz, Q to 2.3, and gain to –10.4.

Testing Band-Pass Filter #2

• Build the circuit and find f_o, f_{ch} and f_{cl} by measuring the input and output voltage of sine waves at frequencies from 50 to 5000 Hz. Calculate the filter's peak gain (V_{out}/V_{in}), bandwidth ($f_{ch} - f_{cl}$) and Q.

• Most filter responses are measured in decibels, or dB. Gain in dB = 20 log (V_{out}/V_{in}). Recalculate gain in dB. Gain at the upper and lower cutoff frequencies should be close to 3 dB below the gain of the filter at f_o.

• To change f_o, increase or decrease both capacitors, keeping their values the same. To increase f_o, decrease capacitance, and vice versa. f_o is directly proportional to the value of the capacitors.

Listening to Your Filters

All this measuring is fine, but it's more fun to actually use your circuits for a practical purpose. Figure 5 shows how to route your rig's received audio through the filter circuit so that you can hear the effect of the filter using headphones from a portable music player. Set your rig to use its widest filter (usually "AM") and then listen to the filter output. The op-amp can't drive a very big load, so keep the audio output level low to avoid distortion.

Suggested Reading

The 2003 ARRL Handbook, pp 16.1-16.2, 16.28-16.29; Horowitz and Hill, *The Art of Electronics*, chapter 5, sections 5.01-5.05. One of the best books for hobbyists on active filters is Don Lancaster's *Active Filter Cookbook*.

The ARRL Web site for this series is **www.arrl.org/tis/info/html/hands-on-radio/**.

Shopping List

• 741 op-amp
• ¼-W resistors of the following values: 2.2 kΩ, 10 kΩ (2 ea), 22 kΩ, 47 kΩ
• 1 kΩ potentiometer (single or multi-turn)
• 56 nF, 33 nF (2 ea), 5.6 nF, and 2.7 nF film or ceramic capacitors (1 nF = 1000 pF = 0.001 µF)
• 2—10 µF capacitors with a voltage rating of 25 V dc or higher

Errata

Experiment #2 mistakenly equated 1 V_{p-p} with 0.7 V_{RMS}. It should be 0.35 V_{RMS}. $V_{RMS} = 1/(2\sqrt{2}) V_{p-p} = V_{p-p}/2\sqrt{2}$.

Next Month

Next month, we'll take a look at the popular "555" timer and use it as an oscillator, a pulse generator and maybe even as a timer!

Experiment #42 — Notch filters

In previous experiments we've looked at low-pass, high-pass and band-pass filters. This time, we're going to look at a different type, the *band-stop* filter. (*Stop* means the same as *Reject*.) A low-pass filter is the same as a high-stop and vice versa. The band-stop filter acts in the opposite way from a band-pass filter — it passes everything except signals inside its *stop band*. These filters have many uses in radio.

Terms to Learn

Notch depth — the amount of attenuation at the notch (reject) frequency.

Notch width — the difference between frequencies at which the notch attenuation is 3 dB.

Pole — a section of a circuit that has a single frequency or time-determining characteristic, such as a resistor-capacitor combination.

Positive feedback — applying a fraction of the output signal to the input of the circuit in such a way as to reinforce the input signal.

Twin-T Notch Filters

Notch filters are just special cases of band-stop filters — they reject just one frequency, such as the tone of an interfering signal or nearby broadcast station. HF radios often have a notch filter built in and may even have an automatic notch filter operated by a digital signal processor that finds and tunes out unwanted tones.

There are a number of circuits for notch filters, but the most common by far is based on the *Twin-T* circuit shown in Figure 1. You can see the twin Ts, one between points 1 and 3 with two resistors of value R and a capacitor of value 2C. The other T is upside down below it with an R/2 resistor and capacitors of value C.

The frequency response of the Twin-T filter is also shown in Figure 1. This is a *passive filter*, since there are no amplifiers or transistors. The ideal Twin-T filter's 3 dB bandwidth (BW) shown in the response is $4f_0$. Since $Q = BW / f_0$, the Twin-T filter's Q is only ¼. This is not a narrow filter!

How does the Twin-T filter work? It's not exactly the most obvious circuit. Start by disconnecting the two T sections at the input and output so that the input to the upper T is at location 1 and its output at location 3. The lower T's input is now at 2 and the output at 4. Assume that no load is placed on the output of either T. The upper T forms a low-pass filter with a cutoff frequency of $f_0 = 1 / (2\pi RC)$. Similarly, the lower section forms a high-pass filter with

the same cutoff frequency.

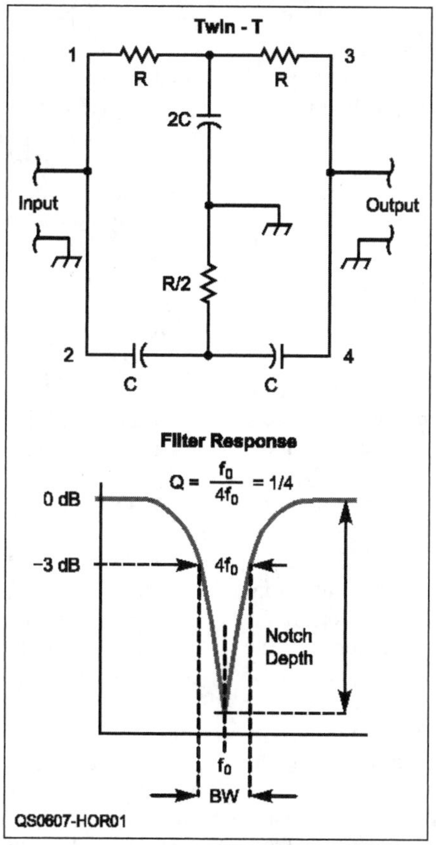

What is important about both of these filters is that the phase shift of the signals through the filters is in *opposite* directions. Phase shift is lagging (negative values) in the upper T and leading (positive values) in the lower T. If you revisit "Experiment #18 — Frequency Response," you'll be reminded that a simple RC filter has 45° of phase shift at the cutoff frequency, whether high-pass or low-pass. (All previous experiments are available to ARRL Members on the Hands-On Radio Web page at www.arrl.org/tis.)

[Note - in the original article, the explanation of how the twin-T circuit works was incorrect and is replaced by an overview of the correct explanation.] Understanding the twin-T circuit's behavior is more complex than just connecting the two filters together, however. The phase shift through each filter is complementary, true, but it is not enough to cause complete cancellation at the filter's center frequency. In fact, at f_0 the phase shift through each T-section is only 63° (one positive and one negative).

When the T-sections are connected together, both at the input and the output, their impedances combine in a more complex fashion than when analyzed separately. A full analysis is beyond the scope of this article, but is available on-line at www.drp.fmph.uniba.sk/ESM/twin.pdf. This analysis shows that by converting each T-section to it's Pi-section equivalent, the impedances of each T-section are now connected in parallel and can be combined mathematically. The result is a single Pi-section circuit whose frequency response goes to zero at f_0. (The technique for converting T-section circuits into Pi-section circuits, also known as a Y-Delta transformation, is described in the Wikipedia entry en.wikipedia.org/wiki/Y-%CE%94_transform.)

Activating the Twin-T

So far, so good, but the filter's low Q of ¼ makes it less than useful for radio applications. Also, for the filter sections to work as designed, the load connected at the output must have a very high impedance. It doesn't take much to upset the phase shift of each T and reduce notch depth dramatically. All it takes to fix these problems is a single op-amp and some positive feedback as shown in Figure 2.

The op-amp in Figure 2 is configured as a *voltage follower* (see Experiment #3) with a very high input impedance and a gain of 1. Voltage followers are used as buffers to isolate a sensitive circuit in this way. The low impedance of the op-amp's output allows it to drive almost any load, as well.

The positive feedback is applied to the

Figure 1 — The Twin-T filter produces a notch by creating two out-of-phase copies of the input signal at the notch frequency, $f_0 = 1 / (2\pi RC)$. Careful matching of the components is required to get good notch depth.

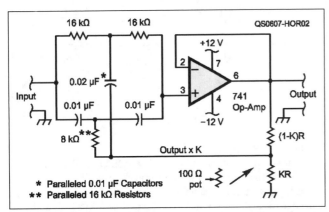

Figure 2 — A practical notch filter is created by adding an op-amp configured as a voltage follower. The voltage divider creates a smaller version of the output that is used as positive feedback to decrease the notch width, increasing filter Q.

ground connection of the two Ts, which have been redrawn in the usual configuration found in books and references. The positive feedback changes the Q of the overall circuit from $\frac{1}{4}$ to $\frac{1}{4}(1 - K)$. K is the fraction of output voltage fed back to the input and varies from 0 (no feedback) to 1 (direct connection). The resistive divider connected to the op-amp output creates a voltage of OUTPUT × K that can be used for feedback. By using a potentiometer connected as a voltage divider, the Q of the filter can be made adjustable as well.

There is one caveat — for the feedback not to affect the filter frequency, the resistance of the voltage divider must be much smaller than the resistors used in the filters. This is accomplished by choosing a small value for R, since the op-amp output impedance is very small.

Build and Test a Notch Filter

The Twin-T filter's performance depends heavily on the component values being close to the exact ratios shown: R and 0.5R, and C and 2C. The values of the resistors and capacitors shown in the figure are standard values except for the 8 kΩ resistor and the 0.02 μF capacitor. You won't find those easily. However, there are two more tricks to learn!

If you pick any old resistors or capacitors out of the junk box, the chances of them being a match are pretty slim, and the different manufacturing processes used will make them act differently as the temperature changes. If you buy a small batch of 10 or 20 components, however, not only do you get a price break per component, they are much likely to be close in value and react the same way to varying temperature.

The second trick is that to make the half and double value components, use two more of the batch connected in parallel. Again, you'll find components out of a batch are much easier to create the value you need.

Start by finding matched resistors. From the batch, use your voltmeter to find four that are close to 16 kΩ. Try to come up with two that are very close in value and a separate pair that in parallel have one-half that value.

Capacitors are a little harder to match, unless you have a capacitance meter. Yet another workbench trick is to build an oscillator

circuit (such as the astable 555 timer circuit in Experiment #5) and pick capacitors that give the same frequency output. (Don't hold the capacitors in your fingers while testing them, since you'll warm them up — yes, it matters!) As with the resistors, try to find two closely matched capacitors and a pair with double that value in parallel.

Build the Twin-T circuit of Figure 1. Apply a 1 V_{P-P} sine wave and measure its frequency response from 100 Hz to 5 kHz. The values shown should result in an f_0 close to 1 kHz. Measure the notch frequency, f_0, and the –3 dB points at which $V_{OUT} = 0.707 \, V_{IN}$. Calculate the filter's Q = BW / f_0 and see how close to $\frac{1}{4}$ it is.

Now add the op-amp as in Figure 2, but not the 100 Ω potentiometer. Quickly check the filter's frequency response at a few points to be sure it's still working okay.

Add the 100 Ω potentiometer as shown in the figure with the wiper set so that each leg of the pot measures 50 Ω. This gives a K of 0.5. What should Q be? Q = $\frac{1}{4}(1 - K)$ = 0.5. Measure the –3 dB points and f_0 to see if you got the right Q.

Have fun and adjust the potentiometer to different values to see the effect on Q. Swap out one of the resistors or capacitors with one whose value is close but not matched, and see what happens to notch depth.

If you still have your cables and headphones or speaker ready from last month, see what audio sounds like when subjected to the notching effect!

More Modern Notch Filters

Notch filters have played an important role in interference rejection over the years. The Twin-T, described above, has been successfully deployed as part of receivers both at IF and AF frequencies. Earlier receivers made use of the deep notch of a single crystal IF filter to provide this function at the same time that it was used to set the receiver bandwidth.

Many of today's receivers have synthesized the notch filter function as a part of a digital signal processor system also used to set the operating bandwidth of a receiver. Like the Twin-T, the DSP filters are available both in IF or AF versions. Unlike the analog systems, some DSP based notch filters are "smart" enough to determine the frequency of a steady interfering carrier and notch it out without operator intervention. This can really help as you try to copy a station on 40 meters with a foreign broadcast station's carrier in your passband!

Shopping List

- 4 each 16 kΩ, ¼ W resistors (buy a batch, if possible).
- 4 each 0.01 μF, film capacitors (buy a batch, if possible).
- 741 op-amp.
- 100 Ω potentiometer.

Recommended Reading

Most filter design textbooks will have a section on the Twin-T filter, including active versions that can also adjust the depth of the notch. Walter Jung's *Op-Amp Cookbook*, published by Howard Sams, also features a tunable notch filter.

Next Month

We've done a lot of work over the past three-and-a-half years, but little of it has been at frequencies above 1 MHz. That's about to change, because next month's experiment will be an initial foray into the world of the oscillator!

Experiment #50 — Filter Design #1

Looking at the block diagrams of radios, I sometimes think this hobby should be called "Amateur Filter Users." Ready-made tables, graphs and simple formulas put filter design within reach of every ham. How about a guided tour?

Terms to Learn

Cutoff frequency — the frequency at which the output is 3 dB below the input.

Insertion loss — the ratio of output power to input power of a filter.

Normalization — specifying quantities as a ratio to fixed reference value.

Stop frequency — the frequency at which required attenuation is reached for the first time.

Defining and Specifying a Filter

You already know that a filter is a circuit that passes some signals while blocking or attenuating others. A filter's behavior at different frequencies is described by its *response*. An idealized low-pass filter response is shown in Figure 1. The vertical axis shows *insertion loss* in dB. The horizontal axis shows frequency on a logarithmic scale.

At low frequencies, the filter has 0 dB of insertion loss — a signal coming out of the filter has exactly the same amplitude as the signal going in. In this idealized filter there is no insertion loss until the *break frequency* is reached. Frequency and insertion loss then increase until the *corner frequency*, f_C, is reached at which ½ of the input signal's power has been lost. From dc to f_C is the *passband*.

The filter's *rolloff* is a measure of how fast insertion loss increases above f_C in dB per octave or decade of frequency. At the *stop frequency*, f_S, the filter first reaches its *required attenuation*. The *stop band* starts at f_S and continues to infinite frequency.

The passive LC-filter circuit most common in radio is the *ladder* circuit shown in Figure 2. There are two types of ladder circuit that have the same response: the shunt input (B) and the series input (C), referring to the connection of the first filter component.

A filter is said to have a certain number of *poles*, referring to the mathematical description of the filter. For the LC filters in Figure 2, the number of poles equals the number of reactances (L and C) in the circuit — five-pole filters are shown. If more

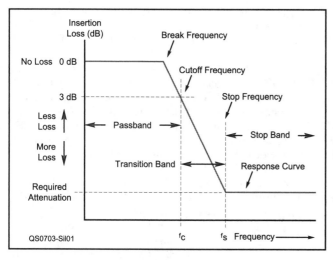

QS0703-Sil01

Figure 1 — A filter's response is specified by key parameters that define its shape. (A low-pass filter is shown here.) The corner and stop frequencies specify the points at which certain amounts of attenuation are required. The number of poles in the filter needed to satisfy those requirements can then be determined.

Prototype Butterworth Low-Pass Filters

n	C1 / L1	L2 / C2	C3 / L3	L4 / C4	C5 / L5	L6 / C6
1	2.0000					
2	1.4142	1.4142				
3	1.0000	2.0000	1.0000			
4	0.7654	1.8478	1.8478	0.7654		
5	0.6180	1.6180	2.0000	1.6180	0.6180	
6	0.5176	1.4142	1.9319	1.9319	1.4142	0.5176
7	0.4450	1.2470	1.8019	2.0000	1.8019	1.2470
8	0.3902	1.1111	1.6629	1.9616	1.9616	1.6629
9	0.3473	1.0000	1.5321	1.8794	2.0000	1.8794
10	0.3129	0.9080	1.4142	1.7820	1.9754	1.9754

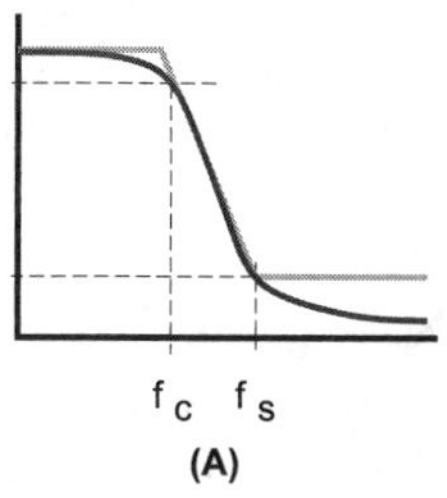

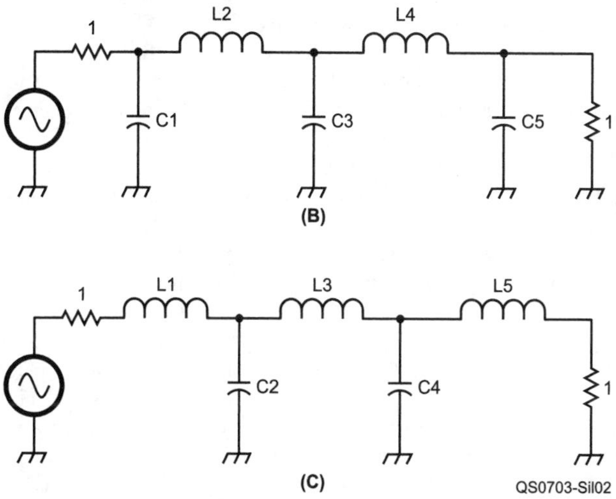

Figure 2 —
A — Table of normalized component values for a filter with a given number of poles, n.
B — The shunt-input filter schematic.
C — The series-input filter.

(A)

(B)

(C)

QS0703-Sil02

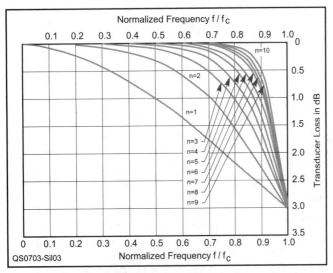

Figure 3 — Response of Butterworth filters in the passband below f_C where normalized frequency is less than 1.0.

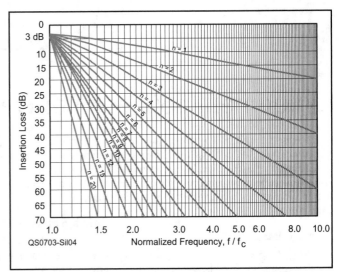

Figure 4 —Response of Butterworth filters in the transition and stop bands above f_C where normalized frequency is greater than 1.0.

poles are needed, alternating L and C elements are added before the output resistor. For example, a six-pole, shunt input filter would add L6 between C5 and the 1 Ω load resistor. The higher the number of poles, the steeper the filter's rolloff and the narrower the transition band.

The simplest ladder filter design is the *Butterworth* filter, named for its inventor. To design a Butterworth low-pass filter, you'll need to know f_C, f_S and the required attenuation. The Butterworth filter has a syrupy smooth response curve as shown at the lower left of Figure 2. Responses for Butterworth filters with different number of poles are graphed in Figure 3 (below f_C) and Figure 4 (above f_C). Different graphs are used to give a clearer view of insertion loss above and below f_C.

Using Filter Design Tables

Butterworth filters are designed by specifying the shape of the response in terms of f_C, f_S and the required attenuation. Frequency is *normalized* to f_C, meaning it is stated as a ratio to f_C. Normalized response graphs and tables produce component values of henrys and farads for filters with a cutoff frequency of 1 and input and output impedances of 1 (normalized values have no units).

Assuming you know f_C, here's how to use f_S, the required attenuation and Figure 4 to produce a normalized filter design:

Calculate the normalized stop frequency = f_S/f_C (normalized cutoff frequency is f_C/f_C = 1).

In Figure 4, find the intersection of the required attenuation with the normalized stop frequency.

Move vertically down from that point until you encounter a response line. The value of n is the number of poles required for your filter — the minimum number of poles that can provide the required attenuation at f_S.

Go to the table in Figure 2 and find the row for the same value of n. Depending on which circuit form you choose, shunt sor series assign the value in the table to the appropriate component.

Converting a Normalized Design

To make the filter work at the frequencies and impedances you want, the component values must be *scaled*. To raise the low-pass filter's f_C from 1 rad/sec, smaller values of L and C are needed. To raise the filter's impedance from 1 Ω, smaller values of C and larger values of L are needed. The equations to perform scaling are not difficult to use:

Scaled L = L × (desired R / 1 Ω) × (1 radian/sec / 2π × desired f_C) [Eq 1]

Scaled C = C × (1 Ω / desired R) × (1 radian/sec / 2π × desired f_C) [Eq 2]

Let's step through a pair of example low-pass filter designs to show how the process works.

Example #1 — A 40 Meter Harmonic Reject Filter

To clean up the output of a 40 meter oscillator, let's say 20 dB of attenuation is required for all harmonics of the 7 MHz fundamental. Choose the oscillator frequency of 7 MHz as f_C, accepting the 3 dB of attenuation. Assume a filter input and output impedance of 200 Ω.

The stop frequency, f_S, is the second harmonic, 14 MHz, so the normalized f_S = 14 / 7 = 2.0. The first response line below the intersection of 20 dB and 2.0 in Figure 4 is n=4, so a four-pole filter is required. If the shunt-input circuit is used (Figure 2B), C1 = 0.7654, L2 = 1.8478, C3 = 1.8478, L4 = 0.7654. Using scaling equations 1 and 2 results in C1 = 87 pF, L2 = 8.4 µH, C3 = 210 pF, and L4 = 3.5 µH. Values for the series-input filter are located on the Hands-On Radio Web site at **www.arrl.**

org/tis/info/HTML/Hands-On-Radio/.

Example #2 — An Audio Hiss Removal Filter

Sometimes, you don't know f_C at the start and have to work with both Figures 3 and 4. Let's design a filter that removes audio hiss by attenuating frequencies below 3 kHz no more than 1 dB and frequencies above 5 kHz (f_S) at least 10 dB. The filter impedance will be 32 Ω to match headphones.

We know f_C, with an attenuation of 3 dB, must be somewhere between 3 kHz and 5 kHz. Start by choosing f_C = 3.5 kHz, making normalized f_S = 5/3.5 = 1.43. From Figure 4, the lowest number of poles providing 10 dB attenuation at a frequency of 1.43 is n=3. Check the attenuation of 3 kHz signals by normalizing 3 kHz to 3/3.5 = 0.86 and look at the line n=3 in Figure 3. At a frequency of 0.86 and n=3, the attenuation will be 1.4 dB — too high, so let's increase f_C to 3.8 kHz, reducing normalized f_S to 1.32. Now the minimum number of poles is n=4. Rechecking the 3 kHz attenuation at a normalized frequency of 3/3.8 = 0.79, the four-pole filter has an attenuation of less than 0.5 dB, satisfying the requirement. We have our filter! Scale the values from the normalized table in Figure 2 — solutions are on the Hands-On Radio Web site.

This example shows how to adjust your filter shape definitions to meet the fixed requirements of frequency and attenuation. Choose an f_C, determine the required number of poles and iterate different values of f_C until the shape meets your needs.

Next Month

We'll extend our discussion of filter design to high-pass and band-pass filters next month. You'll be surprised at the similarities and meet the Butterworth's rippling cousin!

Experiment #51 — Filter Design #2

Last month's column explained some basic terminology of filters: pass and stop bands, rolloff, cutoff and stop frequencies. Normalized design was introduced, in which filter parameters are developed based on ratios to the cutoff frequency. If you haven't read last month's column or are a little shaky on those basics, please reread it as this month's column builds on those ideas.

Terms to Learn

Loaded Q (Q_L) — A band-pass filter's bandwidth when terminated with its design impedance.

Reflection coefficient — A measure of how much power is reflected by a filter.

Ripple — The amount of variation in a filter's passband or stopband.

Review

High-Pass Filter Design

A high-pass filter looks a whole lot like a low-pass filter in a mirror. The design still has all the same key frequencies and frequency ranges of a low-pass filter, but the response is inverted around the cutoff frequency. This is a great illustration of normalization paying off;

as we can use the very same techniques, tables and charts to design a high-pass filter!

In the equations that govern low-pass filter design, if frequency (f) is replaced by 1/f, and capacitors and inductors are exchanged, a high-pass filter response is the result. Looking at Figure 2B from last month's column (Figure 12.11 in *The 2007 ARRL Handbook*), replace each component with its opposite; L for C and C for L. For example, C1 becomes L1, L2 becomes C2, and so forth. This is a high-pass filter. The reciprocals of the normalized values in the table rows are used in the same way. For a fourth-order low-pass series input design (Figure 2C), L1's normalized value is 0.7654. In the high-pass design, the value for C1 in its place is its reciprocal, or 1/0.7654 = 1.3065.

Determination of filter order is done similarly to the low-pass filter. First, find or specify the cutoff frequency (f_C), the stop frequency (f_S), and the required attenuation at f_S in dB. Instead of using the ratio f/f_C as in last month's column to find the filter's order, use f_C/f instead. Below the cutoff frequency, you'll use the chart in last month's Figure 4 and above the cutoff frequency, the chart in Figure 3.

How about an example? If we take the 7 MHz low-pass filter from last month and change it to a high-pass filter instead, the circuit looks like Figure 1. Note that all the C's are now L's and vice versa. The order is the same (n = 4), so the normalized component values are the same. After scaling to 7 MHz and 200 Ω, the component's actual values are L1 = 6 μH, C2 = 62 pF, L3 = 2.5 μH, and C4 = 149 pF.

Something to consider when selecting a filter type — shunt or series input — is the dc response of the filter. If the circuit to which the filter is connected has a dc voltage present, at that point a shunt inductor would short the voltage to ground. You should either use the alternate filter type or place a dc blocking capacitor in series with the filter. The dc blocking capacitor should be large enough to have a negligible reactance at the frequency of signals passing through the filter. For example, a 0.01 μF capacitor would be a good choice for our 7 MHz high-pass filter because its reactance is only 2.3 Ω at 7 MHz and lower at higher frequencies.

Band-Pass Filter Design

The response of a band-pass filter is much

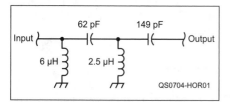

Figure 1 — This 7 MHz high-pass filter was created from a 7 MHz low-pass design by exchanging capacitors and inductors, then performing the same frequency and impedance scaling process.

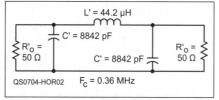

Figure 2 — This filter represents an intermediate step of designing a band-pass filter. It is designed for cutoff at 0.36 MHz, the bandwidth of the final filter, and an impedance of 50 Ω.

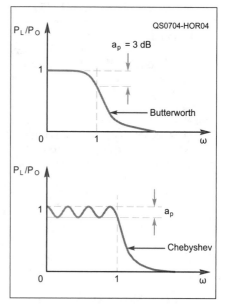

Figure 4 — The difference in passband ripple and rolloff between Butterworth and Chebychev filters.

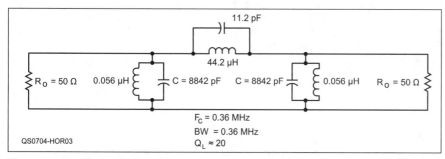

Figure 3 — The final band-pass filter has resonant circuits in place of the individual L and C of the low-pass filter in Figure 2. The tuned circuits scale the frequency of the low-pass filter to its final value and change its response to band-pass.

easier to understand as a pair of filter responses, one low-pass and one high-pass, sharing a common center frequency. For example, take the low-pass filter response graph, turn it around (as for the high-pass filter) and attach the two responses back-to-back. The "zero frequency" of the low-pass filter is now the center frequency of the band-pass response.

To translate the combined responses to a non-zero center frequency, each of the capacitors and inductors in a low- or high-pass filter is replaced with a parallel tuned circuit (for shunt elements) or with a series tuned circuit (for series elements). The order of a band-pass filter is the number of *resonators* in the filter, the number of parallel or series tuned circuits.

Designing a band-pass filter using this common center frequency method consists of finding the actual center frequency and designing a low-pass filter to satisfy the "upper half" of the required frequency response. The "lower half" of the response is created by adding components to create parallel or series tuned circuits, resonant at the filter's center frequency.

The following example of a 40 meter band-pass filter design comes from the *2007 ARRL Handbook*, and starts with four design requirements: $f_C = 7.15$ MHz, 3 dB bandwidth (BW) = 360 kHz, filter impedance = 50 Ω, and a 3-pole Butterworth response characteristic. (This last requirement assumes that the designer has already translated the rolloff requirements into the number of poles, as we learned how to do last month.)

The actual filter center frequency is determined by the two cutoff frequencies: 7.15 + 0.360/2 = 7.33 MHz and 7.15 – 0.36/2 = 6.97 MHz. The filter's frequency of optimum response, $f_O = \sqrt{(7.33 \times 6.97)} = 7.147$ MHz. (There is only a small difference between f_O and the specified f_C because the bandwidth of the filter is small in comparison. For filters with wide bandwidths, the difference between f_O and f_C is much larger.) The *loaded Q* of this filter is $Q_L = f_O$ / BW = 7.147 / 0.36 = 19.8.

Using the process of last month's column, design a low-pass filter of n = 3, f_C = 0.36 MHz, and 50 Ω impedance. You'll find the results in the circuit of Figure 2. (It is good practice to see if you can duplicate the component values.)

Now convert the low-pass filter to a band-pass filter with $f_O = 7.147$ MHz by placing an inductor in parallel with each of the shunt

capacitors and a capacitor in series with the series inductor. The formulas to use are:

L1 = L3 = $1/(C1 \times (2\pi \times 7.147)^2$ and
C2 = $1/(L1 \times (2\pi \times 7.147)^2$

The result should be the circuit of Figure 3.

Filter Design Caveats

If you plan on building filters using this process, you should be aware of two important concerns. Scaling frequency with tuned circuits can result in extreme (large or small) LC ratios in the tuned circuits. The narrower the bandwidth (higher Q_L), the larger the change from low-pass f_C to band-pass f_O and the more extreme the ratios. Extreme LC ratios result in high sensitivity to component values and parasitic effects. Higher Q_L also makes component losses more important, resulting in high insertion loss and poor rolloff. A good rule of thumb is to use this design process only for $Q_L < 10$.

Very wide filters can also be a problem, such as an HF ham-band filter that passes signals from 1.8 to 30 MHz. In this case, $f_O = 7.35$ MHz and BW = 28.2 MHz for a Q_L of 0.26. This type of response falls well above the n = 1 curves, a clue that the design process isn't really suitable. For these filters, use separate low- and high-pass filters "back-to-back," one rolling off below 1.8 MHz and the other above 30 MHz.

Chebychev Filters

Once you start designing filters, you'll rapidly run into the limits of the Butterworth filter. While it has a nice, smooth response, its rolloff is not very steep until large numbers of poles are used. This increases filter expense, size, and loss. An alternate design, the Chebychev filter, uses a mathematical technique that results in more aggressive rolloff.

Figure 4 shows the basic difference between the Butterworth and Chebychev filters. The passband of the Chebychev response contains variations known as *ripple* and specified by a_P. This allows the filter to have significantly steeper rolloff in the transition band. The more ripple is allowed, the steeper the rolloff will be. Chebychev filters also allow the filter's impedance to vary, resulting in a *return coefficient* (RC) of greater than zero. (An alternate type of Chebychev, the eliptic filter, has ripple in the stopband, instead.)

Chebychev filters can be designed using tables similar to those for Butterworth

filters. Instead of the cutoff frequency, f_C, the frequency at which the attenuation first exceeds the passband ripple, a_P, is used, F_{ap}. Start with your rolloff requirement in terms of the number of dB of attenuation at a normalized frequency referenced to F_{ap}. For example, you might need 10 dB of attenuation at $2F_{ap}$. Look at the design table (such as Table 12.3 in the *2007 ARRL Handbook*) column for 10 dB of attenuation. Find the filters that have an f/F_{ap} ratio of less than 2, meaning they will have 10 dB of attenuation before $2F_{ap}$ is reached, meeting your needs. There are usually several possible choices with different numbers of poles and RC. Choose the filter with the lowest number of poles unless the value of RC results in unacceptably high SWR. (Tables of RC to SWR conversion are available in the *2007 ARRL Handbook* or online.) The process of scaling your filter to the required frequency and impedance is the same as for Butterworth filters.

Recommended Reading

The Wikipedia (**en.wikipedia.org**) entries on Butterworth, Chebychev and other types of filters make good online references. There are also free online filter design programs, such as those listed at **www.web-ee.com/Downloads/Filters/filter_design.htm** or the Web applet at **www.users.cs.york. ac.uk/~fisher/cgi-bin/lcfilter**. Log on and experiment with designing your own filters!

The Hands-On Radio Web site FAQ includes a corrected description for the 4:1 balun described in Experiment #48 and some clarification on the design equations used in last month's column. I would like to thank W8JI and W3NQN for their input and I'm glad to know these gurus are keeping an eye on me! Ham radio is lucky to have such resources.

References

The ARRL Handbook, including *ELSIE* — an included LC filter design program on CD-ROM.

The Hands-on Radio Web site, **www.arrl. org/tis/info/HTML/Hands-On-Radio/**.

Next Month

Every shack has one, maybe more than one! I'm talking about the good old SWR bridge, of course. But not everybody understands how they work, so next month we'll take one apart (figuratively) and then you'll know, too.

Oscillators and Buffers

Experiment #5—The Integrated Timer

Background

Timer circuits based on the 555 chip and its many relatives are found everywhere. Although not complex, it can be used to create many different circuits. This month we'll take a look at two popular applications of the legendary 555.

Terms to Learn

• *Astable*—not stable; a circuit that cannot stay in one state.

• *Comparator*—a circuit whose output is indicative of the greater of two of its inputs.

• *Flip-flop*—a digital circuit that "flips" or "toggles" between two states.

• *Monostable*—stable in one state, these circuits stay there until perturbed, then attempt to return to the stable state.

The Integrated Circuit Timer

The 555 integrated circuit timer has proved to be incredibly popular. Inexpensive and versatile, the 555 is used in myriads of circuits. What's inside that makes it so useful?

Figure 1 shows the basic components of a 555. While it is the most complex circuit we've looked at so far, the 555 is easy to break into bite-size pieces. Let's start with the three resistors labeled "R" at the top left of Figure 1. Connected between power input (V_c) and ground, they form a *voltage divider* that divides V_c into two equal steps—one at $\frac{2}{3}$ V_c and one at $\frac{1}{3}$ V_c. These serve as reference voltages.

Connected to the reference voltages are blocks labeled *trigger comparator* and *threshold comparator*. A *comparator* is nothing more than a circuit whose output indicates which of its two inputs is greater. If the + input is greater, the output is *high*. If the – input is greater, the output is at ground or *low*.

The trigger comparator in the 555 is wired so that its output is *high* whenever the trigger input is *less* than $\frac{1}{3}$ V_c and vice versa. Similarly, the threshold comparator output is *high* whenever the threshold input is *greater* than $\frac{2}{3}$ V_c. These two outputs control a

circuit called a *flip-flop*.

The flip-flop output, *Q*, changes to *high* or *low* when the state of its *set* and *reset* input changes. The Q output stays *high* or *low* (it *latches* or *toggles*) until the opposite input changes. When the set input changes from *low* to *high*, Q goes *high*. When reset changes from *low* to *high*, Q goes *low*. The flip-flop ignores any other changes. An inverter makes the 555 output *high* when Q is *low* and vice versa—this makes the timer circuit easier to interface with external circuits.

The transistor connected to Q acts as a *switch*. When Q is *high*, the transistor is *on* and acts as a closed switch connected to ground. When Q is *low*, the transistor is *off* and the switch is open. These simple building blocks—*voltage divider*, *comparator*, *flip-flop* and *switch*—allow us to build a surprising number of useful circuits.

The Monostable or "One-Shot" Multivibrator

The simplest 555 circuit is the *monostable* circuit. This configuration will output one fixed-length pulse when triggered by an input pulse. Figure 2 shows the connections for this circuit. How does it work?

Starting with capacitor C discharged, the flip-flop output, Q, is *high*, which keeps the discharge transistor turned on and the voltage across C below $\frac{2}{3}$ V_c. The circuit is in its stable state, waiting for a trigger pulse.

When the voltage at the trigger input drops below $\frac{1}{3}$ V_c, the trigger comparator output changes from *low* to *high*, which causes Q to toggle to the *low* state. This turns *off* the transistor (opens the switch) and allows C to begin charging toward V_c.

When C reaches $\frac{2}{3}$ V_c, the threshold comparator switches its output from *low* to *high* and that resets the flip-flop. Q returns *high*, turning *on* the transistor and discharging C. The circuit has returned to its stable state. The output pulse length is:

$$T = 1.1\ RC \qquad [1]$$

Notice that V_c doesn't really matter in the timing—the output pulse width is the same with a 5 V supply as it is with a 15 V supply. This is because the 555 design is based on ratios and not absolute voltage levels.

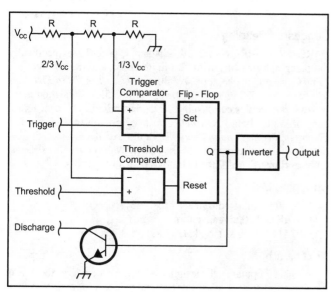

Figure 1—This schematic shows the major circuits inside the 555 timer.

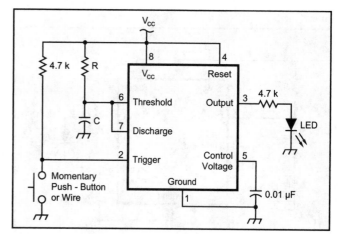

Figure 2—The monostable or "one-shot" circuit. This circuit generates a single pulse when the trigger input is shorted to ground. An LED is used to indicate whether the output is high or low.

Testing the Monostable Multivibrator

- Use the wiring diagram of Figure 2. Let's aim for a 1 second output pulse, which requires RC = 1/1.1 = 0.91. If we choose C = 10 μF, then R = 91 kΩ.
- Connect a 4.7 kΩ resistor between V_c and pin 2. The symbol at pin 2 indicates a jumper to ground—you can use a switch or a piece of wire to temporarily ground pin 2, supplying the trigger pulse.
- The 4.7 kΩ resistor and LED at the output will give a visual indication when the output is *high*.
- The 0.01 μF capacitor at pin 5 filters out any noise that might cause changes in the threshold comparator reference voltage. Pin 4 resets the flip-flop that drives the output and it can be used to prematurely force the output low, regardless of the output state. It should be connected to V_c when not used, to prevent resets from noise. The power supply voltage can be any positive voltage between 4.5 and 18 V.
- With your circuit ready to go, press the switch (or insert the jumper for a brief instant) and watch the output LED light up. It should be on for about 1 second and then turn off until you retrigger the circuit.
- Change either R or C, recalculate the expected output pulse length, and give it a try. R can be a potentiometer, as well, for adjustable pulse length.

The Astable Multivibrator

The opposite of the monostable circuit is the astable circuit in Figure 3. Look carefully at the different connections of pins 2, 6 and 7. Notice, too, that the timing resistor is split into two resistors, R1 and R2. What's happening here?

Let's start from the same state as the monostable circuit, with C completely discharged. In the monostable circuit, it took a trigger signal to get the ball rolling. In the astable circuit, the trigger input is connected directly to the capacitor, so if the capacitor is discharged, then the trigger comparator output must be *high*. Q is *low*, turning *off* the discharge transistor, which allows C to immediately begin charging.

C charges toward V_c, but now through the combination of R1 and R2. As the capacitor voltage passes ⅔ V_c, the threshold comparator output changes from *low* to *high*, resetting Q to *high*. This turns *on* the discharge transistor and the capacitor starts to discharge through R2. When the capacitor is discharged below ⅔ V_c, the trigger comparator changes from *high* to *low* and the cycle begins again, automatically. This happens over and over, causing a train of pulses at the output while C charges and discharges between ⅓ and ⅔ V_c as shown in Figure 4.

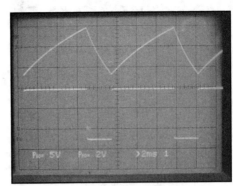

Figure 4—A photo of the oscilloscope showing the capacitor and output voltages for the astable circuit with a 0.1 μF timing capacitor for a 100 Hz oscil-lation frequency. The top trace shows capacitor voltage and the bottom trace the 555 output. Capacitor charging and discharging can be seen clearly.

The design equations are a little more complex for this circuit. The total time it takes for one complete cycle is the charge time, T_c, plus the discharge time, T_d:

$$T = T_c + T_d = 0.693 (R_1 + R_2) C + 0.693 R_2 C$$
$$= 0.693 (R_1 + 2R_2) C \qquad [2]$$

and the output frequency is:

$$f = 1/T = 1.443 / [(R_1 + 2R_2) C] \qquad [3]$$

Let's try it out!

Testing the Astable Multivibrator

- Split the original 91 kΩ resistor into a 62 kΩ for R1 and 39 kΩ for R2. Use the same 10 μF capacitor for C. The total cycle time should be close to 1 second. If you have a stopwatch, count 10 or more cycles and average for a good cycle time measurement.
- You may have noted that the LED is not on and off for equal periods—it's on longer than it is off. This is because the capacitor has to both charge and discharge through R_2. The ratio of on-time to off-time is called the *duty cycle* and is calculated as:

$$\text{duty cycle} = (R_1 + R_2) / (R_1 + 2R_2) \qquad [4]$$

- Experiment with different combinations of R1 and R2 to observe the effect of their ratio on duty cycle. (Keep R1 greater than 1 kΩ to avoid overloading the discharge transistor.) If you have an oscilloscope, watch the capacitor voltage on one channel and the output voltage on the other. Figure 4 shows an example.

Suggested Reading

Read *The ARRL Handbook*, chapter 7, page 7.14, specifically the paragraphs starting with "Multivibrators" and the section "RC Time Constant" in chapter 6. Additionally, see *The Art of Electronics*, pages 517-522. One of the better on-line 555 application notes is **www.doctronics.co.uk/pdf_files/555an.pdf**. If you can, find a copy of Walter Jung's *IC Timer Cookbook* or Howard Berlin's *555 Timer Applications Sourcebook*. Both are excellent, although now out of print. And, remember… the ARRL Web site for this series is **www.arrl.org/tis/info/html/Hands-On-Radio/**.

Shopping List

- 555 timer IC (RadioShack 276-1723).
- 10 μF and 10 nF capacitors.
- 4.7 kΩ (2), 39 kΩ, 62 kΩ, 91 kΩ resistors, ¼ W.

Next Month

Another popular well-designed integrated device is the linear regulator. It is so easy to use that we tend to take it for granted. When you use a power supply, it's likely that one of these is integral to its design. See you next month!

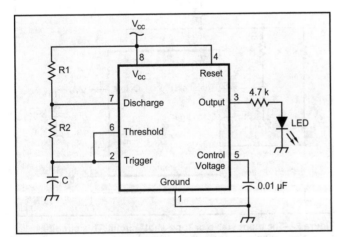

Figure 3—The astable or "free-running" circuit. This circuit generates a continuous train of output pulses.

Experiment #17: The Phase-Shift Oscillator

Any system having gain and a little output to input feedback can quickly become an oscillator. Anyone who has operated a public-address system can attest to that fact! This month we'll look at a very basic circuit that illustrates the fundamental principles of oscillators—the *phase-shift oscillator*.

Terms to Learn

- *Network*—circuits with multiple sections of similar components and multiple input and output connections
- *Latch*—to enter and remain in a steady state
- *Loading*—changing the performance of a circuit by placing an impedance at the input or output

Background

There is an old saying: "Amplifiers are oscillators that *don't* and oscillators are amplifiers that *do*." An amplifier is at the heart of every oscillator, as shown in the block diagram of the basic oscillator in Figure 1. The feedback network is connected so that some of the output signal is fed back into amplifier's input. If this system is going to work as an oscillator at some frequency, two things must occur. The portion of the signal fed back to the input, βV_{OUT}, has to arrive with just the right phase to reinforce and not cancel the input signal. The amplifier also has to have enough gain, A, to compensate for losses in the feedback circuit.

In the block diagram, the output signal, V_{OUT}, is equal to AV_1. V_1 is equal to the input signal, V_{IN}, minus the fraction of the output signal fed back to the input, βV_{OUT}. This means that the overall gain of the circuit is:

$$V_{OUT} / V_{IN} = A / 1 + A\beta \qquad \text{[Eq 1]}$$

All is nice and stable, unless $A\beta = -1$, in which case gain becomes infinite! When this happens, the amplifier's output heads for infinite voltage, but it reaches the power supply voltage and has to stop. Depending on the circuit's design, the output will either *latch* at that voltage or turn around and head for the other limiting voltage (either ground or the opposite power supply voltage). In the second case, we now have an oscillator because the circuit will continue zoom from one voltage to the other in a continuous cycle.

How do we design a circuit such that $A\beta = 1$? Consider that, to a sine wave, multiplying by –1 is the same as adding 180° of phase shift. The requirement for $A\beta$ can then be rewritten to say that the product must be equal to 1 but with a phase shift of 180°. If you assume that all of the phase shift occurs in the feedback circuit and that the amplifier has enough gain to make up for any losses in the feedback circuit, our equation is satisfied and the oscillator *does*!

Figure 2 shows such a circuit, called a *phase-shift oscillator*. To be sure, there are other circuits with better performance, but this one is the closest to the basic circuit we've just discussed. Let's start with the feedback network formed by the three pairs of 10 kΩ resistors and 0.1 µF capacitors. Each forms a low-pass RC filter that shifts the phase of the input signal—0 to 90° as frequency is increased. At some frequency, the phase shift will be 60°. When three identical sections are cascaded, each contributes 60° of phase shift to make 180°, the necessary phase shift to form an oscillator. The frequency at which each section contributes 60° of phase shift is:

$$f = (\tan 60°) / 2\pi RC = 1.73 / 6.28 \, RC = 0.28 / RC \qquad \text{[Eq 2]}$$

For our combination of 10 kΩ and 0.1 µF, that frequency is 275 Hz. At the frequency at which 60° of phase shift occurs, the filter also reduces the amplitude of the input signal by half. If three sections are connected back-to-back, then the total reduction in signal level is $1/2 \times 1/2 \times 1/2 = 1/8 = 0.125$, which is our value of β. To make $A\beta$ at least 1, A must then be at least 8 and that is controlled by the ratio of R_f to R_i. R_f is made variable to allow for adjustment in gain to account for component variations and other effects, as we shall see.

Working with a Phase-Shift Oscillator

For this circuit, you will need a power supply that can provide both positive and negative dc voltages of 6 to 12 V. Since current draw is low, you can use batteries to provide power.

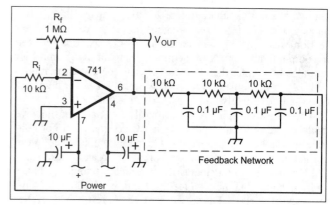

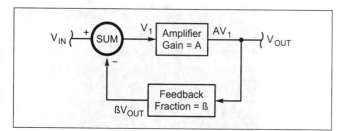

Figure 1—This fundamental block diagram describes an oscillator as a pair of circuits, one providing gain and the other feeding back a fraction of the output signal into the input.

Figure 2—The phase shift oscillator circuit. Each pair of 10 kΩ resistors and 0.1 µF capacitors in the feedback network adds 60° of phase shift at the frequency of oscillation.

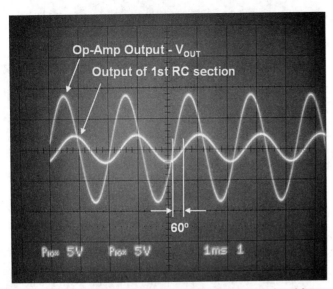

Figure 3—The oscilloscope traces show the output signal from the op-amp and the smaller, phase-shifted signal at the output of the first RC filter section.

- Start by building the circuit of Figure 2. The extra 10 µF capacitors prevent feedback through the op-amp power supply pins. Set the potentiometer for the highest resistance between its connections.
- Connect power and you should see something that looks like a square wave at the output of the op-amp. This shows the op-amp output swinging back and forth between the power supply voltages as it unsuccessfully tries to balance the current in R_f with that coming from the feedback network.
- Reduce the potentiometer resistance to obtain an undistorted sine wave that peaks a volt or so below the power supply voltages as seen in Figure 3. (This may be a touchy adjustment.) If you have a dual-channel oscilloscope, observe the input and output voltages of each RC section and verify that each contributes approximately 60°.
- Measure the period of the output waveform (one complete cycle) and calculate the frequency of the oscillator (f=1/period). Measure the resistance of the potentiometer (R_f) after removing it from the circuit. Compute the amplifier's gain (A=resistance / 10 kΩ).

Design Assumptions

You probably observed that the frequency was a lot different than the initial calculation of 275 Hz—my oscillator's frequency was 476 Hz. The voltage drop across each RC filter section was probably greater than $1/2$—my sections reduced the output to about 0.27 of the input. The gain of the amplifier will also be greater than 8 to compensate for that extra reduction. My potentiometer's resistance was 603 kΩ, for a gain of 60.3—approximately equal to 1 / (0.27 × 0.27 × 0.27).

These discrepancies result primarily from assumptions we made in the design process. Each RC section does not contribute exactly 60° because it is loaded by the next section in the network. That causes extra voltage drop and phase shift. The op-amp also contributes its own small amount of phase shift, meaning that the total feedback phase shift does not have to be exactly 180°. These two errors will result in a higher frequency at which $A\beta = -1$.

To see the effects of op-amp limitations, change the feedback capacitors from 0.1 µF to 0.001 µF. At this frequency, a 741 op-amp can't cause its output to change rapidly enough to keep up and the output waveform will change to something

that looks more like a triangle wave instead, no matter how you adjust amplifier gain.

Buffered Oscillator

The phase-shift and voltage drop errors caused by the loading effects of each RC section can be eliminated by adding a *buffer* between each section. Replace the single op-amp with a quad op-amp such as the LM324. One op-amp section will replace the existing LM741. Add a *voltage follower* between each RC section by connecting an op-amp's output directly to its inverting input and connecting the input signal to the noninverting input. (This circuit is shown in the on-line reference listed below.)

Because the voltage follower presents a very high input impedance to the preceding circuit, each RC section can act more like the ideal filter we envisioned during the design process. The resulting frequency of oscillation and the gain required to achieve oscillation should be within 20% of the calculated values.

Suggested Reading and a Donated Tool

The ARRL Handbook has an extensive chapter on oscillators, although not much on phase-shift oscillators. The section "How Oscillators Work" is highly recommended. A good application note, "The Design of Op-Amp Sine Wave Oscillators" is available on-line from Texas Instruments at **www.ti.com/sc/docs/apps/msp/journal/aug2000/aug_07.pdf**.

Another reader has graciously donated a software tool for Hands-On readers. Bill, N3TR, created a dandy spreadsheet to calculate resistor values for Pi and T attenuators. Enter input power, impedance and attenuation to get resistor values. The spreadsheet is available on the Hands-On Web site: **www.arrl.org/tis/info/html/hands-on-radio**.

Shopping List

- LM741 (RadioShack 276-007) op-amp and (optional) LM324 quad op-amp (RadioShack 276-1711)
- 1 MΩ potentiometer
- 4—10 kΩ, $1/4$ W resistors
- 3 each—0.1 µF and 0.001 µF ceramic capacitors
- 2—10 µF, 16 V (or greater) electrolytic capacitors

Next Month

Our next experiment will move from the workbench over to the blackboard as we discuss frequency response and decibels (dB). Understanding the mechanics and terminology of these important concepts is key to being a successful electronic experimenter.

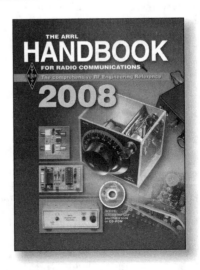

Experiment #31—The Multivibrator

Multivibrator circuits are not only a great way to generate square waves and pulses, but also to become more comfortable with how transistor circuits work. Those of you without oscilloscopes will enjoy this experiment since all measurements can be easily made with a voltmeter.

Terms to Learn

- *Astable*—Not stable in any state, the circuit continually cycles between states.
- *Bistable*—Stable in either state, the circuit stays in one state until disturbed.
- *Monostable*—Stable in only one state, the circuit will eventually return to that state from any other.

The Multivibrator

There are lots of devices that vibrate, that is, jump back and forth between two positions. Buzzers and the familiar "drinking bird" are good examples of vibrators. The electronic equivalent is called a *multivibrator*, outputting a voltage or current that alternates between two values or *states*. You already met such a circuit way back in Experiment #5 on timer circuits. (You can access the previous experiments on the Hands-On Radio Web page— **www.arrl.org/tis/info/HTML/Hands-On-Radio.**) This month, we'll experiment with a simple equivalent built from transistors.

A multivibrator circuit can jump back and forth between its two states in several ways. If it stays in one of the states until an external signal causes it to change, it's called *bistable*. This means the circuit is stable in either state. If it is stable in only one of the states, returning to that state if disturbed, it's called *monostable*. If the circuit is stable in neither state, forever alternating between the two, it's an *astable* multivibrator. All are useful in different applications. For example, the bistable multivibrator is more commonly known to digital designers as a *flip-flop*. In this experiment, we'll take a look at the monostable and astable versions.

The Monostable Multivibrator

"Mono" means "one," so this circuit has only one stable state in which it can remain indefinitely. The most common form of monostable circuit has a stable state and a *quasi-stable* state that it enters following a *trigger* (such as a switch closure or an electronic signal) before returning to the stable state. Electronic monostable multivibrators are often called *one-shots* because they output one pulse for each trigger signal.

Figure 1 shows a simple one-shot circuit using one transistor. If we let the circuit sit undisturbed for a long time, capacitor C will be charged to the voltage at which Q1 is ON. This allows current to flow through R1 and V_{OUT} will be the transistor's saturation voltage, typically less than 0.3 V. If nothing disturbs the circuit, it will stay in this stable state forever.

The one-shot is triggered by a momentary closure of S1. This discharges C and turns OFF the transistor. V_{OUT} is pulled up to V_{CC} by R1. As soon as S1 is released, C begins charging again through R2. When V_B reaches about 0.6 V, Q1 will turn

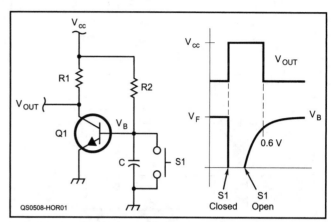

Figure 1—A simple monostable or one-shot multivibrator circuit is triggered by a switch closure.

ON again, pulling V_{OUT} back to the low-voltage state. Capacitor voltage remains at the forward voltage of the base-emitter junction and the circuit is back to the stable state.

The length of the output pulse (after S1 is released) is determined by how long it takes C to charge to 0.6 V through R2. The equation for calculating that time is:

$$t \text{ (seconds)} = RC \ln [\, V_{CC} / (V_{CC} - 0.6) \,]$$

(The natural log, ln, is explained in more detail at **en.wikipedia.org/wiki/Natural_logarithm.**) If you intend to use the circuit for a project, add a 50-100 Ω resistor in series with S1 to limit the discharge current of C.

Building a Monostable Multivibrator

There's no learning like seeing, so grab your prototyping board and have at it! For starters, use a 100 μF capacitor for C, a 2N3904, 10 kΩ for R1 and 470 kΩ for R2. First, calculate the output pulse time, assuming a 12 V supply:

$$t = (470 \text{ k}\Omega) (100 \text{ μF}) \ln [\, 12 / (12 - 0.6) \,] = 2.41 \text{ seconds}$$

Build the circuit and use your voltmeter to measure V_{OUT}. Use a stop watch to estimate the length of your output pulse and compare it to your calculations. My pulse was close to 3 seconds because the capacitor value was greater than 100 μF. Change the values of R2 and C to change the pulse duration.

What happens if you change the power supply voltage? Recalculate the output pulse length with a V_{CC} of 6 V and try it if you have an adjustable supply. This circuit is highly dependent on power supply voltage. There are two ways around the problem; either use a voltage regulator to create a constant power supply voltage or create a design that depends on voltage ratios, such as the NE555 timer IC of Experiment #5.

Astable Multivibrator

The astable circuit of Figure 2 continuously alternates between

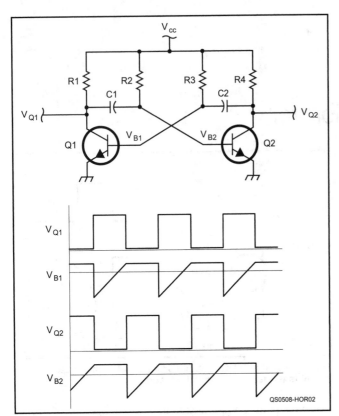

Figure 2—The alternating sequence of capacitors charging and discharging creates the output waveform of the astable multivibrator.

its two stable states. The output can be used as a clock or as a tone. Because the frequency of the switching is not synchronized to any other source, this is a *free-running* circuit.

How does it work? More importantly, how does it start up? For the sake of simplicity, let's assume that C1 = C2, R1 = R4, R2 = R3, and both transistors are the same type. When power is applied, if both transistors were identical, the same base current would flow in both transistors and both would turn on at the same rate, reaching their saturation voltage at the same time. And that would be that. But, the circuit isn't going to be completely symmetric and so one transistor will turn on a little bit faster than the other, say Q1 does.

Since Q1 is turning on a little faster than Q2, the current through R1 is increasing faster than through R4 and the voltage at Q1's collector drops faster than at Q2's collector. This means that more current is going to be pulled through C1 than through C2 and the resulting negative-going voltage transient at the base of Q2 will turn that transistor OFF before it's completely ON. So Q1 wins the race and is ON, while Q2 is OFF. This is stable state 1.

With Q1 ON, the collector side of C1 is nearly at ground, but the other side is charging through R2. Soon, that voltage reaches the turn-on voltage for Q2 and it rapidly turns ON. The sudden drop in voltage at the collector of Q2 results in a negative-going transient at the base of Q1, turning it OFF. The circuit is now in stable state 2.

While in stable state 2, the side of C2 connected to Q2's collector is nearly at ground and the other side is charging through R3. This results in Q1 turning back ON, generating a negative-going transient at the base of Q2 through C1, turning Q2 OFF and returning the circuit to stable state 1, where the cycle begins anew.

The exact equation for the time each transistor is ON and OFF is quite a bit more complicated than for the single-transistor one-shot circuit, but here is a reasonably good approximation:

t (seconds) = RC ln 2 = 0.69 RC and

f (Hertz) = $1/(2t)$ (since there are two halves of each cycle)

This approximation is valid as long as both transistors are driven into saturation when they are ON and if V_{CC} is much greater than the base-to-emitter voltages required to turn the transistors ON. For a 12 V power supply and most transistors, this is true. As V_{CC} is lowered, the approximation will no longer be valid and t will increase. Ready to build one?

Building an Astable Multivibrator

Start with values of 1 kΩ for R1 and R4, 220 kΩ for R2 and R3, and 10 µF for C1 and C2. This keeps operation slow enough for the circuit's behavior to be observed with voltmeters.

First, calculate t = 0.69 RC = 0.69 (220 kΩ) (10 µ)
= 1.52 seconds.

Build the circuit using a 12 V power supply and compare your time to calculated time—mine measured 2.5 seconds due to capacitor tolerances.

Lower the voltage to 6 V and remeasure. The time on my circuit increased to 4.5 seconds.

Return the power supply to 12 V and increase the value of R1 and R4 to 10 kΩ. The collector voltage will rise more slowly as the capacitors are charged through the larger resistance.

Return R1 and R4 to 1 kΩ. Experiment by varying the values of both R2 and R3 or the values of C1 and C2, calculating the expected t each time.

Use different values for R2 and R3 or C1 and C2 to make an asymmetric output waveform.

Shopping List

- 2 each 2N3904 transistors
- 1, 10, 47 and 470 kΩ ¼ W resistors
- 1 each 100 µF capacitor, 2 each 10 µF capacitors, 16 V rating or higher.

Suggested Browsing and a Tip

Internet searching for either "astable multivibrator" or "monostable multivibrator" will turn up a wealth of supplemental information. There is a nice Java applet demonstration of the astable multivibrator at **en.wikipedia.org/wiki/Multivibrator**. On the subject of URLs, alert reader Dick Keller, KF4NS, noticed that the oscilloscope tutorial Web site URL **website.lineone. net/~colin_mccord/Radio/oscilloscope.htm** is case-sensitive and "Radio" must be capitalized, too.

Next Month

You have probably encountered the term "Thevenin Equivalent." Next month we'll learn about it and its dueling dual, the Norton Equivalent.

Experiment #43 — RF Oscillators, Part 1

In Experiment #17 on the "Phase-Shift Oscillator"[1] we explored the idea of using phase-shift and feedback to turn an amplifier into a self-sustaining oscillator. (It's not a bad idea to go back and skim that column.) This month we "turn pro" and move higher in frequency to the world of RF oscillators. In a sense, this is the fundamental building block of radio — without an oscillator there would be no signals to amplify or receive. Along with learning about oscillators, you'll learn about a new way to build RF circuits. This is a two-part experiment — in this installment we'll discuss how RF oscillators work. Next month we'll build and test one.

Terms to Learn

Barkhausen Criterion — For an oscillator to oscillate, the product of gain around the feedback loop must be equal to or greater than unity (1).

Loop Gain — The amount of total gain measured all the way around a feedback loop.

The Oscillator — A Review

An oscillator consists of a means of amplification — a transistor, integrated circuit or vacuum tube — and a feedback network. The feedback network (shown as an LC resonator in Figure 1) is designed so that at the frequency of interest, the product of amplifier gain (A_V in Figure 1) and feedback ratio, β, is equal to or greater than 1. $A_V\beta$ is also known as *loop gain*, the total gain experienced by a signal all the way through the amplifier, the feedback network and back to the input. The requirement that $A_V\beta \geq 1$ is formally known as the *Barkhausen Criterion*. It's important to note that "1" in this case means "an amplitude of 1 and a phase difference of 0°." If A_V is negative (inverting), then β must also be negative, meaning the feedback must have a 180° phase shift.

Signals of the right frequency will be amplified, a portion fed back to the amplifier input, amplified again, and so on, becoming self-sustaining and creating a steady output signal. If the amplitude of the feedback is sufficient, but if the

[1]All previous Hands-On Radio experiments are available to ARRL members at www.arrl.org/tis/info/HTML/Hands-On-Radio.

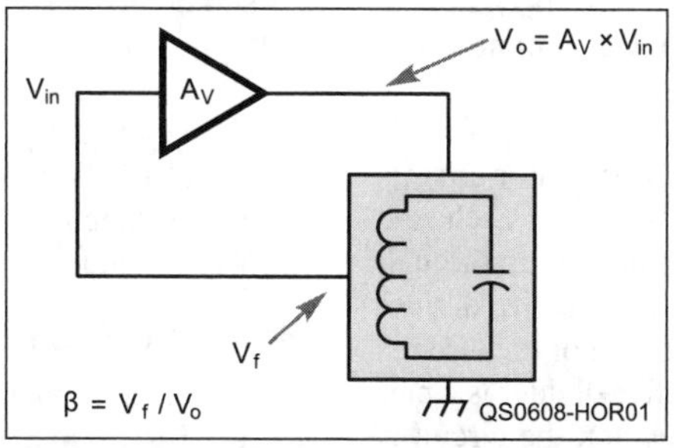

phase difference is not exactly right then the returned portion of the output signal becomes progressively farther and farther out of phase on each trip. The result is that the oscillator's output consists mostly of a fundamental frequency plus small amounts of other signals, usually harmonics, for which loop gain is sufficient and the round trip phase difference is some integer multiple of 360°.

Where does the necessary phase shift come from? Some of the phase shift may come from the amplifier itself. For example, an amplifier such as a common emitter amplifier (Experiment #1) or an op-amp connected to invert its input signal has a phase shift of 180°. The remaining phase shift must come from an external phase shift network, just as we saw in Experiment #17. Any kind of device or circuit that produces a constant phase shift can be used, including RC or LC circuits and even transmission lines. If the amplifier is non-inverting, such as an emitter follower (Experiment #2), the feedback signal must be in-phase with the output signal. As long as the requirements for total loop gain and phase are satisfied, the oscillator will oscillate.

Figure 2 shows three different variations of the same oscillator circuit with the gain provided by a transistor and an LC resonator that is tapped to provide the feedback signal. The resonator serves two purposes: it provides the necessary phase shift at the desired frequency and it acts as a filter for signals in the amplifier loop so that only the desired signals are amplified. (The dc bias and power connections are omitted from the diagram for clarity.) To visualize the common emitter circuit's parallel LC resonator, imagine the capacitors connected together and their connection grounded, as shown by the dashed line.

RF Oscillators

The circuits used in RF oscillators are different than those used for lower frequencies. RC phase shift circuits aren't generally used above a few MHz. The values of R or C become impracticably small, which leaves the oscillator susceptible to parasitic effects that compromise stability and consistency. At these frequencies, it's much easier to use inductors and capacitors to form the phase-shifting resonators.

Most RF oscillators use discrete devices such as a bipolar or FET transistors rather than an op-amp. Most op-amps are designed for use where high gain at low frequencies is needed. A high gain, wide bandwidth op-amp

Figure 1 — An oscillator consists of an amplifier plus a feedback network, shown here as a parallel LC circuit. The resonant LC circuit helps keep unwanted frequencies from being generated.

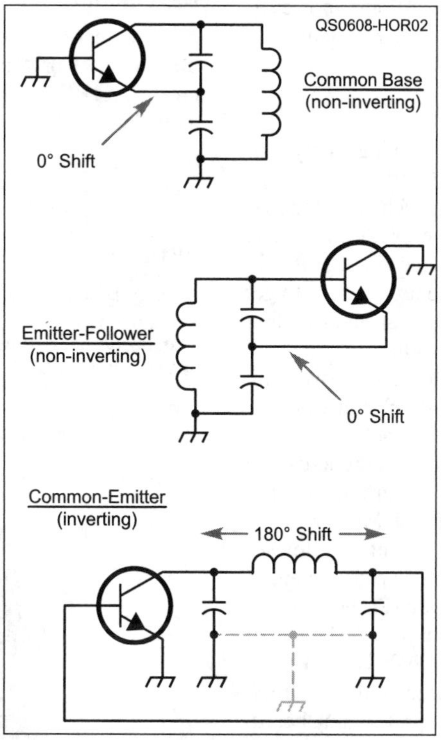

Figure 2 — Three different types of oscillator circuits, all based on the Colpitts design. The type of amplifier circuit determines whether 0 or 180° of phase shift is needed.

is generally much more expensive than discrete transistors such as the 2N3904 (bipolar NPN) or 2N4416 (n-channel JFET) that cost mere pennies and have gain at frequencies up to several hundred MHz. Thus, at RF above 1 MHz, the most effective circuits use a transistor amplifier with feedback. The required phase shift is provided by a resonator such as a parallel LC circuit.

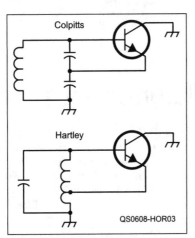

Figure 3 — The Colpitts and Hartley oscillators work on the same principle, but use different connections to the LC resonator to provide feedback.

Meet Mssrs Hartley and Colpitts

Back in the 1920s, two fellows by the names of Hartley and Colpitts came up with the different oscillator circuits of Figure 3 that became popular in radio designs. In each, the feedback comes about by routing part of the emitter circuit through a voltage divider created by two reactances. If the reactive divider is a pair of capacitors, it's a Colpitts oscillator. (All of the circuits in Figure 2 are Colpitts oscillators.) If the reactive divider is a pair of inductors or, more frequently, a tapped inductor, the circuit is a Hartley oscillator. These same circuits are in wide use today at nearly 100 years of age!

The Hartley and Colpitts oscillator circuits are very similar in behavior but their differences may influence the designer's preferred choice. For example, the Hartley has a wider tuning range and fewer components than the Colpitts. The Colpitts, however, avoids the tapped inductor and has several popular variants that provide good stability.

Building Your RF Prototyping Board

In the previous experiments, we've used the plug-in style of prototyping boards. They're very convenient and easy to work with for a variety of circuits, but…they aren't much good for analog circuits that work at frequencies above a couple of MHz. The strips of contacts add too much capacitance to the circuit, often in unpredictable ways. The leads of the components also start to get long enough to have significant amounts of inductance. Providing solid grounds for RF circuits can be very difficult.

Hams have come up with an excellent substitute for working with RF circuits called "ugly" or "Manhattan style" construction. In this style of prototyping, a blank piece of copper-clad PC board is used as a ground plane. Components needing a ground can be soldered directly to the ground plane. To create ungrounded junctions ugly style, high-value resistors (typically 1 MΩ or more) are used as standoffs, costing only pennies. Manhattan style uses small pads of PC board material as standoffs. The pads are either soldered to the ground plane (requires double-sided PC board pads) or hot-glued to the ground plane. (A fine example of Manhattan style building can be seen at **www.wb6kwt.com/2n22.htm**.)

To gain some experience before starting on the oscillator circuit create a new tool for your workbench — an RF prototyping board. You'll need a large piece of single or double sided PC board, at least 8 × 8 inches, and a thick piece of wood as big as or slightly larger than the PC board. Drill mounting holes in the corner of the PC board and attach it to the wooden base with wood screws. This gives you a large surface on which to work, and the base makes it heavy enough to not be dragged about by test leads and cables. I attached rubber feet to the bottom of my wooden base.

Once you've finished (and before each use) scrub the board with a kitchen dishwashing pad to remove fingerprints and oxidation. A swab with some rubbing alcohol will also clean the board of oils and greases. The goal is to have an easy to solder surface.

Next, practice on a non-RF circuit that's easy to build, such as the common emitter amplifier of Experiment #1. (If you are new to "Hands-On Radio," this is a good opportunity to go back and learn about the most common of all amplifier circuits while getting some construction practice.) Once you gain a little experience with this type of construction, you'll find it's a quick and effective way to prototype even complex RF circuits before transferring them to an actual PC board or building them into an equipment enclosure.

Shopping List

Here is the shopping list for next month's oscillator circuit.
- 2 µH inductor — wind your own coil with 8 turns of heavy, 14 to 18 gauge solid wire on a 1½ inch diameter form. The coil should be about 1 inch long.
- 200 pF polystyrene or silver mica capacitor.
- 100 pF air variable or compression trimmer capacitor.
- 2.7 pF and 0.01 µF ceramic capacitors.
- Several 1 MΩ, ¼ W resistors.
- 2N4416 junction field effect transistor (JFET).
- 1N4148 diode.

Recommended Reading

The amateur literature is full of articles about oscillators. These three ARRL books have solid sections on oscillators: *The ARRL Handbook*,[2] *Experimental Methods in RF Design*[3] and *Introduction to Radio Frequency Design*.[4] The *Handbook's* explanation speaks to all levels of readers, while *Experimental Methods* focuses on construction and provides an introduction to the serious design details.

Next Month

Now that you have a basic understanding of oscillators and a brand new RF prototyping board, there's nothing stopping you from creating an RF oscillator, and that's just what we'll do. You'll create a tunable Hartley oscillator — the heart of a 40 meter transmitter!

[2]R. D. Straw, Editor, *The ARRL Handbook of Radio Communications*. Available from your ARRL dealer or the ARRL Bookstore, ARRL order no. 9485. Price, $39.95 plus shipping. Telephone 860-594-0355, or toll-free in the US 888-277-5289; **www.arrl.org/shop/**; **pubsales@arrl.org**.

[3]W. Hayward, W7ZOI, R. Campbell, KK7B, and R. Larkin, W7PUA, *Experimental Methods in RF Design*. Available from your ARRL dealer or the ARRL Bookstore, ARRL order no. 8799. Price, $49.95 plus shipping. Telephone 860-594-0355, or toll-free in the US 888-277-5289; **www.arrl.org/shop/**; **pubsales@arrl.org**.

[4]W. Hayward, W7ZOI, *Introduction to Radio Frequency Design*. Available from your ARRL dealer or the ARRL Bookstore, ARRL order no. 4920. Price, $39.95 plus shipping. Telephone 860-594-0355, or toll-free in the US 888-277-5289; **www.arrl.org/shop/**; **pubsales@arrl.org**.

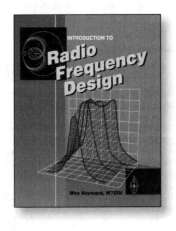

Experiment #44 — RF Oscillators, Part 2

This month, we'll build and test last month's Hartley oscillator, which generates a signal on the 40 meter band. While the soldering iron is heating up, consider the question of how oscillators start oscillating.

Terms to Learn

• Chirp — a slight change in frequency during each dot or dash of a CW signal.
• Drift — long-term, slow changes in frequency usually as a consequence of heating or cooling of the circuit.
• Limiting — a reduction of gain as signal level increases.
• Microphonics — variations in frequency caused by mechanical vibrations.

Getting Started

Where do the "signals of the right frequency" come from to allow the oscillator to start? Oscillators "boot up" by amplifying the random noise — thermal or otherwise — that is present in all circuits. A perfect, noiseless amplifier circuit would not spontaneously oscillate! Noise at the frequencies at which the loop gain ($A_V\beta$) ≥ 1 (see Part 1) is reinforced, eventually becoming a full-fledged signal. Harmonics and other spurious signals are generated at frequencies where the phase shift is just right and enough gain exists.

A Practical Hartley Oscillator

Figure 1 shows a practical circuit for a Hartley oscillator from section 4.2 of *Experimental Methods in RF Design*. As described in that book, the circuit will work from frequencies below the radio range up into the GHz. Take a moment to review the circuit. L1 is tapped, forming the reactive divider characteristic of the Hartley circuit. C1 and C2 in parallel with L1 form a resonant *tank circuit* to determine the oscillator's frequency.

The amplifier is a 2N4416 junction field effect transistor (JFET)

connected as a common-drain circuit with the drain connected to ac ground by C4. Source current flows through the lower part of L1 to provide feedback in-phase with the gate signal. A JFET is used because its high gate impedance means that the tank circuit can be lightly loaded, improving circuit stability. The 2N4416 is an inexpensive transistor designed for good high frequency, low noise performance in oscillator circuits.

What keeps an oscillator's output from turning into a square wave as the amplified signal gets larger and larger with each trip "around the loop"? *Limiting* must occur so that the oscillator doesn't saturate or latch up at the power supply voltage or ground. Limiting is a kind of automatic gain control. As oscillations build, limiting stabilizes the oscillator's gain so that the output level is constant. That is the function of C3, D1 and R1.

Some of the tank circuit signal is extracted through C3 and half-wave rectified by D1. On positive half-cycles, D1 clamps the gate voltage at 0.6 V. On negative half-cycles, D1 allows C3 to charge to the peak negative voltage of the signal. The charge then slowly leaks away through R1. As the oscillation builds, so does negative voltage at the gate. Eventually, the gate-to-source voltage begins to approach pinch-off or cut-off ($V_{GS(OFF)}$) at which point the JFET stops conducting. (The 2N4416's $V_{GS(OFF)}$ varies from –2.5 to –6 V.) Limiting stabilizes loop gain at the point at which the oscillations reduce gain if they grow larger. This keeps Q1 operating linearly, minimizing harmonics and spurious signals.

Building the Oscillator

Figure 2 shows a photo of my circuit, built on a scrap of copper-clad PC material. You can wind a decent coil by clamping one end of the wire in a vise, holding the other end of the wire on the form and rolling the form toward the vise. Don't worry if the coil isn't picture-perfect — the electrons won't notice! Wind eight full turns with at least ½ inch of wire available for making leads. Solder the "cold" or ground end of the coil directly to the PC board.

Support the other end of the coil with C1 and C2. This junction is the "hot" end of the tank circuit. Be sure to mount C1 solidly. Solder D1 and R1 to the PC board and to each other forming an upside-down V. Solder C3 between the coil and the junction of D1 and R1. (Figure 2 shows a "gimmick" capacitor that I tried for C3. A gimmick capacitor consists of a few turns of insulated wire wrapped tightly around each other to give a few pF per inch.)

Bend the leads of Q1 away from each other at right angles. Remove the lead

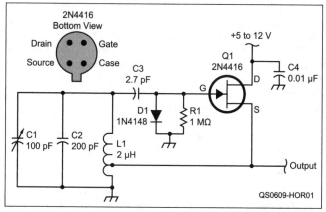

Figure 1 — The practical Hartley oscillator circuit includes limiting so that the level of oscillation is stabilized to reduce the levels of harmonics. Tuning is smoothed by using a smaller trimmer capacitor in parallel with a larger fixed-value capacitor.

Figure 2 — The author's prototype oscillator. The coil is made from heavy wire to support itself. The rest of the components support each other with grounded leads soldered directly to the PC board.

labeled "case." Solder the gate lead to the junction of D1 and R1. Support the drain lead with C4. Use hookup wire to connect the source lead to the second turn of L1 from the grounded end. Be sure you have Q1's leads correctly identified.

Before applying power is a good time to double-check your circuit. It's easy to overlook mistakes while you're building. For example, my oscillator didn't work right away because I misconnected C1 and C2 to the junction of R1 and D1. I had to check my circuit carefully against the schematic diagram to find the mistake. The oscillator still didn't work until I noticed that the color code on R1 was brown-green-brown (150 Ω) instead of brown-black-green (1 MΩ)! Somehow, the wrong resistors had been put in the 1 MΩ tray. Once I had the circuit wired correctly with all correct values, the oscillator sprang to life. Simple errors can happen to anyone. Don't be embarrassed to ask a friend to look over a circuit for you when you get stuck.

Set your power supply to a voltage between +5 and +12 V. Use the grounded end of C4 as the 'scope grounding point. Set C1 about in the middle of its range. When you apply power, the oscillator should immediately begin to oscillate with a signal near 7 MHz and an amplitude of a few volts peak-to-peak.

Measure the period from one peak to the next and calculate frequency as 1/t. If the frequency is in the 40 meter band, congratulations! If it is close to the 40 meter band, adjust C1 (higher C means lower frequency) to bring the frequency into the band. If you can't get a 40 meter signal by tuning C1, reset C1 to mid-range and gently squeeze the turns of L1 closer together (higher L and lower f) or spread them apart until adjustment of C1 brings the frequency into the band. Congratulations — you're a real RF tinkerer now!

Experimenting with the Oscillator

Turn on an HF receiver and find your signal on 40 meters. It should be pretty strong to a nearby receiver. If necessary, turn on your receiver's attenuator so that the signal is registering no more than S-9 +10 or 20 dB. Is the signal drifting slowly higher or lower in frequency? Is it stable or does the level jump around?

Calculate the frequencies of the 2nd, 3rd, 4th and 5th harmonics and find them on the receiver. Are any instabilities you noticed at the fundamental frequency present on the harmonics? If so, they are probably larger, such as a faster rate of drift. Compare the signal strengths of the fundamental and the harmonics.

Turn off power to the oscillator and temporarily disconnect D1 at one end. Power up the oscillator again. The amplitude of the waveform at the oscillator output is now several times greater. Look carefully and you'll also see that the waveform shows some distortion. Figures 3A and 3B show the difference in my oscillator circuit with D1 in and out of circuit. With the diode disconnected, listen to your fundamental again and measure the amplitudes of

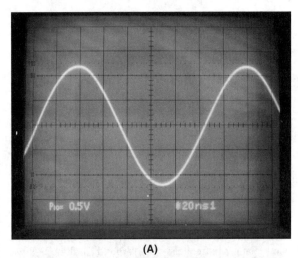

(A)

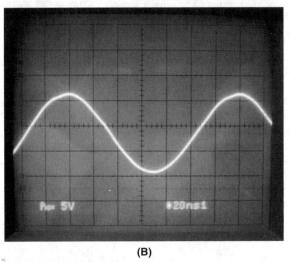

(B)

Figure 3 — At A, the oscillator output with D1 connected is a clean sine wave of 2.5 V$_{p\text{-}p}$. At B, removing D1 disables the limiting circuit. The output is quite a bit larger (16 V$_{p\text{-}p}$), but more distortion is visible.

the harmonics. The extra distortion you saw on the oscillator output is caused by the increased level of the harmonics. Power down again and reconnect D1.

Temperature also affects oscillator stability. Because the components are exposed to free air, the oscillator will change frequency in response to temperature changes. If you have a hair dryer, heat the circuit while tracking the signal on the receiver. Whether the signal goes up or down in response to heat, you'll see a big change. Try focusing the heat on the tank circuit or the transistor to see which is more sensitive.

Bring the hot soldering iron near C1 and C2 to observe the effect of heating those components. Try heating Q1, C3, D1 and R1 one at a time. Similarly, if you have a can of freeze spray or compressed air, try cooling the components individually. You'll quickly understand why master oscillators are often sealed up inside small enclosures and even heated!

You will also hear microphonics, or the response of the oscillator to mechanical vibrations. Just moving the circuit causes the coil to vibrate, changing the frequency noticeably on the receiver. To really hear the frequency change, tap the coil with a pencil! Don't tap too hard or you'll change the resting frequency and have to track it down again. Try tapping the other components to compare their sensitivity. Keeping an oscillator stable is a big challenge!

Finally, reconnect power to the oscillator through a straight key and listen to your signal as you key this micropower transmitter. Listen for the short-term frequency shift of the chirp as the oscillator turns on and microphonics from the thump of the key. Use your call sign since you may get a surprise call from a nearby ham! If you decide to hook the oscillator to an antenna, use a 40 meter filter to reduce the harmonics. A shorted quarter-wave coaxial stub (see Experiment #22) will provide harmonic filtering.

There are lots more experiments to try with your oscillator. Change the tap point on the coil and see what happens to both the frequency and purity of the oscillator waveform. Try changing the value of C3 and R1 to see what effect they have on oscillator stability. Substitute other n-channel JFETs, such as an MPF102. Change the coil and capacitor values to make the oscillator work on higher bands. You'll find the oscillator to be an endless source of interest and you can listen to the effects directly!

Recommended Reading

Now that you have a real, live oscillator on your workbench, go back to the references of last month and review them to cement your understanding.

Next Month

It would be a shame to leave the oscillator without putting it on the air, so next month we'll add a small amplifier and filter. We'll even wind a toroid!

Experiment #45 — RF Amplifiers, Part 1

Last month you built a 40 meter oscillator. This month we'll add a buffer amplifier as an introduction to RF amplifiers. The circuit is adapted from "A First Transmitter" in Chapter 1 of *Experimental Methods in RF Design*.[1]

Terms to Learn

Buffer — A circuit that provides isolation.

Decoupling — Preventing ac signals from flowing between circuits, usually in power supply connections.

Gain-Bandwidth Product — A measure of a transistor's ability to amplify high-frequency signals, numerically equal to the frequency at which gain drops to unity.

Isolation — To insulate from the effects of external circuits or disturbances.

Why Not Just Use the Oscillator?

As you learned, oscillators are sensitive creatures, changing frequency in response to mechanical vibrations and thermal changes. This would show up on the air as chirp, drift and microphonics.

To make the signal "ready for prime time" you need to *isolate* the oscillator both mechanically and thermally. This means building the oscillator in a sturdy and protected way and keeping the components at a constant temperature. Electrical isolation usually involves placing a *buffer* stage between the oscillator and the circuits or loads it drives.

What Circuit Makes a Good Buffer?

Reviewing the single-transistor amplifiers, there are three candidates: the common base, the common collector (or emitter follower), and the common emitter amplifier configurations.[2] What characteristics should a buffer amplifier have? It should place a small load on the circuit it's protecting and be able to drive useful loads. These requirements translate to "relatively high input impedance" (so as not to extract too much power from the oscillator) and "relatively low output impedance" (so that it can drive the typical RF circuit or a feed line).

The common base amplifier has the opposite characteristics: low input impedance and high output impedance. The emitter follower (EF) seems like the natural choice, since its input impedance is quite high and the output impedance low. However, the EF's voltage gain is only 1, limiting the amount of power that can be developed across a low impedance, such as a 50 Ω load.

The common emitter (CE) configuration has both voltage and current gain and medium input and output impedance. This makes it the natural choice as an RF buffer amplifier. Figure 1 shows the circuit we'll use.

The 2N3904 (**www.fairchildsemi.com/ds/2N/2N3904.pdf**) is a low-cost transistor with good RF characteristics. For example, at

moderate values of collector current, its *current gain-bandwidth product*, or f_T, is 300 MHz. (This is a typical value and actual performance varies quite a bit from this figure.) This means that the transistor's ac current gain, which decreases with increasing frequency, will fall to unity at 300 MHz. At lower frequencies ac current gain is higher. For our 7 MHz signal current gain is approximately $300/7 = 43$. A quiescent or Q-point collector current (I_{CQ}) of 5 mA will provide a good compromise between high gain and low power dissipation in the transistor.

Impedance Matching

The CE circuits we've looked at in the past used a resistor as a

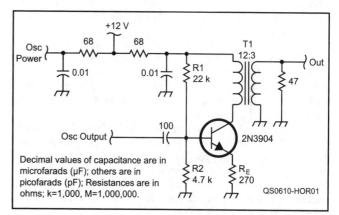

Figure 1 — The Common Emitter amplifier is often used as an RF buffer because of its medium input and output impedances. The 2N3904 is a frequent choice for small-signal RF amplifiers.

Figure 2 — Be sure to keep the buffer output away from the oscillator gate circuits while building the buffer circuit. Route the power leads away from the circuit, as well. This helps prevent unwanted oscillation.

[1]W. Hayward, W7ZOI, R. Campbell, KK7B, and R. Larkin, W7PUA, *Experimental Methods in RF Design*. Available from your ARRL dealer or the ARRL Bookstore, ARRL order no. 8799. Price, $49.95 plus shipping. Telephone 860-594-0355, or toll-free in the US 888-277-5289; **www.arrl.org/shop/**; **pubsales@arrl.org**.

[2]The *Hands-On Radio* experiments for all three transistor amplifier circuit configurations can be found at **www.arrl.org/tis/info/HTML/Hands-On-Radio**.

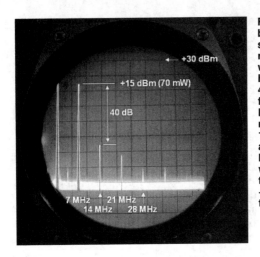

Figure 3 — The buffer output signal at 7 MHz remains clean, with the second harmonic 40 dB below the fundamental. Each division represents 10 dB vertically and 5 MHz horizontally with 0 Hz at the left and +30 dBm at the top.

size of the core determines its power handling limits and the mix determines the inductance per turn of the windings and how much power loss occurs in the core at different frequencies.

Building the Amplifier

Construct the buffer amplifier next to your oscillator as shown in Figure 2. Keep the buffer amplifier components away from the oscillator transistor gate components to prevent unwanted feedback and oscillation. Leave the 100 pF coupling capacitor out of the circuit initially.

To wind the toroid you'll need about a foot of 22 to 28 gauge solid enameled wire. Don't use bare wire as it will short between turns. You may use insulated hookup or wire wrap wire as long as you can get the required number of turns on the core. Solid wire will hold its shape on the core better than stranded wire.

Pull each turn snug. Leave about an inch of wire sticking out of the core for a connection on each end. The turns can be close together or somewhat spread out, but leave room for the other winding. If the coils want to spring out of shape or shift on the core, use a small piece of electrical tape to secure them. The insulation can be removed from enameled wire with a small file — be gentle! Tin the bare leads and install the transformer in the circuit.

Start by making sure that the oscillator works as before. Install the 100 pF capacitor and check the output of the buffer at the 2N3904 collector with your oscilloscope. Distortion indicates biasing problems. Be sure the dc voltages at the buffer's base and emitter are correct before proceeding.

If you have about 1 V_{PP} at the 2N3904 base, you should see about 3 V_{PP} at the collector. Check the output at the 47 Ω resistor. You should see about ¼ the voltage swing at the collector because of the transformer's 4:1 turns ratio.

Figure 3 shows the buffer output spectrum. The scale is 10 dB per vertical division and the top line represents +30 dBm or 1000 mW. The output signal has a power of +15 dBm or 70 mW.

Spurious oscillations at VHF or audio frequencies make the output "fuzzy" or modulated at a low frequency. Separate the oscillator input and buffer output. You may need to move the power supply leads or 'scope probe ground to a new location.

Increase both I_{CQ} and A_V by reducing R_E. Watch for increased waveform distortion or other spurious outputs. Bypass R_E with a 0.01 μF capacitor and observe the output waveform. Listen for and compare the harmonics on a receiver.

Change the transformer turns ratio and observe the effect on gain (higher turns ratio should also increase gain). Change the values of R1 and R2 to adjust the transistor's Q-point and observe the effect on the waveform. Note that changing the Q-point does not affect gain (as long as the waveform is not clipped).

Shopping List

- 2N3904 transistor.
- Ceramic capacitors: one at 100 pF, three at 0.01 μF.
- Resistors, all ¼ W: 47 Ω, two at 68 Ω, 270 Ω, 4.7 kΩ, 22 kΩ.
- FT37-43 toroid core and 12 inches of 24 to 28 gauge solid, enameled wire (see **www.arrl.org/tis** for a list of toroid vendors).

Recommended Reading

Chapter 3 of *Experimental Methods in RF Design* has a good discussion on ferrite inductors and transformers, as does *The ARRL Handbook*, which also includes tables of data about various types of ferrite and powdered-iron cores. The Amidon Web site (**www.amidoncorp.com**) has more information about ferrites under "Product Specification."

Next Month

We will change the oscillator from an LC resonant circuit to crystal control and add an output amplifier for a bit more power, creating a real transmitter that you can put on the air — a homebrew rig that you built yourself!

---

collector load. If the output of the buffer were connected to a medium or high impedance load, a resistor could still be used, but our expected loads — another RF circuit or a coaxial cable — have low impedances, typically 50 Ω.

Because we can't use a resistor as the collector load, a transformer is used to provide an ac load while its primary passes the required dc current. With a 4:1 turn ratio (n), the impedance connected to the transformer secondary is multiplied by n^2 in the primary. A 50 Ω load connected to the secondary then appears as $50 \times 4^2 = 800$ Ω to the collector of the transistor.

Voltage gain, A_V, is approximately the collector load impedance divided by the emitter resistance. The output signal from the transistor shouldn't be clipped or distorted (creating harmonics), so the voltage gain (A_V) must be limited. The input from the oscillator circuit will be about 1 V_{PP}, so we'll start with an A_V of 3. The emitter resistor, R_E, should then be 800 / 3 = 267 Ω, so the standard value of 270 Ω will be used.

We can now design the bias circuit. If I_{CQ} = 5 mA and R_E = 270 Ω, then the voltage at the emitter is 5 mA × 270 = 1.35 V. The base voltage must then be 1.35 + 0.7 = 2.15 V. A value of 4.7 kΩ is chosen for R2 so that the impedance of the base bias voltage divider of R1 // R2 (// means "in parallel") will be at least 10 times the dc base current. Solving the voltage divider equation with a power supply voltage of 12 V: R1 = (12 × 4.7 k / 2.15) − 4.7 = 21.5 kΩ. The standard value of 22 kΩ is used for R1.

A pair of 68 Ω — 0.01 μF low-pass *decoupling* filters are used to prevent ac from flowing between the oscillator and buffer via the power supply, leading to unwanted oscillation.

About Toroids

In the previous experiment, you wound a *solenoidal* inductor. The transformer used here has primary and secondary coils wound on a *toroid* or ring-shaped core. Toroids are a bit harder to wind than solenoids and are a little intimidating to beginners. Like making a contact, the first one is the hardest and it gets easier from there!

In a solenoid, the magnetic field is found both in the core and in the space around the coil. This causes the coil to share its energy with nearby circuits — usually an undesired effect! In a toroid coil, almost all of the magnetic field is contained in the core and very little interaction with nearby circuits takes place. This *self-shielding* property greatly simplifies construction and layout, so toroids are widely used in RF circuits.

The numbers by which toroid cores are identified is another source of mystery. The usual system consists of two numbers: the diameter and the type of material. For example, the core used in this experiment is an FT37-43. This means it has a 0.37 inch diameter and a type-43 *mix* of ferrite. (The FT is a manufacturer label.) The

Experiment #46 — Two Cs: Crystal and Class

Building on the past two "Hands-On Radio" experiments, we will complete a flea-power transmitter with a pair of Cs — a crystal oscillator for good signal stability, and a class C amplifier for a little more "oomph."

Terms to Learn

Amplifier class— describes an amplifier based on the portion of a signal cycle during which the amplifying component (a transistor or tube) is conducting current. Class A amplifiers conduct for 100% of the signal cycle, class B for 50% and class C for less than 50%.

Motional Equivalents — virtual components that represent the electrical equivalents of a crystal's mechanical behavior.

Piezoelectric — a material that produces a voltage in response to mechanical stress.

Crystals

As you no doubt discovered when building the LC oscillator in experiment #44, its signal stability was "not ready for prime time."[1] The large coil converts every vibration into frequency wobbles. The circuit also suffers from thermally induced drift. The solution is to stabilize the operating frequency with a "rock" — a quartz crystal resonator.

The mineral quartz, crystalline silicon dioxide (SiO_2), is a *piezoelectric* material. That is, when a piece of quartz is subjected to mechanical stress, such as squeezing or stretching, the resulting distortion of the crystal's lattice of silicon and oxygen atoms creates a voltage in the direction of the stress. Piezoelectric materials also respond to voltage by expanding or contracting. There are piezoelectric films and ceramics, too.

Quartz is the preferred material for radio-frequency piezoelectric applications because of its low losses, immunity to thermal change and excellent frequency stability. Thin slices of quartz crystals are placed between metal electrodes in holders (the "crystal" electronic component) and used in place of LC circuits in oscillators and filters. The vibrations of current and voltage across the quartz perform the same function as in a resonant LC circuit. (For a more complete discussion of crystals and crystal oscillators, see *Introduction to RF Design*.[2])

Figure 1 shows a crystal's equivalent circuit. L_m

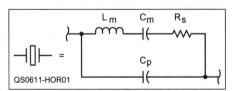

Figure 1 — The equivalent circuit of a crystal translates its mechanical or *motional* behavior into electrical equivalents.

and C_m represent the way the quartz vibrates in response to applied voltage, so they are referred to as *motional equivalents*. C_p represents an equivalent capacitance across the electrodes. R_s represents loss in the material and is usually just 10 or 20 Ω. The resulting component can have an extremely high Q, which in an oscillator helps establish frequency stability. While an LC circuit might have a Q of a few hundred, a crystal can have a Q of 100,000 or more!

Adding A New Crystal Oscillator

For our transmitter to put a good signal on the air, we'll take out the Hartley LC oscillator from the previous experiment and replace it with the circuit of Figure 2. (This circuit is from Section 1.11 of *Experimental Methods in RF Design*.[3]) The crystal's equivalent circuit can't be directly connected, so the feedback connections are

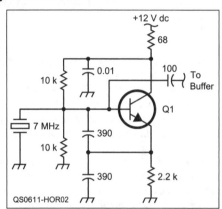

Figure 2 — This is a Clapp oscillator circuit, one of the many variations of the Colpitts family. Feedback is supplied through the tap on the voltage divider formed by the 390 pF capacitors.

external to the crystal. Instead of providing feedback via the resonating inductor as in the Hartley circuit (see experiment #43), a tap between the 390 pF capacitors does the job. This variation of the Colpitts circuit is known as a Clapp oscillator. The 10 kΩ resistors provide operating bias for the transistor and, with a 12 V supply and 2.2 kΩ emitter resistor, set the quiescent collector current at 2.6 mA (see experiment #1 for the necessary calculations).

When rebuilding the oscillator, you can reuse the 68 Ω power supply decoupling resistor and 0.01 μF capacitor. Changes in value of the 390 pF capacitors affect the load on the crystal, so use thermally stable capacitors of the type specified. I recommend a crystal frequency between 7030 and 7045 kHz where other QRP enthusiasts are found.

The oscillator is connected to the buffer amplifier with a 100 pF capacitor connected to the transistor's base, a relatively low impedance point compared to the Hartley circuit FET's high gate impedance. Extracting some signal at this point has relatively little effect on circuit operation or stability.

Class C Output Stage

When you get the oscillator circuit working, you'll likely notice

---

[1]"Hands-On Radio" experiments can be found at **www.arrl.org/tis/info/ HTML/Hands-On-Radio**.

[2]W. Hayward, W7ZOI, *Introduction to RF Design*. Available from your ARRL dealer or the ARRL Bookstore order no 4920. Telephone 860-594-0355, or toll-free in the US 888-277-5289; **www.arrl.org/shop/**; **pubsales@arrl.org**.

[3]W. Hayward, W7ZOI, R. Campbell, KK7B, and R. Larkin, W7PUA, *Experimental Methods in RF Design*. Available from your ARRL dealer or the ARRL Bookstore order no 8799. Telephone 860-594-0355, or toll-free in the US 888-277-5289; **www.arrl.org/shop/**; **pubsales@arrl.org**.

distortion in the oscillator and buffer waveforms that indicate the presence of harmonics. That's okay, as our output stage will add even more before we filter them out! Our amplifiers and oscillators are designed to operate in *class A*, in which collector current flows during the entire signal cycle. (*Class B* circuits have current flow during one-half of the signal cycle and, if designed so that each of two transistors are conducting in alternate half cycles, is called a *push-pull* amplifier.) Class A amplifiers have relatively low gain and power efficiency.

The *class C* amplifier is designed to act as a high gain switch. In this case, a small input signal turns the transistor completely and rapidly on and off. This minimizes power losses in the transistor because $P_{DISS} = I_C \times V_{CE}$ and either I_C or V_{CE} are nearly zero most of the time! The transistor current flows only during a fraction of the signal cycle — about 20-30% or even less. While this is very efficient and can generate a lot of power, it also distorts the signal dramatically, turning it into a series of pulses! Class C amplifiers can only be used if linear reproduction of the input signal is not required, such as for CW and FM modes.

To generate an effective signal on the air, we need to beef up the output of our oscillator and buffer, around 30 mW or +15 dBm, by at least a factor 10, to ⅓ W or so. Many low power (QRP) contacts can be made with a transmitted signal of this level. If you live in Chicago and can make a QSO with Kansas City or New York, you just qualified for the QRP 1000 Miles-Per-Watt award (**www. qrparci.org**)! We'll use a third 2N3904 transistor for the job because of its 300 MHz gain-bandwidth product and 625 mW power dissipation rating.

Figure 3 shows the circuit of our output amplifier, taken from the same source as the crystal oscillator. No bias resistors are needed because the input signal will turn the transistor on only during peaks. The input signal is taken from the secondary of the buffer amplifier transformer. Remove the 47 Ω resistor at the buffer output.

Because the 2N3904 gain is substantial at VHF frequencies, the amplifier might oscillate due to circuit layout. The 10 Ω emitter resistor and 100 Ω base resistor reduce circuit gain enough to prevent oscillation in most cases. If you are using an oscilloscope and the output waveform is stable but "fuzzy" and clears up when a finger is touched to the transistor base, that's an indication your amplifier has a high-frequency oscillation. Add a few pF of capacitance (such as a gimmick capacitor from experiment #44) from the base to ground, spoiling the gain at high frequencies.

Power gain for the class C amplifier is $(V_{CC} - V_E)^2 / (2 \times P_{IN} \times R_L)$. For a gain of 10 and assuming about 1 V across the emitter resistor, we can solve for $R_L = 11^2 / (2 \times 0.03 \times 10) \approx 200 \, \Omega$. Instead of a collector resistor, the RF choke supplies dc power to the transistor, and the RF output circuit is the ac load. (The RF choke has an impedance of about 1000 Ω at 7 MHz and can be ignored.)

Impedance Match and Filtering

Before we can put this transmitter on the air, there are two more functions that must be performed. First, the class C amplifier's output is harmonic-rich and these unwanted signals must be filtered out. Second, the 50 Ω impedance of most antenna systems must be transformed up to the 200 Ω our circuit needs. The L network shown in the Figure 3 does both jobs because the series L and parallel C act as low-pass filters.

Equations for the L network component values can be found in the Hands-On Radio Web site FAQ for experiment #21. The equations for calculating the inductance of toroids are found in section 7 of *The ARRL Handbook* or online at the toroid manufacturer's Web site.

At this low power level, a simple toggle switch can be used as the transmit-receive (TR) switch between the receiver input and transmitter output. If the signal from the transmitter remains uncomfortably strong, either use a regular coax switch for more isolation or use a DPDT switch that shorts the receiver input to ground when the antenna is connected to the transmitter.

You can key the entire transmitter by turning power on and off. If your signal is a little "chirpy" (changes frequency as the oscillator starts up), you can try leaving the oscillator running all the time and only keying power to the amplifier stages. This will leave a very low-power residual signal or *backwave* to leak out through the unpowered amplifier transistors.

You should also check your harmonic levels to be sure they meet the FCC requirement that harmonic levels be at least 43 dB below the fundamental signal. Estimate harmonic levels by listening to them on a receiver and comparing signal levels with the fundamental. Assuming 5 dB per S-unit (a conservative average for signal levels above S3) and an S9+20 dB fundamental, all harmonics should be S4 or less.

Should you decide more harmonic attenuation is required, place the transmitter in a shielded enclosure. There are also many sources of 50 Ω low pass filter designs online and in handbooks. Experiment #22 describes quarter-wave shorted stubs that would pass the 40 meter signal and knock down the even harmonics. Along with the L-network's low-pass characteristics, those options should do the job.

Shopping List

- Capacitors, ceramic: 2 each 0.01 µF, 100 V.
- Capacitors, NPO: ceramic or silver-mica, 200 pF, 2 each 390 pF.
- Crystal: 40 meter CW segment. HC-8 or HC-16 style recommended, with socket.
- Inductor L1 in Figure 3: T50-6 toroid core and 24 inches of 24 to 28 gauge solid, enameled wire.
- Resistors, ¼ W: 2 each 10 Ω, 100 Ω, 2 each 10 kΩ.
- RF choke: 22 µH.
- Transistor: 2 each 2N3904.

Recommended Reading

From the numerous references to previous experiments you can see how we are building up a storehouse of circuitry from which to understand schematics or "roll your own"! I suggest re-reading the referenced experiments to have a complete understanding of your new transmitter.

Next Month

We've dabbled a bit with toroidal inductor and transformers so next month's column will cover a few of the uses of these useful components. Don't get all wound up about it!

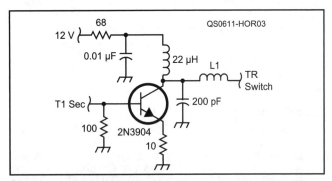

Figure 3 — The output amplifier circuit for the transmitter is operated as class C for maximum gain and efficiency as the transistor is switched on for just a fraction of each cycle. The resulting harmonics are filtered out by the impedance matching L network.

Transmission Lines & Impedance Matching

Experiment #21: The L-Network

This month's experiment moves away from the world of transistors and ICs to visit one of radio's most fundamental designs, the L-network. This building block is the foundation of numerous common impedance matching circuits; the Pi-network—found in amplifiers and the T-network—popular in transmatches. Are its inner workings the black magic of mystical RF designers? Hardly. Read on and find out for yourself!

Terms to Learn

Equivalent series (parallel) circuits—a circuit whose series (parallel) components provide the same impedance at its terminals as the original circuit.

Transformation ratio—the ratio between the input and output impedances of a matching network.

Background

Although radio designers have long used 50 Ω as the standard "system impedance" for antennas and equipment, it seems that hardly any circuits offer 50 Ω impedances without coaxing. Many antennas have a natural impedance far from 50 Ω. What's a ham to do? If you look at the impedance matching equipment and circuits, nearly all have the L-network as part of their pedigree.

The L-network is based on a technique known as *series-parallel transformations*. For any series combination of resistance, R_S, and reactance, X_S, there is a parallel combination of R_P and X_P that looks exactly the same to the voltage applied across the series combination. The same can be said in reverse.

Converting from the series form to the parallel form is governed by the following set of simple equations:

$$Q = X_S/R_S = R_P/X_P = \sqrt{(R_P/R_S) - 1} \qquad [1]$$

$$R_P = R_S (Q^2 + 1) \text{ and } R_S = R_P / (Q^2 + 1) \qquad [2]$$

$$X_S = QR_S \text{ and } X_P = R_P / Q \qquad [3]$$

Depending on which of the variables Q, X_S, R_S, X_S, and R_P that you know, you can solve for the rest. R_P must be greater than R_S. Note that the larger the *transformation ratio* between R_P and R_S, the larger Q becomes. As Q becomes larger, the values of X_S and X_P become more extreme.

The general process of designing an L-network takes four steps:

1) Assign the larger impedance to be transformed to R_P.
2) Determine Q and calculate X_P. X_P is a physical component in parallel with R_P.
3) R_S is already known, so calculate X_S to determine the series equivalent circuit.
4) Add a physical component with $-X_S$ in series with the parallel combination of R_P and X_P.

The orientation of the network—whether the parallel component is at the input or output—depends on whether the input or output impedance is greater. Remember that since reactance is frequency dependent, the L-network will match the two impedances only at one frequency.

The "big trick" is to realize that you can treat a circuit as its electrical equivalent with no change in the electrical outcome. After X_P has been added in parallel with R_P, the impedance of the combination has the correct resistive component, but also has reactance that must be cancelled. It is much easier to figure out what the necessary canceling reactance is if the parallel combination is treated as its series equivalent. The canceling reactance is just equal and opposite the equivalent series reactance.

This is much easier to understand as an example. Let's transform the 50 Ω resistive impedance of matched coaxial cable so that it looks like 10 Ω of resistance to match the collector impedance of a transistor amplifier as shown in Figure 1. Assign the coax impedance to R_P and the collector impedance to R_S. From equation 1, $Q = \sqrt{(50/10) - 1} = 2$ and from equation 3, $X_P = 50/2 = 25$ Ω. Now use Eq [3] to find $X_S = 2 \times 10 = 20$ Ω.

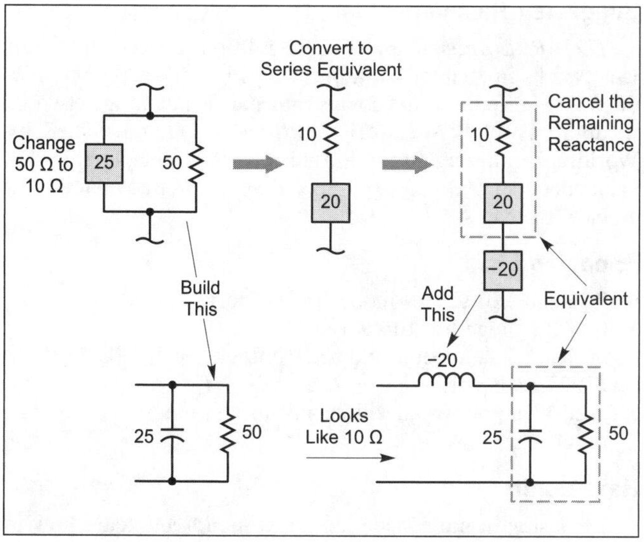

Figure 1—The step-by-step process of designing an L-network by using parallel-series transformations and equivalent circuits.

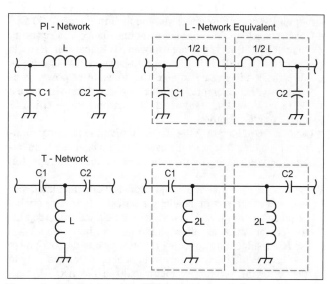

Figure 2—The T-network and Pi-network are easier to understand as a pair of back-to-back L-networks.

Since we want just the 10 Ω of resistance, we must cancel the remaining reactance by adding 20 Ω of the opposite type of reactance in series. This leaves us with only the effective resistance of 10 Ω.

We never did say whether the parallel reactance was inductive or capacitive. The problem is solved either way. However, depending on frequency, the reactance values may be more practical as inductance or capacitance. If the frequency is 28 MHz, for example, the parallel reactance could be either a 0.14 µH inductor or a 227 pF capacitor. Clearly, the capacitor would be a more practical choice to connect between an amplifier output and ground. Thus, the canceling inductance would be 0.32 µH.

What if we were matching the "other" way, from 50 Ω to a higher impedance? In that case, R_P is assigned to the higher impedance and the problem is worked out by the same procedure. The component added in parallel is always next to the higher impedance.

Now that you recognize what the L-network can do, look closely at the Pi and T-networks in Figure 2. Each is just a pair of L-networks back to back. Why are those circuits used rather than just L-networks? The T-network can match a wider range of impedances than an L-network, including impedances that are both higher and lower than the input impedance. The Pi-network uses the two-step transformation of back-to-back networks to provide low-pass filtering for harmonics and to manage the overall Q of the network. Yet both are based on the simple L-network.

Design and Build an L-Network

This experiment assumes that you have an SWR analyzer, such as the MFJ-259, or a similar instrument. You can also use a low power (QRP) transmitter and an SWR bridge. Don't try this with more than a few watts unless you use heavy-duty components that can handle the power level. Use silver-mica, ceramic or air variable capacitors to avoid the parasitic effects of the inductance in other types of capacitors.

Experiment #1

A quarter-wave vertical over a good ground plane has an impedance of about 30 Ω at its resonant frequency. Construct an L-network to match the vertical's impedance (simulated by a 27 Ω resistor) to 50 Ω.

Experiment #2

A loop antenna has an impedance of around 150 Ω. Construct an L-network to match the loop's impedance to 50 Ω.
- Construct a load that simulates the impedance you're trying to match to 50 Ω. If you are using an SWR analyzer, a single resistor will suffice. If you are using a small transmitter, be sure the load is rated to take full transmitter power continuously. For example, 5-150 Ω, 1 W resistors will make a 30 Ω, 5 W load. Use non-inductive carbon composition or metal oxide resistors.
- Using a frequency of 28 MHz, determine the physical component values that have the calculated reactances. Remember that you can start with either a capacitor or an inductor. Use the one easiest to fabricate or obtain.
- Use the closest fixed-value capacitors to your calculated values, add capacitors in parallel (or series), use an air-variable or place an air-variable in parallel with a fixed value capacitor. The air variables allow you to tune for best match.
- Use fixed-value inductors only if you are using the low-power analyzer. Wind the inductors from hookup wire according to the following formula or Figure 6.40 in *The ARRL Handbook* for 1/2 inch or 3/4 inch diameter coils. The on-line calculator at **hawkins.pair.com/radiocalcs.shtml** is also useful.

Figure 3—An SO-239 acts as a good prototyping platform for working with L-networks. An RF analyzer is shown and is convenient, although a low power transmitter and an SWR bridge will work.

$$N = \sqrt{L(18\,d + 40\,l)}\,/\,d \qquad [4]$$

An SO-239 connector makes a good prototyping board for this experiment. Your regular prototype plug-in board won't work well at this frequency.

Follow the four-step procedure presented earlier to calculate your component values. Start by connecting your load resistor directly across the SO-239 to confirm that it is really presenting the expected load to the analyzer: an SWR of 1.7:1 for the 27 Ω load and 3:1 for the 150 Ω load. As shown in Figure 3, connect the SO-239 directly at the analyzer or bridge to avoid the effects of a transmission line on the impedance. Add the L-network between the load and the analyzer.

If you used an adjustable capacitor, tweak the network for optimum SWR. For a perfect match, the resistance will be 50 Ω and the reactance will be 0 Ω. You can stretch (raise) or compress (lower) the coil inductance for the same effect. I had to stretch my coil by about 10 percent. If you don't get a match and you are sure of your connections, double-check your calculations or try an on-line calculator such as **home.sandiego.edu/~ekim/e194rfs01/jwmatcher/matcher2.html**.

Suggested Reading

The ARRL Antenna Book, 20th Edition, covers the use of L-networks in chapter 25, along with Pi and T-networks. Another good reference that covers impedance matching networks in detail is Walt Maxwell's *Reflections II*, published by Worldradio, although this edition is currently out of print. This is an excellent text that explains transmission line concepts in an easy-to-read style.

Shopping List

- 27 Ω and 150 Ω non-inductive resistors.
- 20 or 22 gauge hookup wire.
- An SO-239 connector and a UHF double-male PL-259/PL-259 adapter.
- Fixed-value or air-variable capacitors in the 50 to 200 pF range.

Next Month

Let's stay in impedance land next month and learn how to make a harmonic filter out of one of those mysterious transmission line stubs. Hang onto that SWR analyzer!

Experiment #22—Stubs

Most hams know about transmission line matching and VSWR, but the mechanics of stubs and using them for filtering is often considered mysterious. Like most mysteries, stubs are not hard to design and use if you know the secret. This month, not only will you learn the secret, but you'll build a useful gadget in the bargain.

Terms to Learn

- *Electrical length*—the length of a transmission line in terms of the wavelength (λ) of the energy traveling through it.
- *Termination*—a load attached to a transmission line.

Background

So what is a stub and how does it work? A stub is just a length of transmission line terminated in a fixed impedance, usually a short or open-circuit, in parallel with another transmission line to create a tuning or canceling effect. The tuning and canceling are the result of interference between the RF energy in the two transmission lines. That was simple, wasn't it? Take a deep breath and read on.

Before proceeding, we'll need to review some fundamentals of transmission lines.

Because energy in a transmission line travels slower than in free space, the *physical* length of the transmission line is always *shorter* than its *electrical* length. For example, if a piece of RG-58 is 1 λ long to energy traveling through it, the physical length of the cable will be about two-thirds as long as the wavelength of the same energy traveling in free space.

Impedances in a transmission line repeat every $^1/_2$ λ along the line. (If terminated in its characteristic impedance, Z_0, however, impedance is the same everywhere along the line.) If I terminate any transmission line with a load whose impedance is 100 Ω at some frequency, f, then every $^1/_2$ electrical wavelength away from that load, the transmission line will again present a 100 Ω impedance. If the line is perfectly lossless, I can't tell how many half wavelengths I am from the load.

Open and short circuits reflect 100% of the energy in a trans-mission line. For an open-circuit, the incoming (or *incident*) and reflected voltages are in phase and add together. The incident and reflected currents are out-of-phase and cancel so that there is zero current at the open-circuit. For a short circuit, voltages cancel and currents add.

Stub design is based on these three key elements.

Figure 1 illustrates how a $^1/_4$ λ open stub (stubs are referred to by their electrical length and terminating impedance) creates an apparent short circuit. Imagine a single packet of RF energy just a few cycles long—a very short CW dit. The energy travels in the line from the transmitter, encountering the junction of the stub and the rest of the line. The energy divides between the line and stub. The wave traveling down the stub is phase shifted by 90° because the stub is an electrical $^1/_4$ λ long. At the open-circuit, all of the energy is reflected with the voltages in phase (no additional phase shift). The reflected wave gets another 90° of phase shift going back along the stub for a total phase shift of 180°. At the junction, the out-of-phase voltages cancel or *null*, creating an apparent short circuit. The quarter-wave open stub presents a short circuit at its free end!

Complete reverse only occurs if the stub is completely lossless and exactly $^1/_4$ λ long. Loss reduces the returning voltage, preventing a complete cancellation. Being off-frequency means that the net phase shift won't be precisely 180°. Nevertheless, the range of frequencies over which most of the voltages cancel is sufficient to be useful across a ham band.

What happens if the stub is shorted, instead of open? At the termination, the wave is reflected with voltage phase shifted 180° instead of zero, making the total phase shift 360° in the stub. The voltages now add back together, as if no stub was connected at all. The quarter-wave shorted stub acts like an open-circuit at its free end.

Longer stubs take advantage of the $^1/_2$ λ repetition of impedance. If the quarter-wave stub is doubled in physical length, to become $^1/_2$ λ long, its terminating impedance repeats at the free end. Leaving the physical length alone and doubling the frequency (halving the wavelength) has exactly the same effect so that the terminating impedance appears again at the free end. A stub any number of $^1/_2$ wavelengths long acts as if it were just $^1/_2$ λ long, although with a little more loss.

Harmonic Filtering

By far the most common application of stub is to act as a filter for transmitter harmonics. The free end of a $^1/_4$ λ shorted stub presents an open-circuit at its *fundamental frequency*, but a short circuit at the second harmonic where it is $^1/_2$ λ long. The free end also presents a short circuit at the fourth, sixth, eighth, and so on, harmonics where it is an integral number of $^1/_2$ wavelengths long. While passing energy at the fundamental frequency untouched, all even harmonics are canceled!

Half-wavelength stubs also filter harmonics, but in a slightly different manner. The free end of a shorted $^1/_2$ λ stub presents an open-circuit at one-half its fundamental frequency because there it is a $^1/_4$ λ stub. The stub acts like a short circuit at the fundamental and all harmonics.

Table 1 lists the filtering effect of $^1/_4$ and $^1/_2$ λ stubs cut for

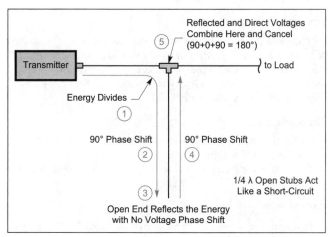

Figure 1—A $^1/_4$ λ stub uses reflections to cancel energy at its free end.

Table 1
Useful ¼ and ½ λ Stubs for Filtering

Stub Type	Passes	Nulls
¼-λ 160-m shorted	160	80,40,20,15,10
¼-λ 80-m shorted	80	40,20,15,10
¼-λ 80-m open	40,20	80
¼-λ 40-m shorted	40,15	20,10
¼-λ 40-m open	20,10	40,15
¼-λ 20-m shorted	20	10
¼-λ 20-m open	10	20

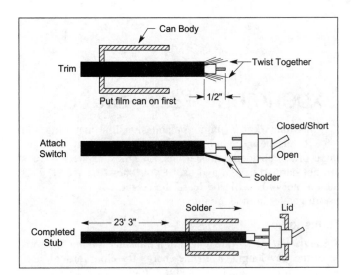

Figure 2—The switched-stub can pass or null energy on 40, 20, 15 and 10 meters.

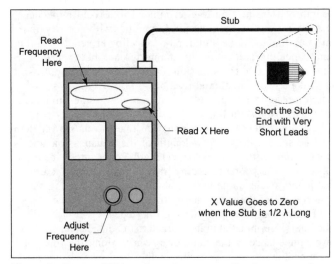

Figure 3—Use an SWR analyzer to measure the frequency at which the stub is ½ λ long.

different ham bands.[1] The possibilities are endless!

The 60, 30, 17 and 12 meter bands are absent from the table because stubs cut to pass or null these bands don't have a similar response in any of the other HF bands. These bands are not *harmonically-related* to other bands.

Design and Build a Multi-Band, Switchable Stub

Taking a look at rows four and five of Table 1, you can see that if a ¼-λ 40-meter stub could be changed from short to open, it would pass or null signals from any of the four highest harmonically related HF bands, 40 through 10 meters. By attaching a switch to the end of an appropriate length of cable, you can do just that, as shown in Figure 2.

Cut 24 feet of coax with a solid polyethylene center insulator, such as RG-58 or RG-213. (You can use foam-insulated coax if you adjust for the different velocity of propagation.) Install a coax connector on one end.

Trim about a half inch of jacket and center insulator from the cable. Twist the shield and center conductor together and attach the stub to your SWR analyzer as shown in Figure 3. Any type analyzer that displays reactance can be used.

Tune for the *lowest* frequency at which the reactance "X" goes to a minimum. Don't watch the SWR value—it will remain high—or the R value. At this frequency the stub is acting like a ½ λ shorted stub, so the frequency should be *twice* the 40 meter design frequency. Measure stubs at a short-circuit frequency because the SWR analyzers give a much sharper and clearer response than for high impedances.

Since you're starting with the stub too long, trim 1 inch at a time and repeat the measurement until the short occurs at twice the desired 40 meter frequency, that is, 14.200 MHz for a 7.100 MHz stub.

When you've reached the desired frequency, replace the short with a toggle switch as shown in Figure 2, cover it with the plastic container and attach the stub to your radio's output with a T connector.

Attach an antenna and listen to signals as you switch the stub from open to shorted on the different bands. You should hear a difference of around 3 S units as you change the stub between "pass" and "null."

Tips on Stubs

I hope you'll try your hand at other types and uses of stubs. If you do, here are some helpful hints:
• Keep the shorting leads *short*!
• Trim open stub shields back from the end of the center insulator by ⅛ inch to prevent arcing from the extra voltage.
• Insulate and waterproof stub ends with shrink wrap or tape to prevent arcing or degrading the cable.
• Use low-loss cable to get the deepest null. RG-213 is good; surplus hardline is even better!

[1]G. Cutsogeorge, *Managing Interstation Interference*, Table 11, International Radio (**www.qth.com/inrad**), 2003.

• Remember that the stub's electrical length must include all adapters, connectors and switches. If possible, trim to length with all such extra items attached.

Suggested Reading

The best book available today on the subject of stubs is W2VJN's *Managing Interstation Interference*[2] with lots of information about all kinds of interesting stubs and applications. The May 2001 *QST* article, "Making a Stub," by Dean Straw, N6BV, may also be helpful.

Shopping List

• Plastic film can or pill bottle
• SPST or SPDT toggle switch
• 25 feet of RG-58 coaxial cable (any solid polyethylene 50 Ω cable will do)

Next Month

It's time for a holiday open house at NØAX's workbench and ham shack! I'll show off my tool box and gadgets to encourage all the Hands-On Radio homebrewers and experimenters. I'd better get started on the clean-up right away!

[2]See Note 1.

Experiment #48 — Baluns

Balun (pronounced *bă-luhn*) is an abbreviation meaning "balanced-to-unbalanced." *Balanced* means *equal and opposite* voltages and current in a signal source, transmission line or load. In addition, a balanced transmission line's conductors are required to be identical, such as in ladder line. *Unbalanced* lines and loads have voltage or current that is higher in one conductor or terminal than the other with one terminal often grounded.

Terms to Learn

- *Balanced load* — a load that presents equal impedances at each terminal.
- *Balanced transmission line* — a symmetric transmission line whose conductors carry equal voltages and currents.
- *Common mode* — currents or voltages that appear equally on all conductors of a transmission line.

Balancing Act

A coaxial transmission line, while balancing voltage and current between the center conductor and inside of the shield, has a third conductor — the outside of the shield — carrying different voltages and currents and so cannot be balanced. At RF, the outside and inside of the shield are effectively separate conductors due to the *skin effect* that causes ac current to flow very near the surface of a conductor. Coaxial feed lines can have completely independent currents flowing on the two surfaces of the shield!

What is a balun, anyway? A balun is an electrical device used to transfer power between balanced and unbalanced loads or lines. Some are wound on cores in the manner of transformers while others are constructed from segments of transmission line. Baluns can be designed to work at a single frequency or over a wide range.

There are two basic types of baluns. *Voltage baluns* force the voltages at their outputs to be equal and out of phase. *Current baluns* force currents at their output terminals to be equal and out of phase. The current balun is the most useful to amateurs because in antenna systems, radiated power is determined by the currents in the antenna and not feed point voltage. In addition, most antennas (even perfectly symmetric ones like dipoles) are not electrically balanced

due to the proximity of other conductors, so equal voltages at the feed point terminals do not guarantee equal currents.

Choke Baluns

Let's begin with a simple design — the *common-mode choke current balun*. This balun connects an unbalanced coaxial feed line to a symmetric, balanced antenna such as a dipole. Figure 1 shows three types of choke baluns: ferrite bead, toroidal and coaxial. (We'll concentrate on baluns that use ferrite cores or beads.) All of them suppress or "choke" common mode RF current flow on the outside of the coax shield by creating an inductance from the outside of the feed line shield. The resulting *common mode impedance* prevents current from flowing along the outside of the shield. The equal and opposite currents inside the feed line are then trans-

Figure 1 — All three of these choke baluns work by forming an inductance from the outside of the coax shield. The resulting reactance blocks RF currents from flowing, while leaving the currents inside the coax unaffected.

ferred *only* to the antenna terminals. Bead baluns are generally the most effective.

By preventing current flow on the outside of the coax shield, currents are forced to be equal in each half of the dipole and the antenna's radiation pattern is not altered by currents radiating from the coax shield. It also reduces RF current on the outside of feed lines that can interfere with other signals and upset power and SWR measurements.

You can make bead baluns by placing ferrite beads over coaxial cable. The outside of the coax shield acts as a "one-turn" winding inside the core while signals inside the coax are not affected. The bead balun in Figure 1 is made from seven Amidon FB-77-1024 beads over RG-213 coaxial cable. Any similar bead made from type 31 or 73 ferrite will work on the HF bands. Use type 43 ferrite for VHF and UHF applications. Wrap the beads with good quality electrical tape (such as Scotch 33), then install the connector or waterproof the exposed conductors.[1]

Stepping Up and Stepping Down

The balun is often combined with a *transmission line impedance transformer*. Although they are often called "baluns," they actually combine the functions of a choke balun and an impedance transformer. (The common-mode choke baluns of Figure 1 are 1:1 baluns, meaning the ratio of input to output impedances is unity.)

Impedance transformers don't change the impedances of whatever is connected to them, but they do convert electrical energy from one ratio of voltage to current (impedance) to another. Impedance ratios of 4:1 and 9:1 are common. For example, a 4:1 impedance transformer has half the current and twice the voltage at the load as it does at the input.

By using a single *bifilar* winding (see Experiment #47), the primary and secondary of the transformer become a transmission line.[2] If the transmission line is then wound

[1]R. D. Straw, N6BV, Editor, *The ARRL Antenna Book*, 20th edition. Chapter 26, Available from your ARRL dealer or the ARRL Bookstore order no 9043. Telephone 860-594-0355, or toll-free in the US 888-277-5289; **www.arrl.org/shop/; pubsales@arrl.org**.

[2]"Hands-On Radio" experiments can be found at **www.arrl.org/tis/info/HTML/Hands-On-Radio**.

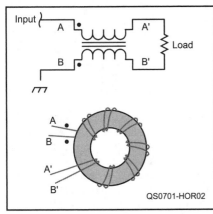

Figure 2 — By making the transformer windings bifilar, a transmission line is created. Winding the transmission line on the toroid core creates the same choking effect as winding a coaxial cable on the core.

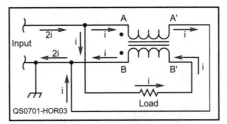

Figure 3 — The common-mode impedance of the transmission line allows ends A-B and A'-B' to be treated independently at RF, while the magnitude and directions of the currents in the two windings must be equal and opposite for a perfectly balanced load. The effect is to cause the input source to see ¼ of the load impedance.

on a toroidal core as shown in Figure 2, it becomes a 1:1 choke balun. The high impedance presented to common mode currents allows us to treat the end labeled A'B' as if it were a separate signal source! Figure 3 shows how to change the 1:1 to a 4:1 balun by connecting the load between the input and output, instead of across the output. (This design is known as a *Ruthroff balun*.) Here's how it works when the load is perfectly balanced.

First, the current *i* at B is equal to and out of phase with the current flowing into A.

The current *i* flowing into B' must be equal to the current at B, so it is equal to the current *i* at A. (Similarly at A' and B.)

The sum of currents from the input signal source is 2*i*, twice what flows in the load.

Since no power is created or lost, the product of voltage and current must be the same in the source and load, meaning the source voltage must be one-half that across the load at twice the current. Thus, the source is presented with one-fourth the impedance of the load.

Having the bifilar winding act as a transmission line is a good thing, but the electrical length of the line (and the various connections) adds a small delay. That delay means that the signal at A'B' is out

of phase a little bit with that at AB. The phase difference also means the currents don't sum exactly and so the impedance the input source sees is not exactly ¼ of the load impedance. The higher the frequency, the longer the line becomes electrically, and the greater the delay and error.

At low frequencies, the common-mode impedance drops to the point where the ends of the line are no longer isolated. These two errors put a definite upper and lower frequency limit on the use of any transmission line transformer.[3]

Building a 4:1 Voltage Balun

This balun can be configured for 1:1 or 4:1 impedance ratios and will handle 1 kW of power from 160 through 10 meters. You'll need an SWR analyzer, such as an MFJ-259, to test the balun or you can experiment with it on the air. (Use low power during tests!)

An FT-240-61 core is selected because type 61 material is designed for use in the HF range, the permeability (μ=125) creates enough reactance, and the 240 size core is large enough to handle the necessary power.

Carefully straighten a pair of 7 foot enameled wires so that there are no kinks or sharp bends. Use small strips of electrical tape to hold the wire together every 2 or 3 inches. Use paper labels to show which wire is A, B, A' and B'.

Wind the balun as shown in Figure 2, spreading the windings evenly around the core and secure the ends of the winding with electrical tape.

Create the 4:1 configuration by connecting an SO-239 connector center conductor to wire A and the shell to B. Connect wire A' to

the shell and leave wire B' unconnected.

Connect the analyzer to the SO-239. Solder a 220 Ω resistor load between wire B' and wire A. Set the analyzer to 10 MHz and confirm that the SWR is about 1:1. If the analyzer has a resistance meter, it should show slightly more than 50 Ω. Replace the 220 Ω resistor with a 390 Ω resistor. SWR should now be about 2:1 and the resistance value slightly less than 100 Ω. Experiment with different resistor values to confirm the 4:1 impedance transformation.

Change to a 1:1 configuration by disconnecting A' from the shell and removing the resistor load. Attach a 100 Ω resistor between A' and B'. Confirm with the analyzer that the SWR is about 2:1. Experiment with other resistor values to confirm the 1:1 impedance ratio.

Reconfigure the balun for 4:1 using the 220 Ω resistor load. Find the frequencies above and below 10 MHz at which the SWR becomes 1.5:1 (resistance value of 75 Ω). These are the frequencies at which the assumptions of negligible line length and sufficient choking reactance break down. Anywhere in the middle, you can use your balun on the air!

Shopping List

- 100, 220 and 390 Ω resistors.
- Coaxial socket, type SO-239.
- FT240-61 ferrite core and 14 feet of 14 gauge solid, enameled or insulated wire.

The AB-240 balun kit includes the above core and wire. It is available from Universal Radio (**www.universal-radio.com**) or Amidon Associates (**www.amidoncorp.com**).

Recommended Reading

The most detailed books on transmission line transformers in the amateur literature are *Transmission Line Transformers* and *Understanding, Building and Using Baluns and Ununs* both by Jerry Sevick, W2FMI.[4] The article "Baluns: What They Do and How They Do It" is a good introduction at **www.eznec.com/Amateur/Articles/Baluns.pdf**.

Next Month

Let's keep the fifth year of Hands-On Radio rolling with a frequently requested topic — how to *read* a schematic. So many articles assume the reader knows them well, when a tutorial might be just what the doctor ordered!

[3]W. Hayward, W7ZOI, R. Campbell, KK7B, and R. Larkin, W7PUA, *Experimental Methods in RF Design*, p 3.33. Available from your ARRL dealer or the ARRL Bookstore order no 8799. Telephone 860-594-0355, or toll-free in the US 888-277-5289; **www.arrl.org/shop/**; **pubsales@arrl.org**.

[4]J Sevick, W2FMI, *Transmission Line Transformers*, order no TLT-4 and *Building and Using Baluns and Ununs*, order no 8982. Both are available from your ARRL dealer or the ARRL Bookstore. Telephone 860-594-0355, or toll-free in the US 888-277-5289; **www.arrl.org/shop/**; **pubsales@arrl.org**.

Experiment #52 — SWR Meters

Like opinions, everybody seems to have an inexpensive SWR meter or two around the shack. They're like "radio voltmeters," used for all sorts of tests and checks of transmitters, antennas and feed lines. But for a piece of equipment so widely used, few of us really understand its basic operating principles.

Term to Learn

Directional coupler — A circuit or structure that samples power flowing in a transmission line according to direction.

Dissection Class

Theoretical discussions of how the SWR meter works are fine, but observation is where real learning takes place. That's all just code for "Let's take one apart!" I dug into the junk box and found the unfortunate device shown in Figure 1. This is a perfectly fine, but defenseless, SWR meter made for RadioShack and sold by the jillions. You can find them at hamfests for a few dollars.

Opening the unit takes only a second — the back cover comes off with two screws, exposing the RF sensing PC board and the front panel components. The PC board also comes loose with a couple of screws, exposing the traces as shown in Figure 2. The case of the unit is plastic, so a thin metal strip is used to provide the ground connection between the input and output SO-239 connectors. Under that strip are the components that form the RF sensing circuit. This particular model can be used as a field strength meter with a sensing antenna plugged into the jack in the middle of the front panel — you can

Figure 1 — This common style of SWR meter is widely available at low cost. Its circuitry is based on the Monimatch design introduced to amateur radio by W1ICP in 1956.

see the pair of RF detection diodes connected to the FWD/REF switch.

The Monimatch

Let's start at the beginning. In the days when most transmission lines were of open-wire or parallel-conductor construction, SWR wasn't really much of an issue. The lines had low loss and as long as your tuner or transmitter output matching network could handle the impedance, there was no reason for concern. When coaxial cable became popular, however, SWR did begin to matter. Line loss and voltage ratings were suddenly something to worry about!

The first widely used circuit for SWR measurement was the "Micromatch."[1] This circuit worked fine electrically, but required a resistance to be inserted in the line and as a result was somewhat awkward to use. The modern SWR meter is a descendent of the "Monimatch," introduced to amateurs

[1]M. Jones, W1PNX, and C. Sontheimer, "The 'Micromatch,'" *QST*, Apr 1947, pp 15-20.

in 1959 by Lew McCoy, W1ICP.[2]

As it turns out, to compute SWR from forward and reflected power, it's not important to know the actual power values, just their ratio, as shown by the following equation for SWR:

$$SWR = [1 + \sqrt{(P_R/P_F)}] / [1 - \sqrt{(P_R/P_F)}] \quad [Eq \ 1]$$

where P_F is the forward power and P_R the reflected power.

For more information on SWR and feedline behavior, try some of the articles on the Technical Information Service "Transmission Lines/SWR" page, **www.arrl.org/tis/info/reflections.html**.

If voltages representing the two powers are provided, it's straightforward to create a circuit that computes SWR. This is the reason for the CAL (calibration) control on the meter. Start by assuming that full-scale indication on the meter represents a power value of 1. (It doesn't matter what the units are.) The meter is set to FWD (indicating the voltage that represents

[2]L. McCoy, W1ICP, "The Monimatch," *QST*, Oct 1956, pp 11-14.

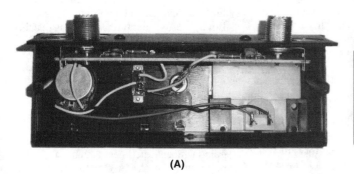
(A)

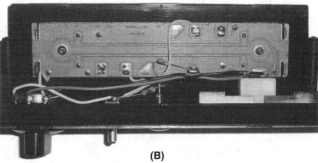
(B)

Figure 2 — Inside the meter, the input and output connectors are mounted directly on the PC board that forms the directional coupler. The layout of the coupler can be seen as the conductor pattern on the PC board at B.

forward power), power is applied, and the CAL control is adjusted so that the forward power indication is the full-scale value of 1. If $P_F = 1$, then Equation 1 simplifies to:

$$SWR = [1 + \sqrt{(P_R)}] / [1 - \sqrt{(P_R)}] \qquad [Eq\ 2]$$

The voltage representing reflected power will always be some fraction of the full-scale voltage, so the meter scale can then be calibrated to read SWR directly, instead of voltage.

The Directional Coupler

The Monimatch circuit of Figure 3 uses inductive and capacitive coupling to create a *directional coupler*. This provides samples of forward and reflected voltage and current from the undisturbed center conductor of the coaxial feed line. The circuit is then calibrated to provide an indication of SWR.

Figure 3 shows how voltages representing reflected power are obtained. Let's let Warren Bruene, W5OLY, tell us how the circuit works in his classic *QST* article from April 1959[3]: "A pickup wire placed parallel to the inner conductor samples the line current by inductive coupling. The voltage e_i induced in the pickup is determined by spacing, length, line current, and frequency. The mechanical dimensions determine the mutual inductance, M. The induced voltage due to line current is:

$$e_i = -j\omega IM = -j\,2\pi f\ell M \qquad [Eq\ 3]$$

where f is frequency in Hz and *j* represents a phase shift of 90°.

"This shows that the higher the frequency, the larger the induced voltage. The sample of line voltage E is picked up by capacitive coupling from the inner conductor to the pickup wire. [This is shown as C_{CPLG} in Figure 3. — Ed.] A current due to this capacitance flows through R and develops a voltage across it; this voltage also increases with frequency because the reactance of the coupling capacitance goes *down* with frequency. That is:

$$e_v = ER/\,X_C = ER\,/-j(1/2\pi fC) = j2\pi fERC \qquad [Eq\ 4]$$

when X_C is much larger than R." D and C form an RF detector that sums e_i and e_v, creating a single voltage proportional to the power in the line.

This is all well and good, but since the line current and voltage contain components of both forward and reflected power, the single resulting output voltage also contains components of both. Happily, we know one more thing that allows us to create the necessary voltages — the voltage components of forward and reflected power created by the induced current, e_i, are 180° out of phase. So e_i *adds* to e_v in the RF detector circuit for forward power and *subtracts* from e_v for reverse power. This creates the two different voltages displayed

[3]W. Bruene, W5OLY (WØTTK), "An Inside Picture of Directional Wattmeters," *QST*, Apr 1959, pp 24-28.

for forward and reverse power.

The different polarities of e_i are obtained by reversing the current sensing pickup. That is why there are two identical pickup circuits in the meter; e_v is the same in both circuits, but the e_i pickup direction is reversed from one to the other. One circuit produces a voltage proportional only to forward power and the other proportional only to reflected power. Display of forward or reflected power is controlled by the switch that selects which voltage is applied to the meter.

Continuing with a note from W5OLY, "Since the current and voltage pickups both increase with frequency, their ratio will stay the same. [The ratio is independent of frequency. — Ed.] The variation in pickup just means that the sensitivity goes down at lower frequencies. This is why the minimum power required to get a full-scale reading is greater on the low-frequency bands." That's why the CAL adjustment is necessary not only at different power levels, but at different frequencies.

The Monimatch directional coupler works no matter where it is installed in the feed line because the forward and reflected voltages and currents have the same amplitude everywhere along the line. (Neglecting feedline loss for the moment.) The standing waves of SWR are created by the varying phase of the components that creates constructive and destructive interference patterns. (Breune's article also contains a good set of diagrams that help understand how this happens.)

For best performance from a Monimatch type of directional coupler, the value of R in one of the detector circuits should be adjusted so that the two circuits produce the same value of e_i for any given current. In addition, balanced detector diodes would also provide better performance at low power levels where the detected voltage level is small enough for variations in the diode forward voltage to introduce significant errors. However, for low-cost equipment, using fixed components is generally "good enough."

The meter scale is calibrated to represent Equation 2 when the calibration adjustment places the voltage representing P_F at full-scale.

Figure 6 of Breune's article shows a graph that describes Equation 1. If you place the edge of a piece of paper perpendicularly across the SWR lines and make a tick mark at each, you'll recognize the scale of the garden variety SWR meter. The meter scale is also modified to account for variations from the non-linearities of the detector diodes at low power levels.

What happens if a 100 W rated SWR meter gets connected to the output of a 1000 W transmitter? Well, *poof*, and you learn what a burnt resistor smells like! Usually, the current sensing resistor and one of the detector diodes are blown. Use the undamaged components to determine the value or part number of a destroyed component.

As you know now, the internal circuitry is very simple. Should you try to repair it? Of course, remembering that if there are no calibration adjustments, the manufacturer calibrated the meter assuming very similar component values. Replace both detector diodes with the same type of diode if you want to maintain low power calibration. The type of diode and its forward drop can be determined if you have a voltmeter with a diode-test function that displays the diode's forward voltage. Choose a pair of diodes with forward drop close to that of the remaining undamaged diode.

Recommended Reading

Along with the *QST* articles referenced in the article, an additional article by Gary Bold, ZL1AN, goes further, showing that the SWR meter will work whether inserted in a feed line or connected to a circuit of discrete components or "a pound of butter" as the article says.[4]

Next Month

As long as we're poking around into RF measuring circuits, let's keep the momentum going with an experiment to understand and build an RF peak detector to use in your shack.

[4]G. Bold, ZL1AN, *The Bruene Directional Coupler and Transmission Lines*, Version 1.1, 6 Dec 2006. **www.physics.auckland.ac.nz/ staff/geb/swr.pdf**.

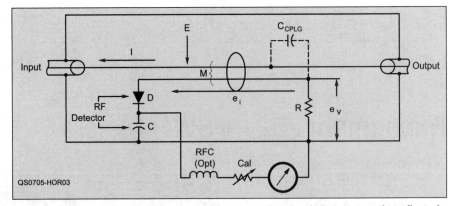

Figure 3 — The half of a Monimatch directional coupler circuit that senses the reflected voltage and current components. The samples of induced voltage e_i and line voltage e_v sum in the RF detector formed by D and C, producing a voltage that drives the meter.

Experiment #57 — Double Stubs

Shorted and open transmission line stubs can be put to work in a lot of useful ways, but sometimes it takes more than a single stub to get the job done. This month, we're going to combine a pair of stubs to get more performance out of the same length of cable.

Terms to Learn

Sub-harmonic — Integer fraction of a fundamental frequency; $f_{FUN}/2$, $f_{FUN}/3$, $f_{FUN}/4$ and so forth.

Velocity factor — Fraction of the speed of light in a vacuum at which electromagnetic waves travel in a transmission line

Stub Basics Review

Start by rereading experiment #22 from November 2004 *QST*.[1] The mechanics of a basic transmission line stub are explained in that article. By choosing the right length for a stub and the type of termination — open or short — fundamentals and harmonics can be nulled or passed at various useful combinations of frequencies.

Table 1 in that first experiment lists useful types of stubs that act as filters on harmonically related amateur bands. Quarter wave ($\lambda/4$) shorted stubs attached to a main feed line pass energy at the fundamental frequency, f_{FUN}, at which the stub is $\lambda/4$ long, nulling even harmonics at which the stub is some integer multiple of $\lambda/2$ long. For example, an 80 meter, shorted $\lambda/4$ stub will null signals on 40, 20, and 10 meters. Attached to the main feed line at the same point, $\lambda/2$ open stubs pass the fundamental (at which they are $\lambda/2$ long) while nulling the first *sub-harmonic*, $f_{FUN}/2$, and its odd harmonics,

[1]All Hands-On Radio columns are available to ARRL members at **www.arrl.org/tis/info/HTML/Hands-On-Radio/**.

$3 \times f_{FUN}/2$, $5 \times f_{FUN}/2$, $7 \times f_{FUN}/2$, etc. A 7 MHz, 40 meter $\lambda/2$ open stub passes 40, 20, and 10 meters while nulling 80. Other nulls of this stub occur at 10.5, 17.5, 24.5 MHz and so forth, frequencies not in amateur bands.

A Resonant Pair

The pair of stubs in Figure 1 are $\lambda/8$ long — a new length that we haven't discussed before. Making an accounting of the phase delay incurred by energy traversing the stub, if the stub is open the total phase delay of the voltage is $45° + 0°$ (at the termination) $+ 45°$ for a total of $90°$. This makes the stub look like a capacitive reactance because the voltage of the returning energy is delayed in phase with respect to the energy in the main feed line. Similarly, the shorted stub has a total phase shift of $45° + 180° + 45° = 270° = -90°$, and it thus looks like an inductive reactance.

The inductive reactance presented by shorted stubs less than $\lambda/4$ long is a function of the coaxial cable's characteristic impedance (Z_0) and the electrical length of the stub in degrees (L_E):

$$X_L = Z_0 \tan (L_E)$$

Similarly, the capacitive reactance of open stubs less than $\lambda/4$ long is:

$$X_C = Z_0 / \tan (L_E).$$

The $\lambda/8$ stub by itself does not work as a filter, but looks like a capacitive or inductive reactance. These can be combined to form resonant circuits. That is precisely what is created by the two $\lambda/8$ stubs connected in parallel and shown in Figure 1 — a paral-

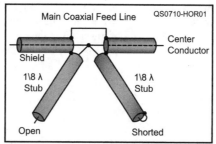

Main Coaxial Feed Line   QS0710-HOR01

Center Conductor

Shield

1\8 λ Stub   1\8 λ Stub

Open   Shorted

Figure 1 — An $\lambda/8$ stub can act like a capacitance or inductance when open or shorted, respectively. A pair of $\lambda/8$ stubs connected in parallel are resonant, just as a parallel LC circuit.

lel resonant circuit! At the fundamental frequency reactance from each stub cancels, just as in an LC tank circuit, so that the combination of stubs looks like an open circuit. Thus, energy at the fundamental frequency passes without any cancellation.

Unlike the capacitor and inductor in an LC circuit, transmission lines change their electrical characteristics as the frequency changes. At $2 \times f_{FUN}$ and at all even harmonics, both stubs are some odd integer multiple of $\lambda/4$ so that one of the stubs acts as a short circuit to cancel the harmonic.

There is an added bonus to this configuration: At $2 \times f_{FUN}$ the $\lambda/8$ shorted stub is a $\lambda/4$ shorted stub and cancels even harmonics of $2 \times f_{FUN}$. (The open stub must be disconnected or switched out.) So from the same length of cable as a $\lambda/4$ stub, you can get the extra filtering behavior for the cost of a switch. Noted filter designer George Cutsogeorge, W2VJN, reports that the double stub even provides a few extra dB of cancellation!

Making a Filter

This configuration is definitely worth building! Compute the length of cable needed to create $\lambda/8$ stubs at 3.55 MHz and cut a pair of stubs that are a few percent long for trimming. A 1 λ stub has a length in feet = VF × 983.6 / f (in MHz), where VF is the *velocity factor* of the cable as shown in Table 1. At 3.55 MHz, for a VF of 0.75 a $\lambda/8$ stub will be 25.97 feet long. One caveat — there can be a fair amount of variation in VF between cables of the same construction. The *ARRL Handbook* shows VF of 0.78 to 0.86 for cables in the RG-8 class. Check the manufacturer's catalog or Web site to get VF for your cable. If you don't know the VF, assume the highest VF to ensure you'll "cut long" and can trim from there. For the cable in the example, I would cut the stub one foot too long and begin trimming.

To trim the stubs, short one end as shown in Figure 2, install a coax connector on the other end, and connect it to your SWR analyzer. Now sweep the frequency while watching the reactance value (X). Find the *lowest* frequency at which X dips to zero (or as low as it will go). This is the frequency at which the stub is $\lambda/2$ long. The stub is $\lambda/8$ long at ¼ of the measured frequency. For example, if you want the stub to be $\lambda/8$ long at

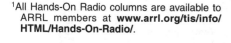

Table 1
Velocity Factor

Cable	VF	Dielectric
RG-58	0.665	Solid polyethylene
RG-58A	0.75	Foamed polyethylene
RG-213	0.665	Solid polyethylene
RG-8X	0.78	Foamed polyethylene
LMR-400	0.85	Foamed polyethylene

Source: *ARRL Handbook*

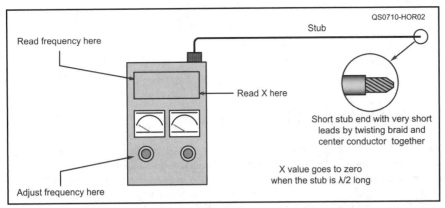

QS0710-HOR02

Stub

Read frequency here

Read X here

Short stub end with very short leads by twisting braid and center conductor together

X value goes to zero when the stub is λ/2 long

Adjust frequency here

Figure 2 — An antenna SWR analyzer, such as the popular MFJ-259/269 series, is used to cut each stub to the proper electrical length. The stub is λ/2 long at the lowest frequency at which reactance (X) approaches zero.

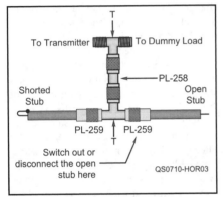

Figure 3 — Connect a pair of λ/8 stubs together using T and barrel adapters. The length of the adapters must be taken into account when trimming the stubs. A switch to disconnect the open stub can be inserted as shown, if needed.

3.55 MHz, the λ/2 frequency should be 4 × 3.55 = 14.2 MHz. Assuming your stub is a little long, trim an inch or two at a time, keeping the short circuit leads, well, short. Twisting the braid and center conductor together will do for determining resonant frequency.

You're not quite done because we still have to include the length of the adapters that connect the stubs to each other and to the main feed line as shown in Figure 3. Start by connecting the stubs together with a T adapter, then add a coax *barrel* (double

female PL-258 adapter, sometimes called a splice) and a second T adapter for the main feed line. Connect one of the remaining open T connector positions to the analyzer with a short coax jumper or a double male UHF adapter.

Checking it Twice

Measure the lowest frequency at which the stubs create a null (where X approaches 0 Ω). This is the second harmonic frequency at which both stubs are λ/4 long and the open stub creates the null. For example, after you add the T connectors you might find the null at 7.050 MHz, meaning the fundamental has shifted down to 3.525 MHz. Trim both stubs at the same time in ½ inch increments until the fundamental frequency is again 3.55 MHz. Solder the short-circuit of the shorted stub. Protect the ends of both stubs by covering them with heat shrink tubing, leaving enough tubing free to fold back over the cable and wrap with electrical tape.

If you plan on switching out the open stub, you'll have to compensate for the length of the switch. Remove the open stub from the T connector and attach it to the analyzer. Find the stub's fundamental frequency as before and write it down. Attach the stub to the coax switch, place a double-female adapter on the switch's common connector and connect the switch to the analyzer. Find the fundamental frequency — it will be lower due to the extra

length of the switch and adapter. Trim the stub until the fundamental frequency with the switch and adapter equals the frequency you recorded. Now you can reconnect the stub-plus-switch-plus-adapter to the T adapter.

Test your stubs by attaching the stub assembly to the feed line from your transmitter to a dummy load. (If you constructed the switchable stub set, the open stub should be switched in.) Transmit on the fundamental frequency you measured before and find its second harmonic on a receiver, noting signal strength in S-units. Repeat the process for the third, fourth, fifth, and sixth harmonics. Now disconnect the pair of stubs from the feed line. Repeat your measurements, comparing the strengths of the harmonics with and without the stubs. You'll find that the stub set nulls the harmonics on 40 and 20 meters, but not on 30 or 15 meters. (You can estimate the depth of the null by assuming each S-unit represents 6 dB.) If you added the coax switch to disconnect the open stub, change the transmitter frequency to 40 meters and confirm that the single stub nulls the harmonic on 20 and 10 meters.

Recommended Reading

As in the first experiment on stubs, I highly recommend W2VJN's *Managing Interstation Interference*.[2] George covers more than just stubs in this useful shack reference. Additional information on stubs is available on K1TTT's excellent Web site at **www. k1ttt.net/technote/techref.html#filters** (click "Filters" in the Topics list).

Next Month

Don't put the analyzer and cutter away quite yet! These two simple pieces of transmission line can do many useful things, but a few combinations of pass and null are off limits to them. One particularly desirable function is to null odd harmonics, such as the harmonic of a 40 meter signal on 15 meters at 21 MHz. Come back next month and find out how.

[2]G. Cutsogeorge, W2VJN, *Managing Interstation Interference*, Table 11, International Radio (**www.qth.com/inrad**).

Experiment #58 — Double Stubs II

Readers of the preceding columns on stubs (Hands-On Radio columns #22 and #57) have learned about the workings of the common quarter ($\lambda/4$) and half wave ($\lambda/2$) versions.[1] We also combined a pair of $\lambda/8$ stubs into a resonant circuit with interesting properties at even harmonics of the fundamental frequency. Thus far, removing odd harmonics seems to be off-limits. Using the dual-stub mechanics employed last month, however, even odd harmonics yield to stub filtering.

The Mystery of the Minus Sign

Before beginning, I apologize for a cut-and-paste error in last month's column. The equation for the impedance of an open stub is $X_C = Z_0 \cot (L_E + 90°)$ or $X_C = -Z_0 / \tan (L_E)$. In reviewing the equations with W2VJN, I developed the following descriptions of how the equations work. You may find them helpful.[2]

A shorted stub presents an increasing positive reactance (inductive) as its length increases from zero to 90°. As it approaches 90°, it also approaches infinite positive reactance (open) and then flips over to infinite negative (capacitive) reactance, gradually reducing to zero reactance at 180° ($\lambda/2$) at which point the cycle begins again. This is the character of the tangent function; positive between 0 and 90°, then negative between 90 and 180°, with a period of 180° ($\lambda/2$), so shorted stub $X = Z_0 \tan (L_E)$.

The open stub presents an infinite negative (capacitive) reactance at zero length, gradually decreasing to zero reactance at 90°. The reactance then becomes positive (inductive) and gradually increases back to infinite reactance (open) at 180° ($\lambda/2$). Thus the behavior of the open stub is $X = - Z_0 \cot (L_E)$; negative between 0 and 90°, then positive between 90 and 180°, with a period of 180° ($\lambda/2$). Note that cot is the cotangent function (cot = 1/tan). The minus sign in the equation for stub reactance is often omitted with the understanding that the reactance is capacitive, X_c.

Students of the Smith chart (**www.arrl.org/tis/info/chart.html**) shown in Figure 1

[1] **www.arrl.org/tis/info/HTML/Hands-On-Radio**
[2] G. Cutsogeorge, W2VJN, *Managing Interstation Interference*, International Radio (**www.qth.com/inrad**), 2003.

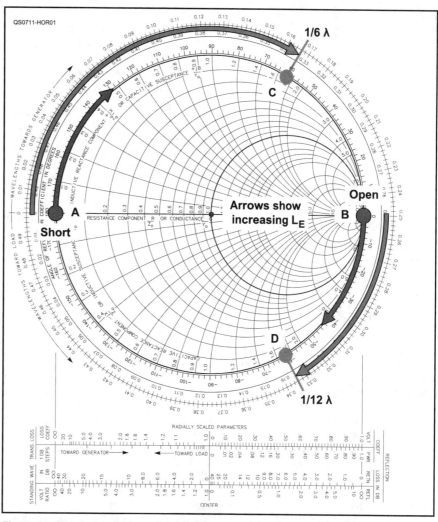

Figure 1 — The Smith chart is a convenient way of describing transmission line behavior. Points A and B and the gray arrows show the changes in impedance of shorted and open stubs as electrical length increases. Points C and D represent the impedance of a $\lambda/6$ shorted stub and a $\lambda/12$ open stub.

can follow the behavior of open and shorted stubs around its outer rim. Beginning from the termination at point A (the shorted stub) or point B (the open stub), increasing the stub's electrical length means its impedance moves clockwise around the chart TOWARDS GENERATOR. A line length of 90° ($\lambda/4$) is represented by moving halfway around the chart, returning to the original point at 180° ($\lambda/2$). Changing the termination from an open to a short also moves the starting point halfway around the chart.

Remember that the equations and the Smith chart are based on electrical length that changes with either physical length or operating frequency. As either increases, so does electrical length.

Thirds, Sixths and Twelfths

Now, on with our story — how to get rid of odd harmonics! For example, that nasty third harmonic of the 40 meter station (7 MHz) is often found to be tearing up the band on 15 meters (21 MHz). A $\lambda/4$ shorted stub can

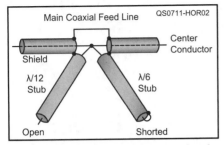

Figure 2 — Connecting a $\lambda/6$ shorted stub and $\lambda/12$ open stub in parallel creates a way to pass a fundamental frequency while nulling its third harmonic.

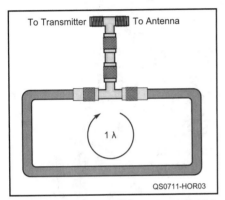

Figure 3 — The odd-looking racetrack stub sends energy on a round trip to create phase delay. This configuration passes even harmonics of the fundamental while nulling the subharmonic f_{FUN} / 2 and its third harmonic.

Table 1
Stub Impedances for Lengths of 50 Ω Z_0 Line

Electrical Length (λ)	Termination	Equation	Z at f_{FUN} (Ω)
1/12	Open	$-jZ_0 \times 1.73$	$-j86.6$
1/12	Shorted	$jZ_0 \times 0.577$	$+j28.9$
1/8	Open	$-jZ_0 \times 1$	$-j50$
1/8	Shorted	$jZ_0 \times 1$	$+j50$
1/6	Open	$-jZ_0 \times 0.577$	$-j28.9$
1/6	Shorted	$jZ_0 \times 1.73$	$+j86.6$
1/4	Open	Short	0
1/4	Shorted	Open	∞
1/2	Open	Open	∞
1/2	Shorted	Short	0

only null even harmonics. $\lambda/2$ open stubs can null a subharmonic (f_{FUN} / 2) and its odd harmonics at $3 \times f_{FUN}$ / 2, $5 \times f_{FUN}$ / 2, etc, but harmonics at $3f_{FUN}$, $5f_{FUN}$, and so forth are tantalizingly out of reach.

As W2VJN points out in his book, one could just cut a $\lambda/4$ shorted stub for 10.5 MHz so that on 21 MHz it becomes a $\lambda/2$ shorted stub, nulling the harmonic. The problem is that the stub is not an open circuit on 7 MHz — it is $\lambda/6$ at 7 MHz and presents a $-j86.6$ Ω impedance that will create an SWR ($Z_0 = 50$ Ω) problem when connected to the transmitter's feed line.

The clue that solves the problem was contained in last month's resonant combination of $\lambda/8$ stubs. A stub with complementary reactance (equal and opposite) at the fundamental frequency (f_{FUN}) cancels the unwanted reactance when connected in parallel with the first stub, creating an open circuit.

To perform the same trick in this case, we'll need a stub that presents $+j86.6$ Ω of impedance. That turns out to be an open stub $\lambda/12$ in length at 7 MHz. When the shorted $\lambda/6$ and open $\lambda/12$ stubs are paralleled, the result is an open circuit at 7 MHz.

At 21 MHz the $\lambda/6$ and $\lambda/12$ stubs become three times as long electrically; $\lambda/2$ and $\lambda/4$, respectively. Figure 2 shows the connection. (If you're following along on the Smith chart, Figure 1 shows the $\lambda/6$ and $\lambda/12$ stub imped-

ances at points C and D, respectively.) The now $\lambda/2$ shorted stub presents a short circuit and so does the now $\lambda/4$ open stub. Both stubs null the 21 MHz harmonic, creating a double null that is extra deep.

Construct this pair of stubs, just as the pair of $\lambda/8$ stubs described in the previous experiment. Use barrel and T connectors to connect the stubs together and then to the main feed line. Remember to account for the lengths of the T connector that joins the two stubs as shown last month.

Measure the attenuation of the stub pair by using a receiver's S-meter to observe harmonic strength on 21 MHz with the stub disconnected. Now connect the stub pair and see what the S-meter reads afterward. Multiply the difference in S-meter readings by 6 dB per S-unit to get the attenuation in dB. (This isn't precise and assumes your S-meter changes the standard 1 S-unit for every 6 dB in signal strength. An oscilloscope, spectrum analyzer or network analyzer will give much more accurate results.) Bring this secret weapon to ARRL Field Day or a multi-operator contest station and you'll be a popular person with the 15 meter crew!

A Racetrack Stub

Here's one of my favorite stubs, just because it looks so odd! Figure 3 shows a 1 λ loop of cable with its ends connected together at a T connector. I can hear you readers exclaiming, "Now, wait a minute!" It looks like an April Fool's prank — but it really works!

By now, you're wise to the knowledge that stubs work because of the relative phases of waves bouncing around inside transmission lines, with the amount of phase difference determined by the line's electrical length. Let's analyze the racetrack stub the same way, beginning with the fundamental frequency, f_{FUN},

at which the loop is 1 λ in circumference.

At the point where the ends of the loop are connected together, energy from the main feed line divides equally. Half of the energy goes clockwise and the other half counterclockwise. At f_{FUN}, the energy undergoes 360° of phase delay and is back in-phase at the junction, so no cancellation takes place. This is also the case at frequencies at which the delay is integer multiples of 360° — all the harmonics of f_{FUN}.

At the subharmonic f_{FUN} / 2, the delay is only 180° so the returning energy is out of phase and cancels energy at that frequency in the main feed line. Wherever the delay is an odd integer multiple of 180° — all odd harmonics of f_{FUN} / 2 — the racetrack stub creates a null. A 14 MHz, 1 λ racetrack stub cancels 7 (f_{FUN} / 2) and 21 MHz (3 × f_{FUN} / 2) signals, while passing 14 and 28 MHz. With the loop cut for f_{FUN} = 7 MHz, 3.5 MHz signals are cancelled, while those at 7, 14, 21 and 28 MHz are passed. Do you have any cable left? Have at it!

Recommended Reading

With your newfound knowledge of stubs, review articles or chapters of books on transmission lines that you may have set aside before. Take a walk through the chapter on transmission lines in *The ARRL Antenna Book* or some of the many articles on transmission lines available through the ARRL's Technical Information Service at **www.arrl.org/tis/info/reflections.html**.[3]

Next Month

All this trigonometry whetted my appetite for a little Smith chart work! Next month we'll unlock a few of the secrets hidden in plain sight among the many circles and arcs that make up one of radio's most useful tools. You might want to prepare by browsing some of the articles at **www.arrl.org/tis/info/chart.html**. We'll put the Smith chart to work on a practical task, too!

[3]R. D. Straw, Editor, *The ARRL Antenna Book*, 21st Edition. Available from your ARRL dealer or the ARRL Bookstore, ARRL order no. 9876. Telephone 860-594-0355, or toll-free in the US 888-277-5289; **www.arrl.org/shop/**; **pubsales@arrl.org**.

Hands-On Radio FAQ

This column makes frequent references to previous columns, all of which are available to ARRL members at **www.arrl.org/tis/info/HTML/Hands-On-Radio**. The Web page is also host to a collection of tools, tips, observations and errata organized by column number.

Experiment #59 — Smith Chart I

The ways and means of transmission lines can be mysterious and hard to understand. Is the venerable Smith Chart a magic talisman of instant knowledge? No, but it is a window on what's happening "inside the line," enabling a better understanding of transmission line mechanics.

Smith Chart Background

QST articles and the Wikipedia Web pages on the Smith Chart (**en.wikipedia.org/wiki/Smith_chart**) are good references with deeper discussions than this column can provide. You can read these articles first or use them as references throughout this column.[1]

Before discussing the chart, let's back up a step. All impedances consist of two *components*, resistance and reactance. Graphically, these components are represented as a pair of axes at right angles, as in Figure 1. The horizontal axis represents resistance — positive to the right of the origin and negative to the left. The vertical axis represents reactance — positive (inductive) above the origin and negative (capacitive) below.

All possible impedances correspond to one point (Z) on that graph based on the values of resistance and reactance. Those two values are the *rectangular coordinates* of the impedance. Hold that thought.

In a transmission line, when a wave of RF voltage and current encounters an impedance different from the characteristic impedance of the transmission line, Z_0, some of the energy in the wave is reflected back along the line. The phase of the voltage and currents making up the *reflected* wave will differ from those in the incoming or *incident* wave depending on the value of the impedance causing the reflection.

The incident and reflected voltage and current waves combine at every point along the line. At each point, the combination results in voltage and current with a phase relationship different from *either* the incident or reflected waves. It is as if the same energy in the line had been applied to an impedance with values of resistance and reactance that

[1]G. Hall, K1PLP, "Smith-Chart Calculations for the Radio Amateur, Part I," *QST*, Jan 1966, pp 22-26, and "Part II," Feb 1966, pp 30-33. Also see D. Walraven, K5DVW, "Understanding SWR by Example," Nov 2006, pp 37-41.

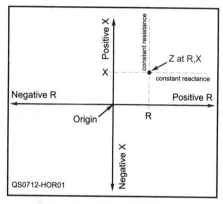

Figure 1 — This graph shows the rectangular coordinates for any impedance against the resistance (R) and reactance (X) axes.

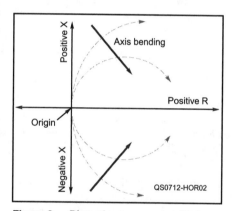

Figure 2 — Distorting or mapping the rectangular graph captures all of its right-hand side impedances inside the circle formed by the bent reactance axes. This is the basis of the Smith Chart.

create the same phase relationship. If you cut the line at that point and replace the section beyond the cut with actual components creating that *equivalent impedance*, there would be no change to the waves in the remaining section of the line.

The voltages and currents of both waves also vary with distance along the line because of the ac nature of the waves. This results in different combinations of incident and reflected voltages and currents and their equivalent impedance. For example, if the equivalent impedance looks like 5 Ω of resistance and +20 Ω of reactance at one point, a bit farther along the line, the equivalent impedance might

be 20 Ω of resistance and –5 Ω of reactance. That means the point on the graph of resistance and reactance also moves around with position in the line, returning to its original combination of voltage and current every half-wavelength ($\lambda/2$).

Smith Chart Construction

What does all this have to do with the Smith Chart? The formulation describing how that impedance point moves around on a graph of rectangular coordinates is defined by

$$Z = Z_0 \left[(Z_L + jZ_0 \times \tan(\beta l)) / (Z_0 + jZ_L \times \tan(\beta l)) \right]$$

The path it describes on the graph does not lend itself to easy use. (βl gives the electrical position along the line.) That path does not lend itself to easy use. What Mr Smith discovered, however, was that if you distort the rectangular graph in a certain way (called a *mapping*), the path becomes a circle!

What is this magic mapping? Imagine yourself standing at the origin of the rectangular graph with the positive resistance axis in front of you and the negative behind. The positive reactance axis starts at your feet and goes straight up and the negative straight down. All of the axes extend to infinity.

Now imagine reaching up over your head and bending the positive reactance axis down in front of you (make your favorite bending noise) in a semicircle whose far end then meets the far end of the positive resistance axis. Do the same for the negative reactance axis, bending it up instead. The negative resistance axis still extends behind you, as straight as ever. This process is sketched in Figure 2.

Step off to the side and view your handiwork. You have created a circle from the two reactance axes bisected by the resistance axis. The infinite points of all three join together at the right of the chart. All of the points that were once in the right-hand side of the rectangular graph are now somewhere inside or on the boundary of that circle. Points on the left-hand side of the rectangular graph are now outside the circle. Nothing has been lost, just squashed or stretched.

The Smith Chart (shown in Figure 3) only contains the circle and what's inside. It ignores everything outside the circle because of the negative resistance value of those points. Originally they were on the left side of the graph. Those impedances can not be present in a transmission line.

The circles and arcs on the Smith Chart show what happens to straight lines on the rectangular graph after remapping. Lines of constant resistance originally vertical and on which all points had the same value of resistance are now nested as *constant resistance circles* that share a common point at the far right of the Smith Chart. That should make sense because all of those straight lines originally went where? To infinity — now the point at the right side of the Smith Chart. Horizontal lines of points having the same reactance are now bent into *constant reactance arcs* with one end on the outer circle (the original vertical reactance axes) and the other end at…yes, that's right…infinity! This distortion results in the path of the impedance point becoming a circle on the Smith Chart as we look at each point along the line.

Making a Circle

You can see how this works by plotting the circle for yourself. You'll need an SWR analyzer that shows both resistance (R) and reactance (X) values. It does not need to show the sign of the reactance.

Cut a piece of 50 Ω transmission line approximately an electrical λ/2 long at 10 MHz. The free-space λ/2 at 10 MHz is 15 meters. If the velocity of propagation of your feed line is 0.66, the length of line needed is 9.9 meters (15 × 0.66).[2] Put a coax connector on one end, short the other end and use your analyzer to find the lowest frequency at which the meter show 0 Ω (or a minimum value) of X. That is the frequency at which the line is electrically λ/2 long. Note this frequency. Replace the short with a 150 Ω resistor. Your SWR meter should now show an SWR of 3:1 and the impedance at the analyzer should be 150 Ω of R and 0 of X. On the rectangular graph, this would be a point on the horizontal resistance axis at 150 Ω.

Print out a copy of the Smith Chart.[3] If you look for the point of 150 Ω of R and 0 of X, you will find it squashed way over in the nest of circles at the right-hand side of the chart — not very easy to use. Mr Smith avoided the problem of big numbers by *normalizing* all of the coordinates to the characteristic impedance of the line, Z0. Normalization replaces the values of all points by their ratio to Z0, in this case dividing them by 50 Ω. So instead of the impedance you just measured being found at 150 on the horizontal axis, it is found at 150/50 = 3.0 instead. Much better! From here on, all of the values you plot on

[2]R. D. Straw, Editor, *The ARRL Antenna Book*, 21st Edition, p 24-20, Fig 23. Available from your ARRL dealer or the ARRL Bookstore, ARRL order no. 9876. Telephone 860-594-0355, or toll-free in the US 888-277-5289; **www.arrl.org/shop/**; **pubsales@arrl.org**.
[3]**www.printfreegraphpaper.com/**.

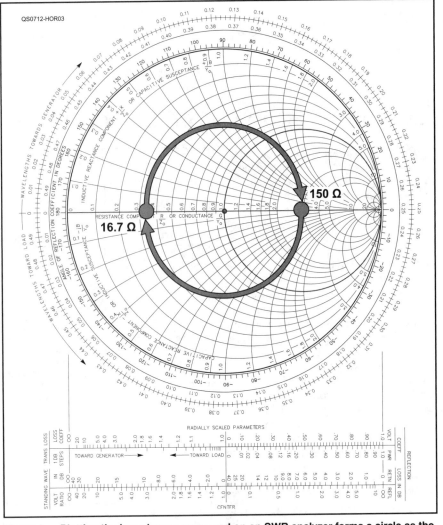

Figure 3 — Plotting the impedances measured on an SWR analyzer forms a circle as the electrical length of a line of fixed length increases with increasing frequency.

the Smith Chart will be the value you read on the meter divided by 50 Ω.

Increase the frequency on the analyzer in 0.5 MHz steps, recording R and X on the Smith Chart. Because the meter may not show the sign of the reactance, assume the reactance values become negative (capacitive) as you increase frequency. Stop when you see the reactance go to zero again, halfway around the Smith Chart at a resistance near 50/3 = 16.7 Ω, plotted as 16.7/50 = 0.33 on the Smith Chart's horizontal axis. This is the frequency at which the line is 3λ/4 long, approximately 13.3 MHz. While you are recording the points, note that the SWR reading does not change.

The points you have plotted should form a semicircle as shown in Figure 3 with its lowest point approximately 0.6 Ω of R and –0.8 Ω of X or an unnormalized impedance of 30 – *j*40 Ω. Continue increasing the frequency until the points return to the horizontal axis near the 3.0 mark at which you started. The line is now 1 λ long and the frequency should be twice what it was when you started. The complete circle of points is called a *constant SWR circle* because all the

points have the same SWR.

If you'd like to see the reason the Smith Chart is so helpful, plot these normalized values on a piece of rectangular graph paper scaled to show 0 to 5 Ω on the horizontal axis and –5 to +5 Ω on the vertical. Egads! Which path would you rather work with? I thought so.

Next Month

This was only the beginning! Next month, we'll explore more of the Smith Chart, so hang on to that analyzer and continue to review the referenced articles and books. I hope the Smith Chart is starting to make a little more sense now!

References

A number of articles on the Smith Chart are listed by the ARRL Technical Information Service's Publication's Search Web page at **www.arrl.org/tis**. Enter "smith chart" in the KEYWORD window. The *ARRL Antenna Book* also discusses the Smith Chart.[4]

[4]See Note 2.

Experiment #60 — Smith Chart Fun #2

Last month's column introduced the Smith Chart and showed how it was constructed. This month, we're going to add more information to the chart in a way that helps design impedance transformation circuits.

Free Admittance!

You now understand how the Smith Chart is created by mapping the usual impedance coordinates from an open-ended rectangular grid into a finite circle. Impedance, however, is not the only way to specify the ratio of voltage and current. Admittance (Y) is the reciprocal of impedance. This reciprocal, $Y = 1/Z$, is just the ratio of current to voltage.

Impedance is sufficient for most problems, but admittance comes in very handy at times. For example, to calculate the combined impedance of three impedances in parallel, $Z_{EQ} = 1 / [1/Z_1 + 1/Z_2 + 1/Z_3]$. If those impedances were first converted to admittances, $Z_{EQ} = 1 / [Y_1 + Y_2 + Y_3]$. Stated another way, $Y_{EQ} = Y_1 + Y_2 + Y_3$. Admittances in parallel add together, just as impedances in series add together.

What's it All About?

Impedance is made up of resistance (R) and reactance (X). Similarly, admittance is made up of conductance (G) and susceptance (B). G and B are the reciprocals of their counterparts in the impedance world; $G = 1/R$ and $jB = -j/X$. Note that $1/j = -j$. Just as the rectangular grid of impedance points can be mapped into the circular Smith Chart, so can the rectangular grid of admittance points. Figure 1 shows the result.

Let's Go to the Charts!

To obtain Figure 1 from a "regular" impedance Smith Chart, first flip the chart horizontally about a vertical line drawn through the center of the chart. That changes all of the constant resistance circles, touching at the right-hand side of the resistance axis (at which $R = \infty$ and $G = 0$), into *constant-conductance circles* that touch at the left-hand side of the axis (where $G = \infty$ and $R = 0$). All of the *constant susceptance* arcs still start on the circle's outer rim, but now meet at the left-hand side of the horizontal axis at $G = \infty$, just as the constant-reactance arcs met at $R = \infty$.

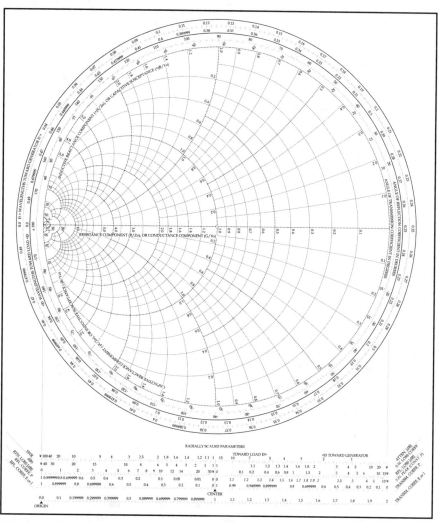

Figure 1 — The admittance-only Smith Chart is inverted from the impedance-only Smith Chart both horizontally and vertically about the center point.

Now, flip the chart vertically about a horizontal line drawn through the center of the chart. This accomplishes the final part of the transformation, adding the effect of the minus sign in the equation $jB = -j/X$. Download an admittance-only Smith Chart from **ece.wpi.edu/~ludwig/EE514/Y_ee3113.pdf** and look carefully at the labels on the outer circle axis near the left-hand side of the chart. You will see that the top label, for example, is INDUCTIVE REACTIVE COMPONENT ($+jX/Z_0$), or CAPACITIVE SUSCEPTANCE ($+jB/Y_0$). Susceptance is normalized, just like

reactance, by dividing it by the characteristic admittance ($Y_0 = 1/Z_0$) of the transmission line. If $Z_0 = 50\ \Omega$, then $Y_0 = 0.02$ S. Note that the symbol for conductance, formerly an inverted omega, is now the letter S for siemens, the unit of admittance.

The Z and Y Smith Chart

Many problems in transmission lines are best worked out using a combination of Z and Y. Some parts of the problem are easiest working with Z, while others are easiest using Y. It would be awfully inconvenient to

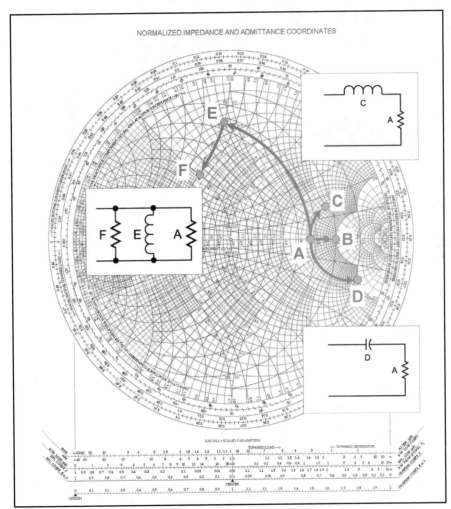

NORMALIZED IMPEDANCE AND ADMITTANCE COORDINATES

Figure 2 — The admittance-impedance version of the Smith Chart has Y-coordinates in red and Z-coordinates in blue so that a transmission line problem can be worked out with whatever set of coordinates work best. Adding components in series and parallel transforms an impedance along circles and arcs representing constant resistance, conductance, reactance and susceptance.

use two separate charts for this, so (hold on to your hat) engineers did the logical thing and printed both sets of coordinates on a single chart. The result would be hopelessly cluttered except that some bright person decided to use two different colors, with the result downloadable at **www.eecircle.com/applets/006/imped_admit_smithchart.pdf**. The admittance coordinates are in blue and the impedance coordinates in red. Print a copy using a color printer, and familiarize your eyes with both sets of coordinates on the chart.

Note that the scales around the outside of the circle and at the bottom of the page are the same for both Z and Y. What single point is the same on both charts? That's right — 1.0 + $j0$ at the very center. That is the only complex number whose reciprocal is the same as the original number!

Smith Chart Chess

The Smith Chart also makes it easy to work out impedance transformation and matching problems by adding impedances and admittances together in series and parallel combina-

tions. Once you know the rules of using it, all sorts of circuit problems can be worked out without any complicated formulas.

The Rules of the Game

There are two simple rules for making the "allowed moves" on the Smith Chart. Rule One — every component is treated as a pure R, L or C. Rule Two — if adding components in series, treat them as impedances and use the red impedance coordinates. When adding components in parallel, treat them as admittances and use the blue admittance coordinates. The result is that you'll be making "moves" on the chart along the arcs and circles, much like a rook in chess has to move along the ranks and files, never diagonally.

Try It to Know It

On the dual-coordinate chart, find the original starting point (point A in Figure 2) for last month's experiment; Z = 150 + $j0$ Ω. Normalized to 50 Ω, that is Z = 3.0 + $j0$ Ω. From here on, we'll work in normalized coordi-

nates and the pre-normalized values will be shown in parentheses where necessary. Add 2.0 Ω (100 Ω) in series with the impedance at Point A. Following Rule Two, this is a series combination, so we'll treat the extra 2.0 Ω as an impedance and add it to the original impedance for an impedance of 5.0 + $j0$ Ω (250 + $j0$ Ω).

This move has to be along a red constant X arc on the chart. Why? Because adding R in series does not change X. Point A lies on the constant X arc representing X = 0 (the horizontal axis), so adding 2.0 Ω of R moves to 5.0 + $j0$ Ω at Point B, also on the X = 0 constant X arc.

Play by the Rules

What if instead of series resistance, we added some series reactance? Rule Two would still apply, but now we would move along a constant-R circle because we're only changing X. Point C is the result of adding +$j2.0$ Ω (100 Ω) of inductive reactance in series with 3.0 Ω. The arrow moves along the constant-R circle labeled "3.0" at the horizontal axis until it encounters the constant-X arc labeled "2.0" at the outer edge of the chart in the inductive reactance (upper) half of the circle. The circuit inset shows the addition of the capacitance (C) to the original impedance (A).

Let's add series capacitance instead. Point D is the result of adding –$j6.0$ Ω of capacitive reactance in series with 3.0 Ω. Once again, the arrow moves along the constant-R circle labeled "3.0," this time in the lower half of the chart, until it encounters the constant-X arc labeled "6.0." The inset circuit shows how the impedances are connected.

What if we add a component in parallel with our original 150 Ω? According to Rule Two, we have to treat both components as admittances, so let's start by converting 3.0 + $j0$ Ω to admittance = 0.33 + $j0$ S…hey, it's the same point!

Let's add a capacitor with $j1.0$ S of capacitive susceptance in parallel to get a combined admittance (remember, they just add together) of 0.33 + $j1.0$ S. Travel along a constant-G circle (because the conductance was not changed) at 0.33 S (between the 0.3 and 0.4 S circles) to the constant-B arc labeled "1.0." This point is shown at E in the figure. Now add 0.67 S of conductance, also in parallel. This moves the point along a constant-B arc to the constant-G circle with a value of 0.33 + 0.67 = 1.0 S. The result is the point F at 1.0 + $j1.0$ S as shown in the inset circuit.

Next Month

You now know the basics of how to plot impedances and admittances on the Smith Chart. Next month, we're going to put that knowledge to work as we revisit Experiment #21 — The L-Network.

Experiment #61 — Smith Chart Fun III

Now that you know the rules of the Smith Chart, why not put it to some real work? This month, we're going to revisit the circuit featured in "Experiment #21 — The L-Network." Being able to see what the L-network is doing on a Smith Chart will definitely make both easier to understand!

Impedance Transformation

Transforming impedances seems mysterious, but it helps me to remember all that's really going on is changing voltage and current relationships. Impedance is, after all, the ratio of voltage to current. No energy is gained or lost in the process, except for any resistive losses.

The Smith Chart is a guide to how those transformations can be made using Ls, and Cs. The process of transformation is described by moving along the various circles and arcs to a point with the desired combination of voltage and current. By assuming only lossless L and C, no energy is lost. Only the relationship between voltage and current is changed.

In most transmission line applications, the goal of impedance transformation is to make the moves needed to get from the load impedance to the center of the chart, where $Z = Z_0$. The moves can be on either the impedance coordinates of the Smith Chart or the admittance coordinates. Typical moves were shown in Figure 3 of last month's column. Note where the last move ended (point F) on the 1.0 S constant-conductance circle that leads to the center of the chart! One more parallel susceptance and the impedance at point A would have been transformed to the system's characteristic impedance, Z_0.

The circuit shown next to point F in that figure is not a very practical one for impedance transformation. The conductance that moves the impedance from point E to point F would dissipate some of the energy. In nearly all cases, only L and C are used to avoid losses. For any impedance on the Smith Chart, there is a combination of one L and one C that will transform it to Z_0 at the chart's center. That combination is the L-network.

The L-Network

If possible, start by downloading Experiment #21 from the Hands-On Radio Web site, **www.arrl.org/tis/info/HTML/Hands-On-**

Radio, and review the L-network's function. The L-network has two components, an inductor and a capacitor, that can be hooked up in four configurations as shown in Figure 1. Referring to the connection of the component closest to the load, they are: series-L, shunt-L, series-C and shunt-C.

Figure 1 also shows the region of the Smith Chart — a surprising appearance of the yin-yang symbol — for which each L-network configuration can achieve the match. This might be confusing. Shouldn't there be *some* combination of values that would allow a single configuration to match any impedance to Z_0? No, and here's why.

Because the L-network is composed only of reactances, all of the moves on the chart must be along constant-R or constant-G circles. Since there are two components, there can only be two moves. Furthermore, the final move that ends at Z_0 has to be along the R = 1.0 Ω or G = 1.0 S circle to reach the center point. (Remember, all impedances and admittances are normalized to Z_0 or Y_0.) The first move, by the component closest to the load, has to move the load impedance point onto one of those two circles. That means the location of the load impedance point determines what kind of component

(L or C) and what type of connection (series or parallel) can do the job. By picking that component, the remainder of the L-network is also determined.

Each type of L-network can match one-half of the possible impedances on the chart, so you have two choices for any given matching problem.

Example #1

Start with the familiar 150 + $j0$ Ω load we began with two experiments ago. It's labeled as point A in Figure 2 and sits on the R = 3.0 Ω and G = 0.33 S circles, shown as black dashed lines on the chart. The goal is to move from that impedance point on the chart to 1.0 + $j0$ Ω at point D. According to the requirements described above, the first move has to be to either the R = 1.0 Ω or G = 1.0 S circle so that a second component can move to the center. In the L-C only L network, moves are restricted further to the constant R or G circles.

There are no moves in impedance coordinates along the R = 3.0 Ω circle that will reach the R = 1.0 Ω or G = 1.0 S circle. That means the first component must be a susceptance in parallel with (shunt) the 150 + $j0$ Ω load and the move will be on the admittance (blue) coordinates — this will be one of the

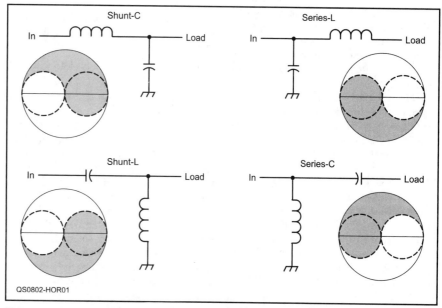

Figure 1 — The four types of L-networks and the regions on the Smith Chart containing impedances they can match.

shunt-type L-networks. There are two moves along the G = 0.33 S circle to get to the R = 1.0 Ω circle at B or C. To get to B, add 0.47 S of Y_C and to C, 0.47 S of Y_L.

Once at B or C, switch to the impedance (red) coordinates. Moving along the R = 1.0 Ω circle to the center is done by adding an equal-and-opposite reactance to cancel the reactive component of the impedance at B or C. The impedance at B is 1.0 + j1.4 Ω, requiring 1.4 Ω of X_C to get to the center point. At C (1.0 − j1.4 Ω), 1.4 Ω of X_L does the same job and the 150 + j0 Ω load is perfectly matched to 50 + j0 Ω! (Note that the reactances or susceptances are not always equal with because the impedance to be matched is not always exactly on the resistance axis.)

This is a single-frequency solution because the components have the necessary reactance or susceptance at only one frequency. If f = 10 MHz, here's how to determine the four component values in the two circuits that will match the load. Start by *denormalizing* the values from the Smith Chart. Multiply X by 50 Ω or Y by 0.02 S. Convert Y to X and calculate C or L from the usual formulas for X. Shunt Y_C and Y_L both have the same magnitude in this particular case, so Y = 0.47 × 0.02 = 0.0094 S = 106.4 Ω. Both series X are also of the same magnitude, X = 1.4 × 50 = 70 Ω.

The components for a shunt-C network (A-B-D on the chart) are:

Shunt C = 1 / (6.28 × 10⁷ × 106.4) = 150 pF
Series L = 70 / (6.28 × 10⁷) = 1.11 µH

And for a shunt-L network (A-C-D):
Shunt L = 106.4 / (6.28 × 10⁷) = 1.69 µH
Series C = 1 / (6.28 × 10⁷ × 70) = 227 pF

These are very close to the calculated values from a double-check using WA7CS' online L-network calculator at **webpages. charter.net/crstrode/calcs/RFcalcs.htm**. Since both of these circuits have reasonable component values, either is suitable for building.

This is how the L-network impedance matching works in general. Make a move to the constant R or G circle on one of the coordinate systems, then flip to the other coordinates and move to the center of the chart.

Build the Network

Now build the L-network by winding a coil and using the closest available fixed capacitor or a variable capacitor. Terminate the network with a 150 Ω resistor and attach the free end to your SWR analyzer. (The online inductance calculator at **www.66pacific. com/calculators/coil_calc.aspx** will help you design your coil.) If you are close, vary the L or C value to observe the effect on matching.

More Examples

Don't stop with just one example! Here's

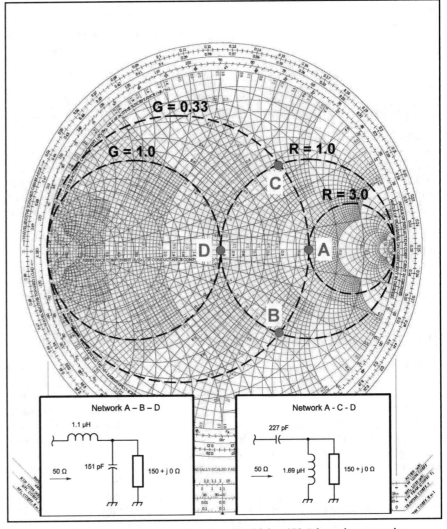

Figure 2 — This example shows the two ways in which a 150 Ω impedance can be matched to 50 Ω using an L-network.

a list of impedances you might encounter when trying to match circuits or feed line impedances:

(100 + j50) Ω, (25 + j0) Ω, (30 + j30) Ω, (200 − j20) Ω

Try to design an L-network to match each of them to 50 Ω.

Print out fresh copies of your Smith Chart and normalize the impedances to 50 Ω by changing (100 + j50) Ω to (2.0 + j1.0) Ω, and so on. Use Figure 1 to select the pair of L-network types that will achieve the match. Then make your moves. Denormalize the resulting values at a frequency of your choosing and double-check using the WA7CS calculator program. (Check your solutions using the WA7CS L network calculator tool.) You can also build the loads by adding the appropriate amount of reactance in series with the specified resistance and test your design. For extra credit, can you figure out where on the Smith Chart an impedance can be matched using an L-network made from two capacitors or two inductors? (The solution is in the recommended reading material.)

Recommended Reading

We've just barely scratched the surface of the Smith Chart and impedance transformation. Along with the references in the previous two experiments, the archives of *High Frequency Electronics* contain an excellent two-part article on matching. Browse to **highfreqelec.summittechmedia.com** and click "Article Archives," then look in the March and April 2006 issue listings for "The Yin-Yang of Matching" by Randy Rhea.

Next Month

We will bid a fond farewell to the Smith Chart (for a while, anyway) and return to topics of interest to the workbench. We'll begin with a discussion of the various resistor types and why their selection matters to successful radio construction projects.

Workshop & Design Techniques

Experiment #18: Frequency Response

When the behavior of a circuit is dependent on frequency—and that's the case with just about any ac circuit—it's important to understand just how that circuit changes with frequency. That behavior description is called the circuit's *frequency response*. In mathematical terms it can be quite complex, but luckily there are some easy-to-understand methods of measuring and displaying frequency response. That's the topic this month and, along the way, we'll review what makes a dB a dB.

Terms to Learn

- *Cutoff or Half-Power Frequency*—the frequency at which a circuit's output is one-half of some specified reference value (usually a maximum value of gain or response).
- *Magnitude Response*—a graph of a circuit's effect on the amplitude of a signal passing from that circuit's input to its output.
- *Phase Response*—a graph of a circuit's effect on the phase shift of a signal passing from that circuit's input to its output.

Background

Technically, frequency response is an equation that describes how a circuit modifies a sine wave signal at any frequency. To most hams and experimenters, frequency response is usually represented as a pair of graphs. One graph, the magnitude response, shows how the circuit affects the signal's amplitude. The other, the phase response, describes the circuit's effect on the signal's phase.

Let's start with the most commonly seen response—magnitude. Figure 1 shows an example: the magnitude response of a band-pass filter. The ratio of output to input amplitude in dB is shown on the Y axis with frequency on the X axis. (If you're not familiar with the decibel, take a detour to the sidebar, Decibels and Ratios.) The curve shows that the input signal is passed to the output with no loss (or 0 dB) between the frequency range of 200 Hz to 5 kHz. Above and below those frequencies the filter removes more and more of the signal until, at 1 Hz, only 1/200th (–23 dB) and, at 500 kHz, only 1/1000th (–30 dB) of the signal remains. At 20 Hz and 20 kHz, we see that the filter passes half of the input signal because the output is 3 dB lower than it is in the *passband*.

Many different types of magnitude measurements can be plotted compared to frequency—voltage, power, brightness, loudness and so on. The object is to show how a quantity or a ratio of quantities varies with frequency.

The phase response (more accurately, phase shift) graph shows how the phase of the circuit's output relates to that of the input for a sine wave signal. Phase is always measured from the input to the output. A negative value, such as –45°, means that the output is lagging the input. Leading phase does not mean that the output signal somehow appears before the input signal. It means only that once the input has been applied for a while, the phase of the output signal is a little ahead of the input.

Figure 2 shows the phase response of a simple low-pass filter. At low frequencies, there is little effect on the phase. As the signal frequency rises, however, there is more and more phase shift until, at the cutoff frequency, there is 45° of lagging phase shift, plotted as a negative number. The phase shift then gradually approaches 90°.

Obtaining a Frequency Response

With computer tools such as spreadsheets, it's easy to do the calculations and make a graph. If you don't have a spreadsheet, then graph paper (use semi-log paper if you can get it,

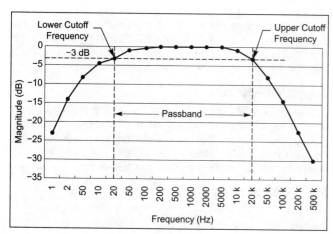

Figure 1—This magnitude response shows the effect of a band-pass circuit on a signal's amplitude as the frequency is varied. The upper and lower cutoff frequencies occur where only ½ of the input power is delivered to the output.

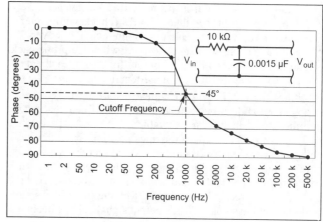

Figure 2—This is the phase response of simple RC low-pass filter. Note that the phase shift at the cutoff frequency is 45°, a trademark of single-pole filters.

Decibels and Ratios

Why use dB? The decibel, or dB, is a mathematically convenient way of "compressing" wide variations in ratio by using logarithms. Since so many electrical phenomena are best viewed as ratios, using dB makes ratio relationships appear as straight lines on graphs.

A ratio between two power levels, P_1 and P_2, is calculated in dB as:

$$dB = 10 \log (P_1/P_2)$$ [Eq 1]

A power ratio of 10:1 is 10 dB, while 1000:1 is 30 dB and 10000 is 40 dB.

To compute dB using voltage (or current) ratios, the constant 10 in equation 1 must be changed to 20. This leads to the mistaken notion that there is "power dB" and "voltage dB"—not true! Where does the "20" come from? Recall that power is equal to V^2/R. Substituting that formula into equation 1 gives:

$$dB = 10 \log [(V_1^2/R) / (V_2^2/R)] = 10 \log [(V_1 / V_2)^2] = 10 \times 2 \log (V_1 / V_2)$$ [Eq 2]

This assumes that the measurement of voltages occurs across the same value of resistance, which is usually the case. You can see that there is only one type of dB. The confusion usually occurs when we are measuring a change in power by a factor of 2, which is always 3 dB. If voltage changes by a factor of 2, that translates to 6 dB and a power ratio of 4. To change power by a factor of 2 requires a voltage change of $\sqrt{2}$ or 1.414. Don't be confused!

Another common ratio rule-of-thumb is the "1-2-5 rule." Have you've ever wondered why meter scales and frequency ranges seem to be calibrated in this sequence? It's because dividing a range this way, for example 1-2-5-10-20-50-100-200-500 Hz, makes the steps in approximately equal ratios which appear equally spaced on a logarithmic axis. This is another way to help ratio relationships appear as easy to grasp straight lines on graphs.

---

with a linear axis for dB or phase and a logarithmic axis for frequency[1] and a pencil will do just fine! A Microsoft *Excel* spreadsheet that you can use to make graphs is available on the Hands-On Radio Web site (**www.arrl.org/tis/info/HTML/ Hands-On-Radio**).

There are some simple rules to follow whether using a spreadsheet or graph paper:

- Measure input and output in the same units, such as volts, and use the same measurement convention, such as RMS or peak-to-peak.
- Measure phase from the input to the output.
- Use 10 × log [ratio] for power and 20 × log [ratio] for voltage or current.

Measure the frequency response of the RC circuit shown in Figure 2. Set your function generator to output a sine wave of several volts. Connect it to V_{in} and monitor it with one oscilloscope channel. Connect the other 'scope channel to V_{out}.

- You can measure the magnitude response with a voltmeter on its ac voltage setting if it will read RMS voltage accurately to frequencies higher than 10 kHz (check your meter's manual). You won't be able to measure phase, however.
- If you have a single channel 'scope, switch the probe back and forth between input and output for each measurement to be sure that the input voltage remains constant.

Follow the 1-2-5 rule for frequency, starting at 1 Hz, measuring input and output voltage and phase. Enter the values into the spreadsheet or make a table.

To measure phase, adjust the trace position so that the zero voltage value of each channel falls directly on the center calibration line of the oscilloscope graticule. Measure the time between the input and output signal zero-crossings. Convert the time to degrees of phase by multiplying by 360f (f is the frequency of the signal). As the output signal voltage becomes smaller, you will have to increase the sensitivity (fewer volts/division) of the display to measure voltage and phase, so use the proper scale for the voltage reading.

[1]Free software for printing graph paper directly to your printer is available at **www.farm.kuleuven.ac.be/pharbio/gpaper.htm**. This will handle many graphing requirements, including log and semi-log plots at up to 6 cycles per axis.—*Ed.*

You will have a magnitude response graph that begins with approximately 0 dB at 1 Hz, reaches the cutoff frequency somewhere near 1 kHz, and steadily declines as frequency increases. The phase response should look a lot like Figure 2.

Swap the resistor and capacitor, with the resistor across the output, forming a high-pass filter. Measure the frequency response of this circuit. The magnitude response will increase with frequency to the very same cutoff frequency, gradually approaching 0 dB. Phase response will start at approximately 90° at 1 Hz, reach 45° at the cutoff frequency, and then gradually drop to 0°. You may find it easier to start at high frequencies and work your way down to 1 Hz.

Advanced Techniques

For actual measurements, you'll want to measure response at more frequencies than are covered by the 1-2-5 rule. For example, to plot a tuned circuit's response, you'll want to measure at several points close to resonance including the cutoff frequencies (where the magnitude is –3 dB exactly), whether or not they are on a 1-2-5 frequency. To use *Excel* for these graphs, use an "X-Y Scatter Plot" chart type and set the X-axis scale to be logarithmic. Enter all frequencies in exact numeric form (not as "200 k," for instance).

Suggested Reading

The 2004 *ARRL Handbook* devotes several pages in Chapter 4 to logarithms and decibel relationships. As an example of how ratio relationships can be plotted as straight lines using logarithmic axes, check out the inductive and capacitive reactance versus frequency graph in Chapter 6.

Shopping List

- 10 kΩ, ¼ W resistor
- 0.0015 µF capacitor, any type

Next Month

Let's get back to the bench next month and learn about a neat circuit—the current source. We'll cover a couple of ways to generate constant current, including one of my favorites, the current mirror.

Experiment #23: Open House in the NØAX Lab

What better way to celebrate the holiday season than with an open house for friends? In the case of Hands-On Radio, it will be "open lab." I'm delighted to wrap up the second year of the column by inviting you to take a look behind the word processor to see where the experiments come from.

The Lab

You may think I must have a big, industrial-sized facility with the latest in technical gadgetry and instrumentation. Not so! While my little shop is fairly well equipped, what makes it play is having the right tools and parts conveniently located. Figure 1 shows that my workbench is "co-located" with my ham shack and office. Having everything within arm's length or a step away has turned out to be a real boon after having had them in separate rooms before.

Even if you have a very small shack, it's a great idea to have a bit of room to do troubleshooting on the spot. You need to have access to antennas and power supplies to really check out the radio equipment. A piece of plywood, fiberboard, or even cardboard, will protect a desktop while you work on the electronics.

Figure 2 shows the equipment layout on the workbench. The bench surface is plywood, which tolerates the various mechanical insults I throw at it. When the plywood gets too grungy, I turn it over or get a new piece. For sensitive electronics work, I unroll a static dissipating mat that stays clean between uses. Heavy-duty tasks get done in the garage where I can really make a mess!

Lighting is very important to being able to work with small parts and dig into equipment. All of the lights are movable—there are two clamp fixtures that can slide horizontally, and one swing-arm lamp that can move in close. I also have some small photoflood bulbs that I can use for photography or when lots of light is needed. A pocket flashlight and a mini-gooseneck lamp illuminate those tight spots. A head-mounted mag-nifier comes in handier with each passing year.

The flooring is linoleum, not carpet. If possible, the floor in your lab should be a smooth surface. Carpeting in a lab environment traps dirt, shavings, metal bits, small parts and solder blobs melt it. If you're stuck with carpet, pick up some of the office rug protectors for rolling chairs and trim them to fit around your workbench. You won't regret it!

The room I use for all three jobs—shack, bench, and office—is just 10×16 feet, so I have to make the most of available space with drawers, shelves and carts. Tools are kept in a rolling set of drawers or in a toolbox. Even the radio equipment is on movable carts or cabinets so that I can easily work in back of the gear.

You can never have too many cables—dc, ac line cords, RF, data—they're all used in today's ham shack. Keeping them straight is another thing. You can see two cable racks in Figure 1, at the left. I also installed a piece of pegboard with long hooks to hold coils of coax and data cables. Avoid throwing your cables in a box. You'll waste a lot of time untangling them and you'll never find the one you want.

My Friends, the Test Instruments

Surveying the workbench shown in Figure 2, you'll see the equipment that I use most often. There are two power supplies; one is a dual 0-20 V dc lab supply and the other a high-current supply designed for powering radios. A Variac is to the left of the supplies—good for testing line-powered equipment.

The function generator and voltmeter are used for almost every experiment and building job. Don't scrimp on a voltmeter. A flexible function generator can substitute for several single-purpose generators and many can be found on the surplus market.

Other favorite instruments include the reliable Bird wattmeter and an assortment of common "slugs" or sensing elements and dummy loads. An MFJ Antenna Analyzer is never far from

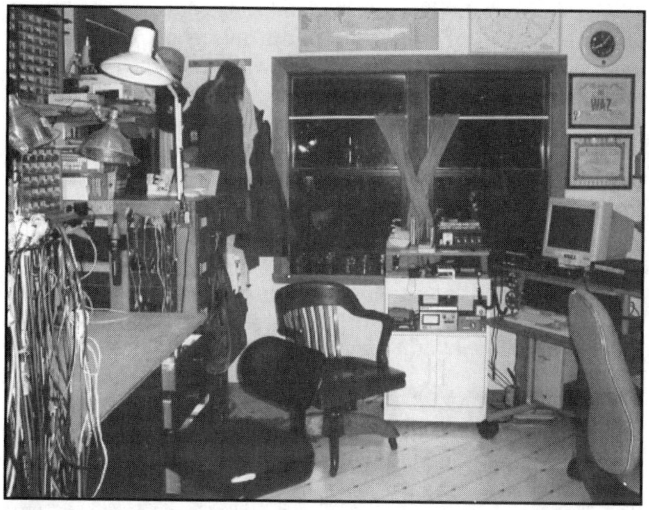

Figure 1—The workbench is surrounded by parts and tools and the shack just a few feet away. Having what I need close by is a big help!

Figure 2—On the bench, you can see the instruments that I use most frequently. Parts bins hold bulk parts and small junk boxes. The oscilloscope is on a rolling cart.

Figure 3—Keeping tools and parts in a toolbox means they're always in the same place and ready to go when you are.

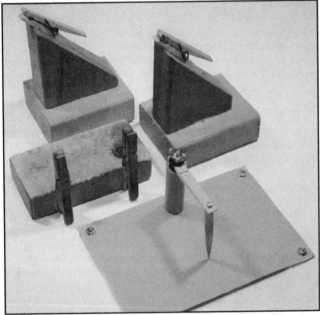

Figure 4—These handy homemade gadgets make working on cables and surface-mount parts a lot easier. Wooden materials won't melt or gouge. And, if charred or damaged, they're easy to replace.

my bench, either. I picked up a small gel-cell battery to run the analyzer; it's paid for itself several times over.

While I've certainly used a lot of oscilloscopes, I'm happy with my 15-year-old Hitachi 4-channel model. With a bandwidth of 100 MHz, it handles everything I'd use a 'scope for in ham radio. Above that frequency, a spectrum analyzer is more likely to do the job. There are lots of scopes like it available as surplus. The Hands-On Radio Web site (**www.arrl.org/tis/info/HTML/Hands-On-Radio/**) has numerous links to sources of test equipment. I found the 'scope cart at a hamfest for $15 where it did double duty as a shopping cart for the day!

The Trusty Toolboxes

My faithful, go-everywhere, hold-everything, toolboxes are shown in Figure 3. I splurged on the pallet case from Jensen (**www.jensentools. com**) years ago and I've never regretted it. The case is big enough to hold a spare voltmeter, soldering gear, spare parts and cables.

The tackle box has turned out to be a great way to store

coax connectors and adapters. It contains everything I need to build or repair cables. All of my adapters are kept sorted and handy. Tackle boxes are inexpensive and great for all sorts of similar uses.

Along with tools and instruments, I find myself keeping a rather large collection of electronic parts and hardware. You can keep them in individual drawers or in cardboard parts bins. I like both, and I keep a few junk boxes going for parts and components, as well.

Buying parts one or two at a time is the most expensive way, so I try to buy extra. Hamfests are a great source of spare parts, too. Sometimes, entire parts cabinets are sold with parts inside. You can keep your lab well stocked by keeping a list of needed stuff in a notebook. When you see a sale or bargain, you'll know exactly what you need.

Gadgets

No shack and lab tour is complete without mentioning a special gadget or two. Figure 4 shows some of my all-time favorites—gadgets that I have used year-in and year-out. Just clothespins and wood? Yes! The three pin-and-block gadgets on the left make working with cables and connectors a lot easier. They hold wires and metal securely without biting into hot plastic. The clothespin jaws are rounded for a firm grip and spring-loaded for easy adjustment. All it takes is wood screws and/or glue to make a set of these.

The odd-looking apparatus in the front is the latest incarnation of my surface-mount "third hand." The printed-circuit board is placed on the cardboard and maneuvered under the point of the dowel (which swivels and can be raised or lowered). The tiny SMT parts are held on the board by the point of the dowel for me to solder. When the cardboard or dowel wear out, I replace them. I encourage you to make a set for yourself and improvise!

Organization and Cost

The best part about my lab (to me) is that I can put my hands on any tool, part, or instrument in seconds. The biggest barrier to accomplishment is the wasting of time or having your train of thought derailed as you go on a "tool hunt" or root around for parts. Keep your workbench reasonably organized and free of junk (well, mostly free) and you will reap benefits in fun and efficiency. There's nothing like getting an idea and being able to sit right down and build it!

You may be totaling costs in your head and thinking: "I can't afford to buy all of that!" Remember, this is my collection of more than 35 years of electronic-ing. My workbench is a work-in-progress—I am continually trading or upgrading. I always buy the highest quality materials I can afford, especially avoiding cheap tools. Start with the basics (**www.arrl.org/tis/info/homebrew.html**) and keep going. The holiday season is the time for big tool sales, as well (hint, hint)!

Thanks for taking part in my open house. I hope it will encourage you to build and repair your own circuits and equipment. I started a long time ago with modest capabilities and improved, step-by-step, with the help of friends and uncounted articles in *QST* and other magazines and books. Good luck!

Shopping List

- Wooden, spring-loaded clothespins
- Scraps of 2×4 wood, thick cardboard and ¼ inch dowel
- Glue, wood screws and machine screws/nuts/washers

Next Month

How do you know if a transistor or an IC needs a heat sink before it fails? How do you choose one properly? We'll take a look at basic thermal analysis in the next installment of Hands-On Radio and meet an old friend, Ohm's Law, in disguise!

Experiment #24: Heat Management

When you're working with electronics, there are lots of instances when you have to deal with heat—usually too much of it. How much is too much? How do you move it around? Let's find out.

Terms to Learn

- *Thermal resistance*—the resistance to heat flow
- *Junction*—the region of the semiconductor in which heat is generated
- *Ambient temperature*—the temperature of the air surrounding a component

Introduction

Everywhere that current flows, heat is dissipated. As you know, for a resistor, the amount that must be dissipated is $P_d = I^2 R$. In general, wherever a voltage drop and current flow exist at the same time, $P_d = V \times I$. Heat is released into the surrounding air through the component's body or via its leads into the supporting circuit board or even to other components. If there is too much heat, the component can change its characteristics or suffer damage. It's up to the circuit designer to "take the heat" and make sure that doesn't happen. To do that, you have to understand a fundamental relationship of heat transfer.

Ohm's Law for Heat

Don't panic—no thermodynamics is involved! If you're comfortable with Ohm's Law, you'll recognize this new equation right away:

$$\Delta T = T_a - T_b = T_{ab} = P \times \theta_{ab} \qquad [1]$$

Temperature drop, ΔT, is equal to the power dissipated, P, times the thermal resistance, θ from point a to point b. If you think this looks a lot like $V = I \times R$, you're right. T can be thought of as a "heat voltage," P as a sort of "heat current," and θ_{ab} as "heat resistance." T is usually specified in °C, P in watts, and θ in °C/W.

The more power that flows through a given thermal resistance, the higher the temperature drop will be. Subscripts "a" and "b" are the two physical locations between which the heat flow occurs. If several different thermal resistances are encountered by the heat flow, then the total thermal resistance is $\theta = \theta1 + \theta2 + \dots + \theta n$, just like resistors in series. Temperatures at each step are calculated just like voltages in a voltage divider. Armed with this equation, we can now take four steps to manage heat. Figure 1 illustrates how this works—just like Ohm's Law.

1. Determine How Much Heat Is Generated

Here is a list of the heat generating equations for common components:

Resistor: $P_d = I^2 \times R = V^2 / R = V \times I$

Diode, SCR, or TRIAC: $P_d = V_f \times I_{avg}$ where V_f is the forward voltage drop and I_{avg} is the average forward current

Transistor: $P_d = V_{CE} \times I_C = V_{GS} \times I_D$

Inductor, Capacitor, Transformer: $P_d = I^2 \times R_{LOSS}$

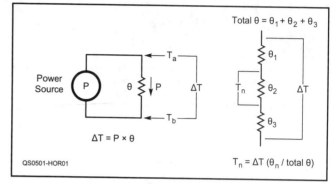

Figure 1—The basics of managing heat are very similar to using Ohm's Law for resistors.

If the current is ac, use rms values. For either dc or ac currents that are intermittent, multiply P_d by the duty factor of the current. For example, if a resistor only carries current in pulses that are on three-quarters of the time, multiply P_d by 0.75.

When you are using an IC, sum up all of the power dissipation from each significant source of heat. These are usually the IC's outputs. Include the power dissipated inside the IC by multiplying the power supply voltage times the current drawn by the IC.

2. Determine Maximum Power or Temperature

"Bulk" components, such as resistors and capacitors, generate heat mostly throughout or along their bodies. Some maximum continuous power dissipation, P_d max, is specified, such as for a $1/2$ W resistor. An ambient temperature is also specified for P_d max, because that determines the temperature at one end of the component's thermal resistance.

Semiconductors, on the other hand, generate heat in the very small volume of the material that conducts current. This small source of heat is generally referred to as the *junction*. For semiconductors, thermal resistance is specified between the heat-generating junction and the surrounding, or ambient conditions, as θ_{ja}. This is sometimes referred to as the *free-air thermal resistance*.

If the semiconductor is intended to be used with a heat sink, θ_{jc} is specified as the thermal resistance from the junction to the case of the transistor, which might be a metal tab or just the external plastic surface. The total thermal resistance, θ_{ja}, then becomes the sum of θ_{jc} and whatever thermal resistance exists from the case to ambient conditions, θ_{ca}.

The internal structure of semiconductors must be kept below some maximum temperature, T_{jmax}, or it will be destroyed. For devices made from silicon, this is usually 150°C. For a given amount of power dissipation, the junction temperature will be:

$$T_j = T_{ambient} + (P \times q_{ja}) \qquad [2]$$

If you calculate T_j and find it to be less than T_{jmax}, then you

Figure 2—Several heat sink styles are shown with different thermal resistances from 15 to 55°C/W. Insulated mounting hardware for TO-220 packages is at the lower right.

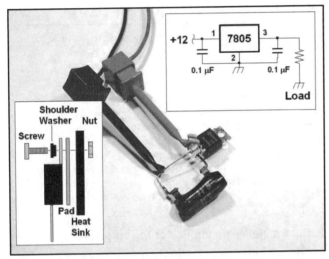

Figure 3—Using a heat sink with a 7805 voltage regulator circuit. The sink dissipates the power generated from dropping the input voltage.

can stop there. You have to be careful when assuming an ambient temperature—in an enclosure, actual ambient temperature may be quite a bit higher than room temperature. You also need to include a safety factor when deciding on what an acceptable junction temperature will be—25% or 35°C is reasonable.

If you find T_j to be on the high side, you must reduce either P or θ_{ja}. Reducing P depends on the application of the component. Reducing θ_{ja} means helping the component pass heat more effectively through its outer surface, since θ_{jc}, the thermal resistance from the junction to the outer surface, is fixed.

3. Selecting a Method To Get Rid of the Heat

There are two common methods of removing excess heat from a component. The first is to cool it by moving enough air across the component to keep $T_{ambient}$ as low as possible. This will work for relatively low power dissipations of up to a watt or so with small components.

To remove higher amounts of heat, a heat sink is required to lower θ_{ca}. A heat sink can be anything sufficiently massive and thermally conductive to conduct heat away from the component so that it can be dissipated. For example, the metal enclosure of many handheld radios acts as the heat sink for the output amplifier, getting rather warm during prolonged transmissions.

4. Select An Appropriate Heat Sink

Heat sinks, like those shown in Figure 2, are specified by their thermal resistance, in °C/W. The rating tells you how much the surface temperature of the case and heat sink will rise per watt of heat. This is generally a natural convection figure, assuming that the only air movement is caused by warm air rising. Larger heat sinks for high power will have different values of θ_{ca} given for various amounts of airflow.

To select a heat sink, you need to know (or select) a maximum body or junction temperature. Calculate the amount of power the component must dissipate. Estimate the ambient temperature. Remember that θ_{jc} is fixed, so you calculate the maximum case temperature. The required thermal resistance is:

$$\theta_{ca} = (T_c \max - T_{ambient}) / P$$
where $T_c \max = T_j \max - (P \times \theta_{jc})$ [3]

Select a heat sink with this thermal resistance or less.

An Example of Heat Management

Three-terminal voltage regulators used in power supplies often require heat sinking. One of the most common applications is dropping a 12 V dc input voltage to 5 V dc with a 7805 for use with digital logic. (You can find the 7805 data sheet at **www.ee.washington.edu/stores/**.) This circuit is shown in Figure 3. Construct it by tacking the components together, since the current levels will be a little high for a solderless breadboard.

To test this circuit, you'll need a beefy load that can draw up to 1 A. A 5 Ω, 5 W resistor can either be purchased or constructed from a combination of resistors. It will get warm!

- Start with a light load of 100 Ω. The total power dissipated in the load is $V^2/R = 25/100 = \frac{1}{4}$ W. The regulator dissipation will be equal to the voltage across it (12 V–5 V) times the current through it, $P_d = 7 \times 0.1 = 0.7$ W.
- If you have a thermometer or temperature measuring probe, take a temperature reading of the case, Tc. Calculate the junction temperature of the regulator by using the data sheet's value for θ_{ja}: $T_j = 0.7$ W × 5°C/W+Tc.
- Now attach the big load and turn on the power. The case of the regulator will get *quite* hot so don't touch it. The regulator has to get rid of 7 V × 1 A = 7 W! Calculate T_j for P_d=7W. The regulator will quickly enter thermal shutdown cutting off output current at high temperatures.
- Attach the heat sink as shown in Figure 3. Turn on the power once again and check temperature again. Cooler, isn't it? If you can measure temperature, calculate T_j.
- Experiment with different types of heat sinks, scraps of PC board material or metal, or a metal enclosure.

Shopping List

- 7805 voltage regulator (RadioShack 276-1770)
- TO-220 heat sink (RadioShack 276-1363) and mounting hardware (RadioShack 276-1373)
- Two 0.1 µF, 25 V capacitors
- 100 Ω, $\frac{1}{4}$ W and 5 Ω, 5 W resistor (or equivalent)

Suggested Reading

The ARRL Handbook contains a very good discussion of heat sinking and sink selection. Aavid-Thermalloy also has a short tutorial on picking heat sinks at **www.aavidthermalloy.com/technical/papers/semisize.shtml**.

Next Month

Generating nearly every digital signal is the job of a circuit gem called a totem-pole output. Seeing as they're so common, wouldn't it be nice to learn how they work? You'll get a neat circuit to use for projects around the shack, too!

Experiment #27: Scope Tricks

Once you've learned how to use the basic functions of an oscilloscope, do you get the feeling that there's much more lurking behind that front panel? This month we'll uncover a trio of tricks for your 'scope toolbox.

Terms to Learn

- Graticule—the grid of horizontal and vertical lines that serve as reference marks on the 'scope display.
- Time base—the circuit that controls the horizontal movement of the 'scope trace with time.
- Trace—the illuminated path followed by the electron beam across the 'scope display.

Introduction

If you've been doing the experiments in this column with the aid of a 'scope, you've used the basic functions to display signals from two separate channels. There are many useful ways to put the 'scope's power to work. Each scope is slightly different and yours may not have all of these features. Even so, learning about them will help you understand your 'scope even better or shop for one more knowledgeably. Start by finding your 'scope's operating manual. It will show you how to set the controls for each of the functions you're about to use.

X-Y Display

There's no reason why the horizontal position of the electron beam has to represent time. The X-Y mode uses the signal from one of the vertical input channels to control the horizontal position of the trace. Look for an XY or X-Y setting or switch in the time base section of the 'scope front panel and turn X-Y mode ON.

In X-Y mode, one of the vertical input channels (usually channel 1 or A) is connected to the horizontal deflection circuit instead of the usual timing signal. This becomes the X input and its sensitivity and position settings now control horizontal movement. The horizontal axis is calibrated in volts/division, just like the vertical channel. With no input to either channel, set the beam position to the very center of the

display graticule using the channel position controls.

Connect your 1 kHz, 1V sine wave to both the X and Y channels. Set both channels to a sensitivity of 0.5 V/div. You will see a diagonal line from lower left to upper right as the signal's voltage moves the beam back and forth. Reduce the frequency to 1 Hz to see the beam moving. Return to 1 kHz and change to a square wave. You'll see a pair of dots, one in the upper right and one in the lower left. These represent the two voltages present in the square wave with a fainter line between them. Return to a low frequency and use different waveforms, imagining how they look as voltages against time. (It's easy to switch back to the usual display.)

X-Y mode can be used for measuring phase. Figure 1 shows how to calculate phase shift between two sine waves of the same frequency by measuring the deviation from a straight line as the two signals push the electron beam around. Build the R-C circuit and use 'scope probes to connect the circuit input to the X channel and the output to the Y channel.

You'll see an ellipse instead of a straight line because the output signal is not an exact replica of the input. It's delayed a few microseconds by the R-C circuit and somewhat lower in amplitude. Measure the "height" of the ellipse on the vertical axis as shown in the figure. Center the ellipse on the horizontal axis. Measure both the outside height and where the ellipse crosses the center scale. Convert these measurements to a phase difference with this equation:

Phase shift = arcsin (B/A) = arcsin (1.4 div / 1.9 div) = 47.5°

There is a detailed tutorial for making this measurement at **photon.iyte.edu.tr/~mgunes/ Circuit_Lab_Manual_exp8_01. pdf**. Change signal frequency and component values to see how changing the phase shift affects the display.

If you have a second oscillator available, set them both to the same frequency and voltage, connecting one to each of the 'scope's inputs. Now increase the frequency of the generator connected to the vertical channel. Pretty neat! Fans of the old "Outer Limits" TV show will recognize the pattern as the frequency of the

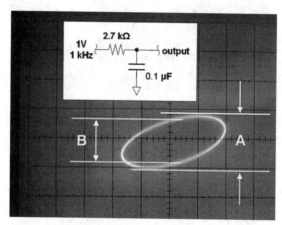

Figure 1—Phase shift of sine waves can be measured by using Lissajous figures displayed on the 'scope's X-Y display.

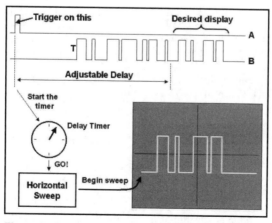

Figure 2—Delayed sweep allows you to see short-lived signals that occur well after an event used to trigger the 'scope.

Y-axis signal becomes two and three times that on the horizontal. These are called *Lissajous figures*.

Another use of the 'scope's X-Y display is for assessing linearity of amplifier circuits. The op-amp circuits of Experiment #3 (available at the Hands-On Radio Web site, **www.arrl.org/ tis/info/HTML/Hands-On-Radio/**) make a good example. Build the noninverting amplifier with a gain of 3 or 4. Connect the input to the X channel and the output to the Y channel. With a small input signal, you'll see the familiar diagonal line, showing that the input is a faithful replica of the input. With both channel sensitivities the same, the line will be steep, the slope reflecting the gain of the amplifier. Now increase the input signal until the output begins to clip as the power supply voltages are reached. You see the line grow, then flatten horizontally when increasing the input does not cause an increase in the output. Change to the inverting amplifier circuit and the line will rotate to the opposite diagonal.

Delayed Sweep

The next useful 'scope trick is *delayed sweep*. This delays starting the sweep of the trace across the display after the triggering event by an adjustable period of time. This is particularly useful when the portion of a signal you want to look at occurs a long time after an event that causes it. The basic functions of delayed sweep are illustrated in Figure 2. The short pulse on channel A is the triggering signal, but the portion of interest in the signal on channel B occurs much later. If you tried to trigger from the signal on channel B, it would be displayed starting at point T, too soon to see the detail you want.

Normally, the "start sweep" signal from the triggering circuit causes the horizontal sweep circuit to drive the trace across the display immediately. When using the delayed sweep function, an adjustable timing circuit in the 'scope creates a delay. When the timer expires, the trace begins its sweep across the display.

One method of using delayed sweep is to use the trigger at point T to begin the delay. Another method is to trigger from a separate signal that occurs prior to the portion of the signal you want to view. Both of these situations are illustrated in Figure 2. Which one you choose depends on the characteristics of the signal you wish to observe and what triggering signals are available.

Experiment with the first method by connecting a 10 Hz square wave to one of the 'scope's inputs. (Turn off X-Y display mode first.) Trigger on the positive-going edge of the square wave, with the sweep speed set so that you can see one complete cycle. What if you wanted to measure the speed at which the generator output changes from positive to negative? At this low sweep speed, you won't be able to zoom in for high-speed detail. (Try it.)

Your 'scope's manual will tell you how to delay the sweep and how to adjust the delay. Set the sweep speed to 1 ms/division and adjust the delay until the falling edge of the signal is visible on the display. The delay will be approximately $1/2$ of the signal's period, or 50 ms. By adjusting the delay and sweep speed, you should be able to observe the falling edge with a resolution of microseconds/division. At this speed, instability in your generator (called *jitter*) may become visible.

Triggering Modes—Ext/Line/TV

The triggering circuits and controls of your 'scope are another rich area to explore. Most of the time, the AUTO or NORM settings will work fine, but there are three other choices you should become familiar with (if your 'scope includes them).

The EXT setting (for External) is a separate input channel dedicated to the triggering circuit. Although you can't display it, a signal connected to the EXT input can control triggering just like a regular input. This allows you to synchronize the display of two inputs to a third signal. Imagine trying to display two channels of stereo audio synchronized to a drumbeat. The drumbeat can be used to trigger the sweep without using a vertical input channel.

In LINE mode, the triggering circuits sample the waveform from the ac power line and trigger the sweep once per cycle. This mode is used when observing signals synchronized with the ac line voltage without requiring a potentially unsafe connection directly to the power line. Set your generator to output a 60 Hz waveform and select LINE triggering. Since the generator is not locked to the ac line frequency, its signal will drift or slide across the screen. Adjust the generator to stabilize the waveform on the screen. Try again at 120 Hz and multiples of 60 Hz.

The final pair of settings, TV-V and TV-H, are not available on all 'scopes, but are quite useful for working with video signals. "V" stands for "vertical frame" and "H" for "horizontal line." (For a complete explanation of composite video signals, try the tutorial at **www.maxim-ic.com/ appnotes.cfm/appnote_number/734.**)

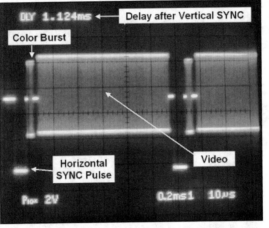

Figure 3—A video signal can be observed by using the TV-V and TV-H triggering modes. This figure shows one horizontal line of the frame.

With a composite video signal connected to one of the input channels, a triggering circuit set to TV-V or TV-H will lock on to the sync pulses that control a TV or video display. You can then view any portion of a video signal. Figure 3 shows one line of a video signal that was obtained by connecting a VCR's VIDEO output (not the Channel 3 or 4 output) to the 'scope, triggering in TV-V mode (one sweep for each frame every $1/30$ of a second), and using delayed sweep to display the first displayed horizontal line of the signal, a solid blue screen! For an interesting experiment, monitor a close-captioned signal and look for the 21st line of the frame. You'll see the text where the video normally resides.

Shopping List

- 2.7 kΩ resistor
- 0.1 µF capacitor

Suggested Reading

Start with the manual for your 'scope manual. All of these functions, plus others are described there. Try them out! For a refresher on 'scope functions, I recommend the 'scope tutorial at the Web site **www.mccord.plus.com/ Radio/oscilloscope.htm**.

Next Month

One amplifier configuration we haven't yet covered is the Common-Base or Common-Gate. These are often used in preamplifier configurations. Tune in next month and find out why!

Experiment #34—Technical References

Working with the varied types of electronics in ham radio requires information on lots of topics. No one can know everything, but where do you get it all? By knowing where to look, that's where!

Introduction

Behind every successful electronics whiz is a collection of magazine articles, encyclopedic tomes and Web sites. As your interest in electronics grows, you'll find that adding a new source of technical information is just as important as obtaining a new collection of components. This month, I'll recommend some technical references, spurring you on to launch your own collection of information.

From Bookshelf and Cabinet

There is no on-line reference that can equal the convenience of a printed book or article. One can get a little excessive in collecting them, and I am happy to brag that my library has more than 30 feet of volumes on everything from antique electric machines to digital signal processing. A filing cabinet stuffed with articles is a few feet away. Nonetheless, you can go an awfully long way with just a few key references and a judicious eye about what to clip and keep.

Let's start with good technical references that will find a happy home with any Hands-On Radio reader.

- The current The *ARRL Handbook for Radio Communications*[1]—the best technical bargain on the planet. It will never be far away from your workbench.
- *Reference Data for Radio Engineers* published by Howard Sams—pricey new, but widely available used for less than $20. The book covers an incredibly wide range of useful topics with useful formulas, graphs and nomographs for quick answers.
- *The CRC Handbook of Chemistry and Physics and Standard Math Tables and Formulae*—these have the answers to tough questions. Almost any edition will serve the typical hobbyist's needs since the laws of physics and math don't change very often.
- A recent edition of the *National Electrical Safety Code*—consult this before doing anything power related.
- Introductory college level circuit analysis and semiconductor circuit textbooks (available used for a fraction of the new price) will help explain a difficult subject or calculation.

Following these *broadband* references is a suite of cookbook style paperbacks, all available used or from the library:

- Don Lancaster's *TTL Cookbook, CMOS Cookbook* and *Active Filter Cookbook* were instant classics and have provided a useful reference for circuit designers since the 1970s.
- Walter Jung's *Op-Amp Cookbook* and *IC Timer Cookbook* are also timeless and a wellspring of design guidance.

[1]Available from your local ARRL dealer, or from the ARRL Bookstore, ARRL order no. 9493 hardcover; 9485 softcover. Telephone 860-594-0344, or toll-free in the US 888-277-5289; **www.arrl.org/shop/**; **pubsales@arrl.org**.

- *The Art of Electronics* by Horowitz and Hill won't come cheap, even used, but will provide hours of enjoyable reading, explaining a wide variety of subjects.

As your interest and ability in electronics grows, you'll find more magazines and articles to be potential keepers. Before getting out the scissors, though, check out the Web site of the magazine to see if the article is available for downloading. Disc space is cheap! You might also consider purchasing the magazine's yearly CD-ROM. The back issues of a century of ARRL magazines take up about the volume of a loaf of bread! (Then you can donate your paper issues to a school, club, or library.)

To manage the articles you do file away, apply a little organization to keep your filing system from becoming a piling system:

- When filing a paper article, discard others if they're obsolete or redundant.
- Save electronic articles with a file name like "keywords—author" to make it easy to find while browsing. The actual title and publication information will still be in the file.
- Use a disc indexing or search program, such as *Windows FindFast* or Google's desktop search utility. This also helps when you forget in what folder you put the article!

ARRL Technical Information Service

Before we get to the wide world of the Web, let's take a tour of one of ham radio's most useful tools, the ARRL's Technical Information Service or TIS. Start by logging on to **www.arrl.org/tis**—go on, I'll wait! The TIS home page has several sections, beginning with a link to the *How Do I?...* page. Following this link leads to a listing of dozens of topics covering most ham radio technologies.

Each topic has its own page beginning with a short introduction, some applicable references, a comprehensive set of *QST*

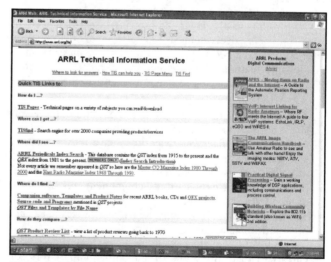

Figure 1—The ARRL's Technical Information Service is available to all, providing a wide variety of support to designers, builders and operators. You will also find product reviews and a comprehensive article index.

articles, links to appropriate vendors, organizations, and other Web pages on the subject. In the bibliography section, automatic keyword searches plumb the ARRL publications database.

Back at the TIS home page, the next feature is the *Where Do I Find?...* link to a vendor database. Enter a keyword for the device, material, or equipment you're looking for and—presto!—you get a list of vendors with the product you are seeking. For example, everybody knows you can't buy radio crystals any more, right? Wrong! Enter *crystals* into the search window and a half-dozen vendors are returned, including a specialist in Heathkit crystals! This feature is particularly useful when you are looking for something the major catalog houses aren't likely to stock. The database can also be downloaded as a program for you to use off-line.

The *Periodical Search* feature on the home page is my favorite part of TIS. You can search by keyword, author name or call, column, year or month, or publication. For example, entering a keyword of *stub* and a call of *NØAX* quickly finds *Hands-On Radio Experiment #22*, titled "Stubs." If you're trying to get rid of a nasty RF bite from your microphone, entering *RF* and *Feedback* in the title/keyword window returns a list of 10 helpful *QST* articles. The collected information of these publications goes back nearly 100 years and covers any ham radio topic you can imagine.

Along with the article index, this section also includes links to software, design templates, supplemental notes, corrections, and addenda to both articles and books. Organized by year, the files go back to the early 1990s. This is where you'll find software for a microprocessor-based project, for example.

The TIS page is also where you'll find links to product reviews and comparisons done in the ARRL lab, links to columns such as "The Doctor Is IN" and, yes, "Hands-On Radio" is there, too. The home page concludes with some helpful suggestions about finding solutions to technical questions. The TIS gives you access to nearly 100 years of radio knowhow, a vendor referral service, a repository with software and design aids galore, and detailed product reviews. What are you waiting for?

Internet Resources

I first understood the power of the Internet when, years ago, needing to reinstall an old hard drive, I was advised to enter the model number into my search engine of choice at the time, *AltaVista*. Instantly the necessary information appeared! Today, the Web is vastly larger and growing faster than ever. To keep from being overwhelmed, I keep several comprehensive sites bookmarked because I find that they contain or point to quality information. This is easier than searching the entire Web every time or trying to keep my own list current. Here are a few I visit regularly:

- **AC6V.com**—not just an electronics site, but a comprehensive "portal" with numerous links on many topics; the *Homebrew* and *Tech Reference* links have information on electronics and building.
- Discover Circuits (**www.discovercircuits.com**)—tons and tons of circuits, explanations, component links, and an on-line forum for extra help.
- Circuit Sage (**www.circuitsage.com**)—specializes in RF and high-performance analog circuitry.
- WA7CS's RF Calculators (**webpages.charter.net/crstrode/calcs/RFcalcs.htm**)—lots of standalone calculators for radio circuits.
- You'll also find a number of incredibly generous tutorial and course collections available for the browsing.
- VK2TIP's Electronics Tutorials (**electronics-tutorials.com**)—a comprehensive list of tutorials on radio and electronics-related topics.

Figure 2—Web-EE's site offers a number of excellent tutorials on electronics topics ranging from test equipment to data communications.

- Open Directory Project Tutorials Listing (**dmoz.org/Science/Technology/Electronics/Tutorials**)—master listing of other tutorials and instructional sites.
- WebEE Tutorials (**www.web-ee.com/primers/Tutorials.htm**)—another excellent listing of electronics and radio-related tutorials.
- US Navy Electricity and Electronics Training Series (NEETS—**www.phy.davidson.edu/instrumentation/NEETS.htm**)—a US Government introduction to the fundamentals.

Component Information Data Sheets

The Web also has done away with the need to keep a big pile of those big always-out-of-date data books on electrical components. You can find complete information on nearly any part on the Internet. The easiest way is to enter the part number and *"data sheet"* (with the quotes) into a search engine. You will find links to both vendors and private groups. If you are only interested in pin or lead assignments and basic specs, both will do. If you need the detailed specs for a special or demanding use, be sure to use a vendor's site. Data sheets for many common parts can be found at the University of Washington's Electrical Engineering Department site, **www.ee.washington.edu/stores**.

Caveat Anagnostes

"Let the reader beware"—information used by hobbyists often comes from unverified and non-reviewed sources. Web sites and magazine articles often contain errors, either by the author or added by the publisher. Look for feedback and corrections in subsequent issues of the magazine or on the 'net. See if other articles on the topic reference the one you have and whether they support or dispute it. For example, there is a tremendous amount of electro-mythology associated with SWR and impedance matching.

Suggested Reading

This whole lesson has been suggested reading! Your assignment is to put all of these useful Web sites into your list of "Favorites." You should also set aside some time to go Web surfing through the links contained in the reference sites.

Next Month

Past experiments have assembled a marvelous little collection of gadgetry. Now it's time to see how some of them work together! Next month, we're going to take a look under the hood at a commercial linear power supply to see how all the pieces work together and learn about an overvoltage protection circuit in the bargain!

Experiment #49 — Reading and Drawing Schematics

The old days of hand-drawn schematics by draftsmen in pen and ink (and typewriter correction fluid) are over for many of us, but just using a fancy schematic editor program is no guarantee that the end product will be easy to "read." A computer is satisfied if all the component leads are accounted for and appear somewhere on the printed page. A human reader needs more — what it takes to have a readable schematic and how to approach reading one, are the topics of this month's column.

Terms to Learn

Bus or rail (ground or power) — A common connection shared by many individual components.

Bus (digital) — A set of parallel connections between devices carrying several digital bits of information.

History and Mission

In the late 19th century, as electrical systems became more and more complex, engineers needed more and more sophisticated methods of describing them. Century-old magazines contain *pictorial diagrams* with the physical location of each component. Quickly outgrown, they were replaced by *ladder diagrams* that show component symbols connected between parallel power *buses* or *rails*. Ladder diagrams are still used today for power wiring — check the manuals or internal labels of your major electrical appliances. The terms *bus* and *rail* are still used to refer to common connections, even though they may not be long, straight conductors.

By 1930, the form of the *schematic* (the word was invented in 1894) and most of the

symbols used today had become the standard method of describing an electronic circuit. The journey had taken nearly 50 years from the time electricity became widely used. A standardized schematic was crucial to the development of the electronic industry. This was because a visual description was the only way to share the complex information necessary to build complex equipment such as multiband superheterodyne radios — the personal computers of their day.

A schematic diagram performs three primary functions. It serves as a symbolic connection diagram (not a construction diagram), illustrating the circuit's design. It also serves as a troubleshooting aid. Like an electrical alphabet, it also allows the exchange of complex design information using a symbolic description of circuits and equipment.

Related to the schematic is the *block diagram,* which shows the functional pieces making up the circuit. (Remember, you studied block diagrams to get your ham license!) A block diagram is often "page 1" of a schematic package, providing an overview of the circuit and familiarizing the reader with the important features and connections. Figure 1 from Experiment #40 is an example of how a block diagram provides a high-level view of a circuit, supported by detailed schematics for each part of the circuit.[1] An example of a schematic diagram can be found on page 36 of this issue.

[1]Experiment #40 — VOX (and all Hands-On Radio experiments) can be downloaded by ARRL members at **www.arrl.org/tis/info/ HTML/Hands-On-Radio**.

Reading a Schematic

Before tackling a schematic, familiarize yourself with the symbols and conventions used on schematics. Each edition of *The ARRL Handbook* begins with a table of schematic symbols.[2] More symbols, including downloadable sets of symbols, can be found online at **www.kpsec.freeuk.com/symbol.htm**.

Here's the process I use in reading an unfamiliar schematic for the first time. Think of it as "Divide and Conquer" — partitioning the schematic into easily digestible sections.

• Make some copies to write on. Making notes in different colors for different purposes (such as green for signal paths) helps a lot.

• Scan the entire schematic and try to identify the major functions and components. Draw lines around the parts of the circuit (IC) that perform related functions. If necessary, make your own block diagram.

• Identify the important input and output signals and their connection points. Add labels if necessary.

• Trace and label the flow of the important signals through the schematic using the block diagram.

• Identify and label control signals and internal connections for the major functions and components.

• Dig in to understand the circuitry in each section. You may not understand every

[2]R. D. Straw, Editor, *The ARRL Handbook for Radio Communications.* Available from your ARRL dealer or the ARRL Bookstore, ARRL order no. 9760. Price, $44.95 plus shipping. Telephone 860-594-0355, or toll-free in the US 888-277-5289; **www.arrl.org/shop/**; **pubsales@arrl.org**.

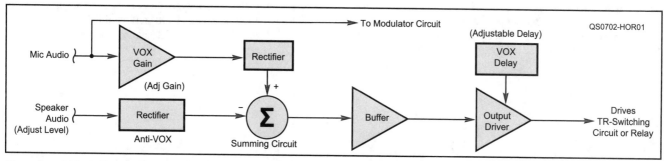

Figure 1 — A block diagram illustrates how a circuit works by breaking it into separate functions. The nature of each function is described and the connections between functions are identified. Detailed schematics can then show the circuit that implements each function.

component's purpose, but try to grasp the general operation.

At this point, you have a pretty good feel for how the entire circuit is put together and how signals flow on the schematic. This method works for both analog and digital circuits.

Now perform a more detailed inspection. If there are integrated circuits with multiple symbols (such as a quad NAND gate or dual op-amp), identify each part of the IC. Look for any unfamiliar symbols and identify them. Read any notes or legends on the drawing.

Drawing a Schematic

Imagine yourself as the schematic's reader. Keep the schematic's mission in mind and provide the necessary information to fulfill it. Start with a block diagram. Arrange the blocks on the page so your reader will be able to follow the flow and function of the circuit described by the blocks. Identify every important signal. If the schematic is to be distributed, have a friend review it for clarity.

Try to follow these general guidelines for drawing schematics. Signal flow from input to output is usually shown from left to right although this may not be possible for all digital circuits. Place external connections at the sides of the drawing. Place components together that perform a common function. Label important signals and component groups. If available, include waveforms or voltages that describe normal operating conditions. Be sure to identify and date your schematic or assign a revision number to avoid later confusion between versions.

Always (always!) use standard symbols and never (never!) use different symbols to represent the same component. For example, unless your circuit has more than one type of ground, use one ground symbol consistently. If the circuit has special connection requirements, such as separate grounds for digital and analog signals, be sure to show this clearly and add a note if necessary. Each component should have a *designator* to identify the type of component (R, C, L, IC, J, T, etc) and which one it is (1, 2, 3, 4, etc).

On analog circuit schematics, the most positive power supply voltage should be at the top of the drawing and the most negative

at the bottom. On digital schematics, use buses for multiple parallel signals such as data and address signals. For a complex IC, such as a microprocessor, it is preferable to group the connections by function instead of pin number.

Example 1 — VFO Schematic

Both of the schematics for Examples 1 and 2 are available on the Hands-On Radio Web site in the FAQ section for Experiment #49. Each schematic is available as a PDF file — download and print the files to work through the examples and suggested exercises. An annotated schematic with the suggested additions is also provided.

The Vackar VFO was designed by G3PDM and is included in most recent versions of *The ARRL Handbook*. (Its schematic is also available as Figure 10.15 in the 2007 edition.) This schematic shows good layout and readability. While it is missing some labels and designators, here are its high points:

• The 2N3819 oscillator FET and the associated components to its left form the oscillator. Draw a line around the oscillator components and label this stage OSCILLATOR.

• Locate the special temperature compensating capacitor's model and part number.

• Draw a line around the buffer stage components (the 2N3794's and the associated R and C). Label this stage BUFFER.

• Positive dc power is at the top of the diagram along with the filtering and regulation components. Draw a line around the decoupling circuit for the oscillator, including the 6.2 V, 1 W Zener diode and the 2.2 mH choke.

• Observe that the schematic clearly shows that it is important to have a single physical ground point for the oscillator components.

• Locate the dashed line that shows the circuit should be completely shielded. Locate the feedthrough capacitor through the shield in the upper right (although no value is given).

• For more practice with analog schematics, try Figure 19.78 of the *2007 ARRL Handbook*. It includes ICs, package and connector diagrams, and plenty of circuit sections. This schematic is also available on the Web site.

Example 2 — TiCK-4 Keyer Schematic

The second example schematic is of a basic digital circuit, the TiCK-4 keyer (Figure 19.34 in *The 2007 ARRL Handbook*). This schematic illustrates several good practices:

• The processor (U1, a 12CE674 PIC microprocessor) is the major component of the circuit and correctly placed in the middle. Identify the power and ground connections.

• Each input and output to the circuit is arranged logically around the processor. Label each signal line and trace it from the processor to the appropriate connector.

• Draw dashed lines around each of the functional groups: voltage regulator, keying and paddle interface circuits, sidetone and programming connections.

• A single asterisk on R2 and R3 lead the reader to the note that these are rig-dependent components. Locate the optional audio annunciator (LS1) shown with dashed lines.

• A more complex digital schematic to practice reading in this way can be found on page 37 of the May 2006 issue of *QST*. This circuit, also a keyer, adds a second digital IC and uses a more complex processor. There are several more inputs and outputs, but all are still nicely separated for clarity.

Your Assignment

Draw a complete schematic of the RF oscillator and output amplifier that were constructed in Experiments #43 through 46. Start with a block diagram showing the oscillator, the buffer and the output amplifier. Draw a single-page schematic that includes all of those circuits connected together. Ask a friend to review your work. Then think up a good name for this mighty transmitter, like "Annihilator V" or "40 Meter Landslide." More information about schematics and components in general is available in the classic *QST* series "First Steps in Radio" by W1FB at **www.arrl.org/tis/info/frsteps.html**.

Next Month

If you've looked at the filter design chapters of *The ARRL Handbook* or an engineering text, the tables and graphs may have given you blurry eyes and a headache! Next month, we'll start a guided tour through the process of designing your own filters.

Experiment #56 — Design Sensitivities

Sensitivity is important in ham radio, and in more ways than just the ability to hear signals. When designing an electronic circuit, it's important to know which component values are critical. It might be critical to choose just the right type of component or even change the design to be more tolerant of component variations. In this column, we'll introduce sensitivity and how it's calculated.

Terms to Learn

Tolerance — allowable variation around the nominal value, usually given in percent (%) or parts per million (ppm).

Nominal value — the specified value of a component.

Standard value — a series of normal production values commonly specified for components.

Actual value — the measured value of a component.

Ideal value — an exact value resulting from a design calculation.

Typical value — a common value exhibited by components of the specified type.

Component Values

When designing a circuit, a calculator will spit out values with many digits, such as 4.83456 kΩ or 373.29 pF. It would be difficult to order components with these *ideal values*, however. You might use variable components carefully adjusted to those exact values, but what about inductors and transistors? What about measurement errors? Adjustment won't work very well. The usual technique is to use the closest *standard value* and accept any resulting differences in performance.

Where do standard values come from? If you open a catalog or look at a list of available component values, you'll recognize a series of familiar numbers such as those for "5%" components seen in Table 1. The percentage value refers to the component's *tolerance*. Each component's value is centered in a *tolerance window* centered between those of its neighbors. For example, a 12 Ω resistor with a 5% tolerance may have an actual resistance anywhere from 12 − 5% = 11.4 Ω to 12 + 5% = 12.6 Ω. The next lowest neighbor, 11 Ω, has a tolerance window ranging from 10.45 Ω to 11.55 Ω, overlapping the lower edge of the 12 Ω window from 11.4 Ω to 11.55 Ω.

Exercise Set #1

Use the same procedure as in the preceding paragraph to see if the 36 Ω standard value's tolerance window overlaps with the edges of the 33 Ω and 39 Ω windows. Find the tolerance window for a 68 Ω, 10% resistor. Go to your junk box and find up to 10 resistors with the same value marked on their surface in text or with paint bands. Using a volt-ohm-milliammeter (VOM), measure the value of each resistor and calculate the difference in percent from the marked value. If you have more than one VOM, measure the resistors *again* using the second VOM. (This is a good exercise to perform with a couple of friends, sharing resistors and meters.) Make a histogram of each set of values as shown at **en.wikipedia.org/wiki/Histogram** and compare the results. Not only do resistor values vary, but measurements by different meters vary, too!

Ideal, Nominal and Actual

The value indicated by those component markings, such as "103" on a ceramic capacitor meaning 10×10^3 pF = 10 nF = 0.01 μF, is the *nominal* value. It's almost certainly *not* the component's *actual* value because of the allowed tolerance, such as 5% or 10%. As you just saw in Exercise Set #1, there can be a significant amount of variation between components of the same nominal value!

A design calculation produces an *ideal* value, such as 1.0927 MΩ. The closest *standard* value is chosen for the design and that is the nominal value of the component. When the nominal values of each component are used to calculate circuit parameters such as gain or frequency response, the result is the nominal value for that parameter. If measured, the component and parameter will have a third value, the *actual* value. Actual values determine the actual value of circuit parameters — how the circuit actually functions.

Designers have to take into account this progression from ideal to actual, even for transistors and ICs. For example, the dc gain or β of a transistor is specified to have a minimum and maximum acceptable value, along with a *typical* value, representative of how most components will behave.

Because the values of the components vary from component to component, the performance of the circuit in which the component is used will also vary. Sometimes the variations are quite small compared to the amount of change in the component value. In other circuits, small variations can have big effects on performance. Circuit designers must take into account the relationship between component variation and circuit performance. This is called *design sensitivity*.

Calculating design sensitivity for a particular component begins with choosing the design parameter of interest. For example, in an antenna tuner circuit, sensitivity may be calculated with respect to range and not for harmonic rejection or power dissipation.

Table 1
5% and 10% Standard Values

5% Standard Series

| 10 | 11 | 12 | 13 | 15 | 16 | 18 | 20 | 22 | 24 | 27 | 30 | 33 | 36 | 39 | 43 | 47 | 51 | 56 | 62 | 68 | 75 | 82 | 91 |

10% Standard Series

| 10 | 12 | 15 | 18 | 22 | 27 | 33 | 39 | 47 | 56 | 68 | 82 |

For 1% standard series see **www.rfcafe.com/references/electrical/resistor_values.htm**.

Only the value of the component under investigation is changed. Other component values are kept constant so that the calculated sensitivity depends only on changes in the value of the selected component.

Sensitivity is often expressed in % of parameter change per % of component change — % per %. If in the tuner circuit a change in 5% of a capacitor's value results in a 10% change in matching range, the sensitivity of range to capacitor value is 10% / 5% or 2% per %. (Sensitivity can also be expressed in electrical units, such as Ω / pF or V / μH, if that is most useful to the designer.) Amplifier and filter circuits often have sensitivity expressed as dB per % of change.

Exercise Set #2

Read the very first *Hands-On Radio* column (Feb 2003) about the "Common-Emitter Amplifier" shown in Figure 1 and find the equation for voltage gain; $A_V \approx -R_C/R_E$.[1] We'll determine voltage gain sensitivity to both R_C and R_E. Assume nominal values for R_C = 3.9 kΩ and R_E = 220 Ω. The nominal value for midband gain is approximately –17.7. What is the actual value of gain if either R_C or R_E vary by 5%? (Either –18.6 or –16.8) The sensitivity of gain to R_C = change in gain / change in R_C value = [(–18.6 –17.7) / –17.7] / 5% = 5.08% / 5% ≈ 1% / %, meaning that for every percent R_C changes, gain will change by the same amount. (The sensitivity for changes in R_E = –1% / % because as R_E increases, the gain is reduced.) Sensitivity to changes in R_C or R_E could also have been expressed in dB / %. A sensitivity of 1% / % = 0.04 dB / %.

Exercise Set #3

Read the *Hands-On Radio* column on "Notch Filters" from July 2006 and find the equation for center frequency, f_0, of the Twin-T circuit shown in Figure 2. Let's assume that all of the Rs and Cs are exactly matched. If this circuit is going to be used in your backpack station, it will probably be subjected to temperature swings. How much will the filter's center frequency change with temperature as the capacitors heat and cool?

Most audio circuits use film capacitors. A common temperature coefficient for film capacitors is –150 ppm / °C. (The capacitor

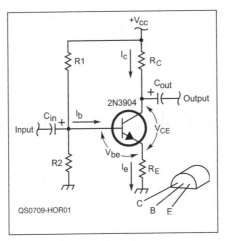

Figure 1 — The common-emitter amplifier's gain is determined by the ratio of R_C and R_E.

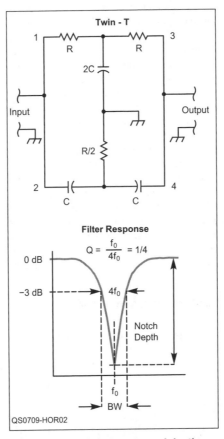

Figure 2 — Notch frequency and depth depend on careful matching of component values. Temperature changes can upset that balance.

expands, increasing the separation between electrodes and reducing capacitance.) A change of 10 ppm is 0.001%, so the capacitor has a "tempco" of –0.015% / °C.

Start by computing the sensitivity of f_0 to the value of C as in the previous Exercise — change the value of C by a few percent and see how much f_0 changes as a result. (We're assuming both capacitors change temperature equally and so both can be treated as a single component.) You'll find the sensitivity of f_0 to C is –1% / %; as C increases, f_0 decreases. For C to change 1%, temperature must change by 1 / 0.015 = 66.6°C, which is equivalent to 1 / 66.6 = 0.015% / °C. So the sensitivity of f_0 to temperature is –0.015% / °C. If f_0 is 1 kHz at room temperature (23 °C), taking it outside into the hot sun at 35 °C, the change of 12° will result in f_0 changing by 0.015% × 12 = 0.18% or 1.8 Hz.

Worst Case and Monte Carlo

In Exercise #2, what is voltage gain if R_C increases by 5% and R_E decreases by the same amount (–19.6)? Vice versa? (–16.0). The *worst case* values of gain occur when both components vary to the maximum amount allowed and in ways that change the circuit parameter in the same direction. In a complicated circuit, finding the worst-case scenario can be very difficult. As a result, circuit designers use the *Monte Carlo* method in which all significant component values are varied randomly within their specified tolerance windows. The resulting values of the circuit parameter, such as gain, also vary randomly. As more and more component value combinations are tried, gradually the extreme worst case values of gain are found. Obviously, this requires a computer to perform the necessary calculations and display the results.

Recommended Reading

How about some more practice in computing sensitivities? You can use any of the *Hands-On Radio* circuits that define a parameter in terms of component values. For a slightly trickier calculation, take a look at the August 2004 column on "Current Sources" and determine the sensitivity of load current (I_{LOAD}) to transistor gain (β) for the current mirror.

Next Month

We haven't visited transmission lines in a while, so let's learn some more about stubs and the use of the nearly ubiquitous SWR analyzer instrument. You'll need an oscilloscope to make the necessary adjustments and measurements. If you don't have one, buddy up, or make this one a club project.

[1]ARRL members can download Hands-On Radio columns from **www.arrl.org/tis/info/HTML/ Hands-On-Radio.**

Parts List

The following components are used for the experiments shown in this book.

Resistors (ohms)	Qty	Experiment	Notes
10	2	2, 13, 15, 16, 46	
27	1	21	
39	2	13	
47	1	10	
51	1	13, 26	
68	2	45	
75	2	13	
100	1	2, 13, 15, 16, 24, 29, 37, 46, 48	
150	1	21	
220	1	48	
270	1	1, 28, 45	
330	1	6, 28, 29, 38	
390	1	48	
470	7	8, 28, 29, 37	
510	1	9, 55	
1k	10	2, 3, 8, 12, 28, 29, 31, 33, 36, 37, 39, 40, 55	
1.2k	1	2	
1.5k	1	1, 28	
2.2k	1	4, 8, 11, 14	
2.7k	1	27	
3.9k	1	3, 6	
4.7k	2	5, 8, 9, 45, 54	
5.1k	1	6	
6.8k	1	1, 28, 55	
10k	4	2, 3, 4, 7, 17, 18, 30, 31, 40, 41, 46, 54	
15k	1	2	
16k	4	42	
22k	1	2, 4, 11, 41, 45	
27k	1	11	
39k	1	1, 5, 28, 41	
47k	1	4, 31	
56k	1	41	
62k	1	5	
75k	1	41	
91k	1	5	
120k	1	39	
220k	1	11	
270k	1	38	
470k	1	31	
680k	1	38	
1M	several	43, 55	

Power Resistors

	Qty	Experiment
5Ω, 5W	1	24
50Ω, 10W	2	9(2)
100Ω, 1W	1	10, 32

Potentiometer (all values are ohms)

	Qty	Experiment
100	1	28, 42
1k	1	3, 4, 14
10k	1	3, 8, 11, 12, 14, 54, 55
20k	1	9
50k	1	10
100k	1	1, 2, 38, 41
1M	1	17, 39, 40

Capacitors

	Qty	Experiment
50 to 200 pF, fixed-value or air-variable	1	21, 43
2.7 pF, ceramic	1	43
100 pF, polystyrene or ceramic	1	45, 46
200 pF, polystyrene or silver mica	1	43, 46
390 pF, polystyrene or silver mica	2	46

Resistors (ohms)	Qty	Experiment	Notes
1 nF, 50V ceramic	3	17, 37	
1.5 nF, film or ceramic	1	18	
2.7 nF, film or ceramic	1	4	
5.6 nF, film or ceramic	1	4	
10 nF, film or ceramic	4	5, 25, 27, 42, 45, 46	
16 nF, film or ceramic	2	41	
33 nF, film or ceramic	2	4	
56 nF, film or ceramic	1	4	
0.1 μF, 50 V ceramic	4	8, 12, 17, 24, 26, 38, 39, 40, 43	
1 μF, 25 V electrolytic	4	7, 40	
1 μF, 35 V tantalum	1	6, 8	
10 μF, 25 V electrolytic	3	1, 2, 3, 4, 5, 7, 17, 28, 31	
100 μF, 15 V tantalum	2	15, 16	
100 μF, 35 V electrolytic	2	10, 30, 31	
4700 μF, 15V electrolytic	2	10, 38	

Inductors and Cores			
2 μH	1	43	8 turns, $1^1/2$" dia, 1" long
100 μH, 1 amp	1	15, 16	
22 μH	1	46	rated for 50 mA
1 mH	1	26	
FT37-43 or equivalent	1	45	
FT240-61 or equivalent	1	48	
T50-6 or equivalent	1	46	

Transformers			
115 V Pri, 12.6 V Sec	1	10, 33	
1000 ohm - 8 Ω audio transformer	1	33	

Transistors			
2N3904	2	1, 2, 19, 20, 25, 28, 31, 40, 45, 46	
2N3906	1	19, 25, 40	
2N4401	1	8	
2N4416	1	43	
2N7000	1	39, 40	
TIP31	1	9	
TIP42	1	38	
IRF510 MOSFET	1	9, 12, 15, 16	
SCR, 100 V, 8 A	1	10	

Diodes and Rectifiers			
1N4733A	1	6, 38	
1N4148	4	6, 7, 14, 25, 26, 30, 39, 40, 42, 54, 55	
1N5819	1	15, 16	

Integrated Circuits			
78L-05, -08, -12, or -15 voltage regulator	1	25	
4N35 Optocoupler	1	14	
741 op amp	2	3, 4, 8, 17, 19, 42, 54, 55	
555 timer	1	5	
LM317 op amp	1	8	
LM311 Comparator	1	11, 38	
LM324 quad op amp	1	17	
CD4028 BCD-to-Decimal Decoder	1	37	
CD4029 Up/Down Counter	1	36	
CD4511 BCD-to-7-Segment Decoder	1	37	

Lights and Displays			
Bulb, 12 V	1	10	
LED, Red	5	11, 36, 39, 40	
LED, Green	1	39	
7-Seg Display, Common-Cathode	1	37	

Resistors (ohms)	Qty	Experiment	Notes
Miscellaneous			
40-meter crystal in HC-8 or HC-16 holder	1	46	7030-7045 kHz recommended
14 ga. solid, enameled wire	14 feet	48	
20 or 22 ga. Solid wire	10 feet	21	
24 to 28 ga. Solid wire	3 feet	45, 46, 47	
SO-239 connector	1	21, 48	
UHF double-male adapter	1	21	
plastic film can or pill bottle	1	22	
SPST or SPDT switch	1	22	
RG-58 coaxial cable	25 feet	22	
Wooden spring-loaded clothespins		23	
Scraps of 2x4 wood		23	
Thick cardboard		23	
¼ inch dowel		23	
Glue		23	
Wood screws		23	
#6-32 machine screws		23	
#6-32 nuts		23	
#6 flat washers		23	
DPST switch	2	30	
TO-220 heat sink	1	24	
Mounting hardware for TO-220 heatsink	1 set	24	
1.5 V AAA or 9 V battery	1	32	

Quick References

Resistor Color Code

Color	Value	Multiplier	Tolerance
Black	0	x 1 (10^0)	
Brown	1	x 10 (10^1)	1%
Red	2	x 100 (10^2)	2%
Orange	3	x 1000 (10^3)	
Yellow	4	x 10,000 (10^4)	
Green	5	x 100,000 (10^5)	0.5%
Blue	6	x 1,000,000 (10^6)	0.25%
Violet	7	x 10,000,000 (10^7)	0.1%
Gray	8	x 100,000,000 (10^8)	0.05%
White	9	x 1,000,000,000 (10^9)	
Silver		x 0.1 (10^{-1})	5%
Gold		x 0.01 (10^{-2})	10%
No color			20%

For more information on resistor markings: **www.radio-electronics.com/info/data/resistor/resistor_col_code.php**

Capacitor Value Markings

###L (Three numbers and a letter)
Numbers 1 and 2 are value digits
Number 3 is a multiplier; 0 - x1, 1 - x10, 2 - x100, 3 - x1000, 4 - x10,000
Letter denotes tolerance; J - 5%, K - 10%, L - 20%

##p or ##n
Numbers 1 and 2 are value digits
p denotes pF, n denotes nF

For more information on capacitor markings: **www.radio-electronics.com/info/data/capacitor/capacitor-markings.php**

Drill Sizes Commonly Used in Electronics

Size Number	Diameter	Next Largest Fractional Size	Clears Screw Size	For Self-tapping Screw Size
11	0.191"	13/64"		10
19	0.166"	11/64"	8	
21	0.159"	11/64"		10-32
25	0.149"	5/32"		10-24
28	0.140"	9/64"	6	
29	0.136"	9/64"		8-32
33	0.113"	1/8"	4	
36	0.106"	7/64"		6-32
43	0.089"	3/32"		4-40
44	0.086"	3/32"	2	
50	0.070"	5/64"		2-56

Complete drill bit table: **en.wikipedia.org/wiki/Drill_and_tap_size_chart**

Metric System of Units

Prefix	Symbol	Multiplication Factor
tera	T	10^{18}
giga	G	10^{9}
mega	M	10^{6}
kilo	k	10^{3}
centi	c	10^{-2}
milli	m	10^{-3}
micro	μ	10^{-6}
nano	n	10^{-9}
pico	p	10^{-12}

Dimension Conversions

25.4 mm/inch	0.0393 inch/mm
2.54 cm/inch	0.393 inch/cm
30.48 cm/foot	0.0328 foot/cm
0.305 meter/foot	3.28 foot/meter
0.914 meter/yard	1.094 yard/meter

Voltage Conversions

Sine or square wave	VPEAK-TO-PEAK = 2 x VPEAK
Sine wave	VRMS = 0.707 x VPEAK, VPEAK = 1.414 x VRMS
Square wave	VRMS = VPEAK

Decibel Conversions

Power to Decibels	dB = 10 log10 (Power 1 / Power 2)
Voltage to Decibels	dB = 20 log10 (Voltage 1 / Voltage 2)
Decibels to Power	Power 1 = Power 2 x antilog10 (dB / 10)
Decibels to Voltage	Voltage 1 = Voltage 2 x antilog10 (dB / 20)

The antilog or inverse log function is often labeled log-1 on calculators.

Where to Find Component Data Sheets

Source	Web Site
Datasheet Archive	www.datasheetarchive.com
NTE (manufacturer of cross-reference parts)	www.nteinc.com
Open Directory Project	www.dmoz.org/Science/Technology/Electronics/

Reference/Application_Notes_and_Data_Sheets	
Datasheet Café (directory of manufacturer datasheet sites)	www.datasheetcafe.com

Vendors for Electronic Components & Supplies	
ARRL Technical Information Service Vendor Cross-Reference	www.arrl.org/tis/tisfind.html
All Electronics	allelectronics.com
Digi-Key Electronics	www.digikey.com
Jameco	www.jameco.com
Mouser Electronics	www.mouser.com
MCM Electronics	www.mcmelectronics.com
Marlin P Jones & Associates	www.mpja.com
Mouser Electronics	www.mouser.com
Ocean State Electronics	www.oselectronics.com
RadioShack	www.radioshack.com
Ramsey Kits	www.ramseyelectronics.com
Tower Electronics	www.pl-259.com
Velleman	www.vellemanusa.com/engine.php

Technical Reference and Tutorial Web Sites

All About Circuits	**www.allaboutcircuits.com**
American Radio Relay League's Technical Information Service	**www.arrl.org/tis**
ARRL Analog Electronics, EC012	**www.arrl.org/cce**
ARRL Digital Electronics, EC013	**www.arrl.org/cce**
ARRL Hands-On Radio	**www.arrl.org/tis/info/HTML/Hands-On-Radio**
Arrick Robotics	**www.robotics.com/robots.html**
Battery University	**www.batteryuniversity.com/partone.htm**
Colin McCord's Oscilloscope Tutorial	**www.mccord.plus.com/Radio/oscilloscope.htm**
Discover Circuits	**www.discovercircuits.com**
Op-Amp Electronics	**www.opamp-electronics.com**
US Navy Electricity and Electronics Training Series	**www.phy.davidson.edu/instrumentation/NEETS.htm**
Radio-Electronics	**www.radio-electronics.com/index.php**
Web EE Tutorials	**web-ee.com/primers/Tutorials.htm**
Williamson Labs	**www.williamson-labs.com**

Books and Magazines

Active Filter Cookbook, by Don Lancaster
The ARRL Handbook
The Art of Electronics, by Horowitz and Hill
Circuit Cellar, **www.circuitcellar.com**
Circuitbuilding for Dummies, by Ward Silver NØAX
CMOS Cookbook, by Don Lancaster
Electronic Circuits 1.1 and Electronic Circuits 1.2, by Intellin Organization
Electronic Formulas, Circuits, and Symbols, by Forest Mims
Electronics for Dummies, by McComb and Boysen
Electronic Projects for Dummies, by Boysen and Muir
Tab Electronics Guide to Understanding Electricity and Electronics by Randy Slone
Nuts and Volts Magazine, **www.nutsandvolts.com**
Op-Amp Cookbook, by Walter Jung
Power Supply Cookbook, by Marty Brown
Timer, Op-Amp, and Optoelectronic Circuits, by Forrest Mims
Understanding Basic Electronics, by Larry Wolfgang WR1B

Semiconductor Diode Specifications[†]

Listed numerically by device

Device	Type	Material	Peak Inverse Voltage, PIV (V)	Average Rectified Current Forward (Reverse) $IO(A)(IR(A))$	Peak Surge Current, I_{FSM} 1 s @ 25°C (A)	Average Forward Voltage, VF (V)
1N34	Signal	Ge	60	8.5 m (15.0 μ)		1.0
1N34A	Signal	Ge	60	5.0 m (30.0 μ)		1.0
1N67A	Signal	Ge	100	4.0 m (5.0 μ)		1.0
1N191	Signal	Ge	90	15.0 m		1.0
1N270	Signal	Ge	80	0.2 (100 μ)		1.0
1N914	Fast Switch	Si	75	75.0 m (25.0 n)	0.5	1.0
1N1183	RFR	Si	50	40 (5 m)	800	1.1
1N1184	RFR	Si	100	40 (5 m)	800	1.1
1N2071	RFR	Si	600	0.75 (10.0 μ)		0.6
1N3666	Signal	Ge	80	0.2 (25.0 μ)		1.0
1N4001	RFR	Si	50	1.0 (0.03 m)		1.1
1N4002	RFR	Si	100	1.0 (0.03 m)		1.1
1N4003	RFR	Si	200	1.0 (0.03 m)		1.1
1N4004	RFR	Si	400	1.0 (0.03 m)		1.1
1N4005	RFR	Si	600	1.0 (0.03 m)		1.1
1N4006	RFR	Si	800	1.0 (0.03 m)		1.1
1N4007	RFR	Si	1000	1.0 (0.03 m)		1.1
1N4148	Signal	Si	75	10.0 m (25.0 n)		1.0
1N4149	Signal	Si	75	10.0 m (25.0 n)		1.0
1N4152	Fast Switch	Si	40	20.0 m (0.05 μ)		0.8
1N4445	Signal	Si	100	0.1 (50.0 n)		1.0
1N5400	RFR	Si	50	3.0 (500 μ)	200	
1N5401	RFR	Si	100	3.0 (500 μ)	200	
1N5402	RFR	Si	200	3.0 (500 μ)	200	
1N5403	RFR	Si	300	3.0 (500 μ)	200	
1N5404	RFR	Si	400	3.0 (500 μ)	200	
1N5405	RFR	Si	500	3.0 (500 μ)	200	
1N5406	RFR	Si	600	3.0 (500 μ)	200	
1N5408	RFR	Si	1000	3.0 (500 μ)	200	
1N5711	Schottky	Si	70	1 m (200 n)	15 m	0.41 @ 1 mA
1N5767	Signal	Si		0.1 (1.0 μ)		1.0
1N5817	Schottky	Si	20	1.0 (1 m)	25	0.75
1N5819	Schottky	Si	40	1.0 (1 m)	25	0.9
1N5821	Schottky	Si	30	3.0		
ECG5863	RFR	Si	600	6	150	0.9
1N6263	Schottky	Si	70	15 m	50 m	0.41 @ 1 mA
5082-2835	Schottky	Si	8	1 m (100 n)	10 m	0.34 @ 1 mA

Si = Silicon; Ge = Germanium; RFR = rectifier, fast recovery.

[†]For package shape, size and pin-connection information see manufacturers' data sheets. Many retail suppliers offer data sheets to buyers free of charge on request. Data books are available from many manufacturers and retailers.

Suggested Small-Signal FETs

Device	Type	Max Diss (mW)	Max V_{DS} (V)	$V_{GS(off)}$ (V)	Min gfs (µS)	Input C (pF)	Max ID (mA)[1]	f_{max} (MHz)	Noise Figure (typ)	Case	Base	Applications
2N4416	N-JFET	300	30	−6	4500	4	−15	450	4 dB @400 MHz	TO-72	1	VHF/UHF amp, mix, osc
2N5484	N-JFET	310	25	−3	2500	5	30	200	4 dB @200 MHz	TO-92	2	VHF/UHF amp, mix, osc
2N5485	N-JFET	310	25	−4	3500	5	30	400	4 dB @400 MHz	TO-92	2	VHF/UHF amp, mix, osc
2N5486	N-JFET	360	25	−2	5500	5	15	400	4 dB @400 MHz	TO-92	2	VHF/UHF amp. mix, osc
3N200 NTE222 SK3065	N-dual-gate MOSFET	330	20	−6	10,000	4-8.5	50	500	4.5 dB @400 MHz	TO-72	3	VHF/UHF amp, mix, osc
3N202 NTE454 SK3991	N-dual-gate MOSFET	360	25	−5	8000	6	50	200	4.5 dB @200 MHz	TO-72	3	VHF amp, mixer
MPF102 NTE451 SK9164	N-JFET	310	25	−8	2000	4.5	20	200	4 dB @400 MHz	TO-92	2	HF/VHF amp, mix, osc
MPF106 2N5484	N-JFET	310	25	−6	2500	5	30	400	4 dB @200 MHz	TO-92	2	HF/VHF/UHF amp, mix, osc
40673 NTE222 SK3050	N-dual-gate MOSFET	330	20	−4	12,000	6	50	400	6 dB @200 MHz	TO-72	3	HF/VHF/UHF amp, mix, osc
U304	P-JFET	350	−30	+10	27		−50	—	—	TO-18	4	analog switch chopper
U310	N-JFET	500 300	30 30	−6	10,000	2.5	60	450	3.2 dB @450 MHz	TO-52	5	common-gate VHF/UHF amp,
U350	N-JFET Quad	1W	25	−6	9000	5	60	100	7 dB @100 MHz	TO-99	6	matched JFET doubly bal mix
U431	N-JFET Dual	300	25	−6	10,000	5	30	100	—	TO-99	7	matched JFET cascode amp and bal mix
2N5670 mix,	N-JFET	350	25	8	3000	7	20	400	2.5 dB @100 MHz	TO-92	2	VHF/UHF osc, front-end amp
2N5668	N-JFET	350	25	4	1500	7	5	400	2.5 dB @100 MHz	TO-92	2	VHF/UHF osc, mix, front-end amp
2N5669	N-JFET	350	25	6	2000	7	10	400	2.5 dB @100 MHz	TO-92	2	VHF/UHF osc, mix, front-end amp
J308	N-JFET	350	25	6.5	8000	7.5	60	1000	1.5 dB @100 MHz	TO-92	2	VHF/UHF osc, mix, front-end amp
J309	N-JFET	350	25	4	10,000	7.5	30	1000	1.5 dB @100 MHz	TO-92	2	VHF/UHF osc, mix, front-end amp
J310	N-JFET	350	25	6.5	8000	7.5	60	1000	1.5 dB @100 MHz	TO-92	2	VHF/UHF osc, mix, front-end amp
NE32684A	HJ-FET	165	2.0	−0.8	45,000	—	30	20 GHz	0.5 dB @12 GHz	84A		Low-noise amp

Notes:
[1]25°C.
For package shape, size and pin-connection information, see manufacturers' data sheets.

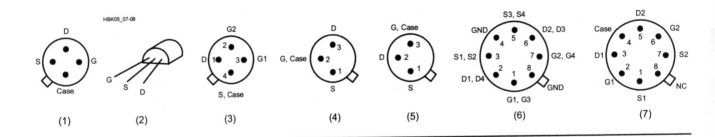

HBK05_07-08

(1)　(2)　(3)　(4)　(5)　(6)　(7)

Low-Noise Transistors

Device	NF (dB)	F (MHz)	f_T (GHz)	I_C (mA)	Gain (dB)	F (MHz)	$V_{(BR)CEO}$ (V)	I_C (mA)	P_T (mW)	Case
MRF904	1.5	450	4	15	16	450	15	30	200	TO-206AF
MRF571	1.5	1000	8	50	12	1000	10	70	1000	Macro-X
MRF2369	1.5	1000	6	40	12	1000	15	70	750	Macro-X
MPS911	1.7	500	7	30	16.5	500	12	40	625	TO-226AA
MRF581A	1.8	500	5	75	15.5	500	15	200	2500	Macro-X
BFR91	1.9	500	5	30	16	500	12	35	180	Macro-T
BFR96	2	500	4.5	50	14.5	500	15	100	500	Macro-T
MPS571	2	500	6	50	14	500	10	80	625	TO-226AA
MRF581	2	500	5	75	15.5	500	18	200	2500	Macro-X
MRF901	2	1000	4.5	15	12	1000	15	30	375	Macro-X
MRF941	2.1	2000	8	15	12.5	2000	10	15	400	Macro-X
MRF951	2.1	2000	7.5	30	12.5	2000	10	100	1000	Macro-X
BFR90	2.4	500	5	14	18	500	15	30	180	Macro-T
MPS901	2.4	900	4.5	15	12	900	15	30	300	TO-226AA
MRF1001A	2.5	300	3	90	13.5	300	20	200	3000	TO-205AD
2N5031	2.5	450	1.6	5	14	450	10	20	200	TO-206AF
MRF4239A	2.5	500	5	90	14	500	12	400	3000	TO-205AD
BFW92A	2.7	500	4.5	10	16	500	15	35	180	Macro-T
MRF521*	2.8	1000	4.2	−50	11	1000	−10	−70	750	Macro-X
2N5109	3	200	1.5	50	11	216	20	400	2500	TO-205AD
2N4957*	3	450	1.6	−2	12	450	−30	−30	200	TO-206AF
MM4049*	3	500	5	−20	11.5	500	−10	−30	200	TO-206AF
2N5943	3.4	200	1.5	50	11.4	200	30	400	3500	TO-205AD
MRF586	4	500	1.5	90	9	500	17	200	2500	TO-205AD
2N5179	4.5	200	1.4	10	15	200	12	50	200	TO-206AF
2N2857	4.5	450	1.6	8	12.5	450	15	40	200	TO-206AF
2N6304	4.5	450	1.8	10	15	450	15	50	200	TO-206AF
MPS536*	4.5	500	5	−20	4.5	500	−10	−30	625	TO-226AA
MRF536*	4.5	1000	6	−20	10	1000	−10	−30	300	Macro-X

*denotes a PNP device

Complementary devices

NPN	PNP
2N2857	2N4957
MRF904	MM4049
MRF571	MRF521

For package shape, size and pin-connection information, see manufacturers' data sheets. Many retail suppliers and manufacturers offer data sheets on their Web sites.

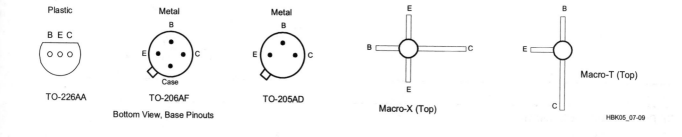

Plastic

B E C

TO-226AA

Metal
B

E   C

Case

TO-206AF

Metal
B

E   C

TO-205AD

Bottom View, Base Pinouts

E

B ⊏───○───⊐ C

E

Macro-X (Top)

B

E ⊏───○

C

Macro-T (Top)

HBK05_07-09

General-Purpose Transistors

Listed numerically by device

Device	Type	V_{CEO} Maximum Collector Emitter Voltage (V)	V_{CBO} Maximum Collector Base Voltage (V)	V_{EBO} Maximum Emitter Base Voltage (V)	I_C Maximum Collector Current (mA)	P_D Maximum Device Dissipation (W)	Minimum DC Current Gain h_{FE} $I_C = 0.1$ mA	Minimum DC Current Gain h_{FE} $I_C = 150$ mA	Current-Gain Bandwidth Product f_T (MHz)	Noise Figure NF Maximum (dB)	Base
2N918	NPN	15	30	3.0	50	0.2	20 (3 mA)	—	600	6.0	3
2N2102	NPN	65	120	7.0	1000	1.0	20	40	60	6.0	2
2N2218	NPN	30	60	5.0	800	0.8	20	40	250		2
2N2218A	NPN	40	75	6.0	800	0.8	20	40	250		2
2N2219	NPN	30	60	5.0	800	3.0	35	100	250		2
2N2219A	NPN	40	75	6.0	800	3.0	35	100	300	4.0	2
2N2222	NPN	30	60	5.0	800	1.2	35	100	250		2
2N2222A	NPN	40	75	6.0	800	1.2	35	100	200	4.0	2
2N2905	PNP	40	60	5.0	600	0.6	35	—	200		2
2N2905A	PNP	60	60	5.0	600	0.6	75	100	200		2
2N2907	PNP	40	60	5.0	600	0.4	35	—	200		2
2N2907A	PNP	60	60	5.0	600	0.4	75	100	200		2
2N3053	NPN	40	60	5.0	700	5.0	—	50	100		2
2N3053A	NPN	60	80	5.0	700	5.0	—	50	100		2
2N3563	NPN	15	30	2.0	50	0.6	20	—	800		1
2N3904	NPN	40	60	6.0	200	0.625	40	—	300	5.0	1
2N3906	PNP	40	40	5.0	200	0.625	60	—	250	4.0	1
2N4037	PNP	40	60	7.0	1000	5.0	—	50			2
2N4123	NPN	30	40	5.0	200	0.35	—	25 (50 mA)	250	6.0	1
2N4124	NPN	25	30	5.0	200	0.35	120 (2 mA)	60 (50 mA)	300	5.0	1
2N4125	PNP	30	30	4.0	200	0.625	50 (2 mA)	25 (50 mA)	200	5.0	1
2N4126	PNP	25	25	4.0	200	0.625	120 (2 mA)	60 (50 mA)	250	4.0	1
2N4401	NPN	40	60	6.0	600	0.625	20	100	250		1
2N4403	PNP	40	40	5.0	600	0.625	30	100	200		1
2N5320	NPN	75	100	7.0	2000	10.0	—	30 (I A)			2
2N5415	PNP	200	200	4.0	1000	10.0	—	30 (50 mA)	15		2
MM4003	PNP	250	250	4.0	500	1.0	20 (10 mA)	—			1
MPSA55	PNP	60	60	4.0	500	0.625	—	50 (0.1 A)	50		1
MPS6531	NPN	40	60	5.0	600	0.625	60 (10 mA)	90 (0.1 A)			1
MPS6547	NPN	25	35	3.0	50	0.625	20 (2 mA)	—	600		1

Test conditions: IC = 20 mA dc; VCE = 20 V; f = 100 MHz

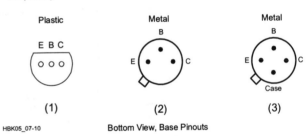

Plastic
E B C
(1)

Metal
B
E C
(2)

Metal
B
E C
Case
(3)

Bottom View, Base Pinouts

HBK05_07-10

RF Power Amplifier Modules

Listed by frequency

Device	Supply (V)	Frequency Range (MHz)	Output Power (W)	Power Gain (dB)	Package†	Mfr/ Notes
M57735	17	50-54	14	21	H3C	MI; SSB mobile
M57719N	17	142-163	14	18.4	H2	MI; FM mobile
S-AV17	16	144-148	60	21.7	5-53L	T, FM mobile
S-AV7	16	144-148	28	21.4	5-53H	T, FM mobile
MHW607-1	7.5	136-150	7	38.4	301K-02/3	MO; class C
BGY35	12.5	132-156	18	20.8	SOT132B	P
M67712	17	220-225	25	20	H3B	MI; SSB mobile
M57774	17	220-225	25	20	H2	MI; FM mobile
MHW720-1	12.5	400-440	20	21	700-04/1	MO; class C
MHW720-2	12.5	440-470	20	21	700-04/1	MO; class C
M57789	17	890-915	12	33.8	H3B	MI
MHW912	12.5	880-915	12	40.8	301R-01/1	MO; class AB
MHW820-3	12.5	870-950	18	17.1	301G-03/1	MO; class C

Manufacturer codes: MO = Motorola; MI = Mitsubishi; P = Philips; T = Toshiba.

†For package shape, size and pin-connection information, see manufacturers' data sheets. Many retail suppliers offer data sheets to buyers free of charge on request. Data books are available from many manufacturers and retailers.

Power FETs

Device	Type	VDSS min (V)	RDS(on) max (Ω)	ID max (A)	PD max (W)	Case†	Mfr
BS250P	P-channel	45	14	0.23	0.7	E-line	Z
IRFZ30	N-channel	50	0.050	30	75	TO-220	IR
MTP50N05E	N-channel	50	0.028	25	150	TO-220AB	M
IRFZ42	N-channel	50	0.035	50	150	TO-220	IR
2N7000	N-channel	60	5	0.20	0.4	E-line	Z
VN10LP	N-channel	60	7.5	0.27	0.625	E-line	Z
VN10KM	N-channel	60	5	0.3	1	TO-237	S
ZVN2106B	N-channel	60	2	1.2	5	TO-39	Z
IRF511	N-channel	60	0.6	2.5	20	TO-220AB	M
MTP2955E	P-channel	60	0.3	6	25	TO-220AB	M
IRF531	N-channel	60	0.180	14	75	TO-220AB	M
MTP23P06	P-channel	60	0.12	11.5	125	TO-220AB	M
IRFZ44	N-channel	60	0.028	50	150	TO-220	IR
IRF531	N-channel	80	0.160	14	79	TO-220	IR
ZVP3310A	P-channel	100	20	0.14	0.625	E-line	Z
ZVN2110B	N-channel	100	4	0.85	5	TO-39	Z
ZVP3310B	P-channel	100	20	0.3	5	TO-39	Z
IRF510	N-channel	100	0.6	2	20	TO-220AB	M
IRF520	N-channel	100	0.27	5	40	TO-220AB	M
IRF150	N-channel	100	0.055	40	150	TO-204AE	M
IRFP150	N-channel	100	0.055	40	180	TO-247	IR
ZVP1320A	P-channel	200	80	0.02	0.625	E-line	Z
ZVN0120B	N-channel	200	16	0.42	5	TO-39	Z
ZVP1320B	P-channel	200	80	0.1	5	TO-39	Z
IRF620	N-channel	200	0.800	5	40	TO-220AB	M
MTP6P20E	P-channel	200	1	3	75	TO-220AB	M
IRF220	N-channel	200	0.400	8	75	TO-220AB	M
IRF640	N-channel	200	0.18	10	125	TO-220AB	M

Manufacturers: IR = International Rectifier; M = Motorola; S = Siliconix; Z = Zetex.

†For package shape, size and pin-connection information, see manufacturers' data sheets. Many retail suppliers offer data sheets to buyers free of charge on request. Data books are available from many manufacturers and retailers.

Logic IC Families

Type	Propagation Delay for CL = 50 pF (ns) Typ	Max	Max Clock Frequency (MHz)	Power Dissipation (CL = 0) @ 1 MHz (mW/gate)	Output Current @ 0.5 V max (mA)	Input Current (Max mA)	Threshold Voltage (V)	Supply Voltage (V) Min	Typ	Max
CMOS										
74AC	3	5.1	125	0.5	24	0	V+/2	2	5 or 3.3	6
74ACT	3	5.1	125	0.5	24	0	1.4	4.5	5	5.5
74HC	9	18	30	0.5	8	0	V+/2	2	5	6
74HCT	9	18	30	0.5	8	0	1.4	4.5	5	5.5
4000B/74C (10 V)	30	60	5	1.2	1.3	0	V+/2	3	5 - 15	18
4000B/74C (5V)	50	90	2	3.3	0.5	0	V+/2	3	5 - 15	18
TTL										
74AS	2	4.5	105	8	20	0.5	1.5	4.5	5	5.5
74F	3.5	5	100	5.4	20	0.6	1.6	4.75	5	5.25
74ALS	4	11	34	1.3	8	0.1	1.4	4.5	5	5.5
74LS	10	15	25	2	8	0.4	1.1	4.75	5	5.25
ECL										
ECL III	1.0	1.5	500	60	—	—	−1.3	−5.19	−5.2	−5.21
ECL 100K	0.75	1.0	350	40	—	—	−1.32	−4.2	−4.5	−5.2
ECL100KH	1.0	1.5	250	25	—	—	−1.29	−4.9	−5.2	−5.5
ECL 10K	2.0	2.9	125	25	—	—	−1.3	−5.19	−5.2	−5.21
GaAs										
10G	0.3	0.32	2700	125	—	—	−1.3	−3.3	−3.4	−3.5
10G	0.3	0.32	2700	125	—	—	−1.3	−5.1	−5.2	−5.5

Source: Horowitz (W1HFA) and Hill, *The Art of Electronics—2nd edition,* page 570. © Cambridge University Press 1980, 1989. Reprinted with the permission of Cambridge University Press.

Three-Terminal Voltage Regulators

Listed numerically by device

Device	Description	Package	Voltage	Current (Amps)
317	Adj Pos	TO-205	+1.2 to +37	0.5
317	Adj Pos	TO-204, TO-220	+1.2 to +37	1.5
317L	Low Current Adj Pos	TO-205, TO-92	+1.2 to +37	0.1
317M	Med Current Adj Pos	TO-220	+1.2 to +37	0.5
338	Adj Pos	TO-3	+1.2 to +32	5.0
350	High Current Adj Pos	TO-204, TO-220	+1.2 to +33	3.0
337	Adj Neg	TO-205	−1.2 to -37	0.5
337	Adj Neg	TO-204, TO-220	−1.2 to -37	1.5
337M	Med Current Adj Neg	TO-220	−1.2 to -37	0.5
309		TO-205	+5	0.2
309		TO-204	+5	1.0
323		TO-204, TO-220	+5	3.0
140-XX	Fixed Pos	TO-204, TO-220	Note 1	1.0
340-XX		TO-204, TO-220		1.0
78XX		TO-204, TO-220		1.0
78LXX		TO-205, TO-92		0.1
78MXX		TO-220		0.5

Device	Description	Package	Voltage	Current (Amps)
78TXX		TO-204		3.0
79XX	Fixed Neg	TO-204, TO-220	Note 1	1.0
79LXX		TO-205, TO-92		0.1
79MXX		TO-220		0.5

Note 1—XX indicates the regulated voltage; this value may be anywhere from 1.2 V to 35 V. A 7815 is a positive 15-V regulator, and a 7924 is a negative 24-V regulator.

The regulator package may be denoted by an additional suffix, according to the following:

Package	Suffix
TO-204 (TO-3)	K
TO-220	T
TO-205 (TO-39)	H, G
TO-92	P, Z

For example, a 7812K is a positive 12-V regulator in a TO-204 package. An LM340T-5 is a positive 5-V regulator in a TO-220 package. In addition, different manufacturers use different prefixes. An LM7805 is equivalent to a mA7805 or MC7805.

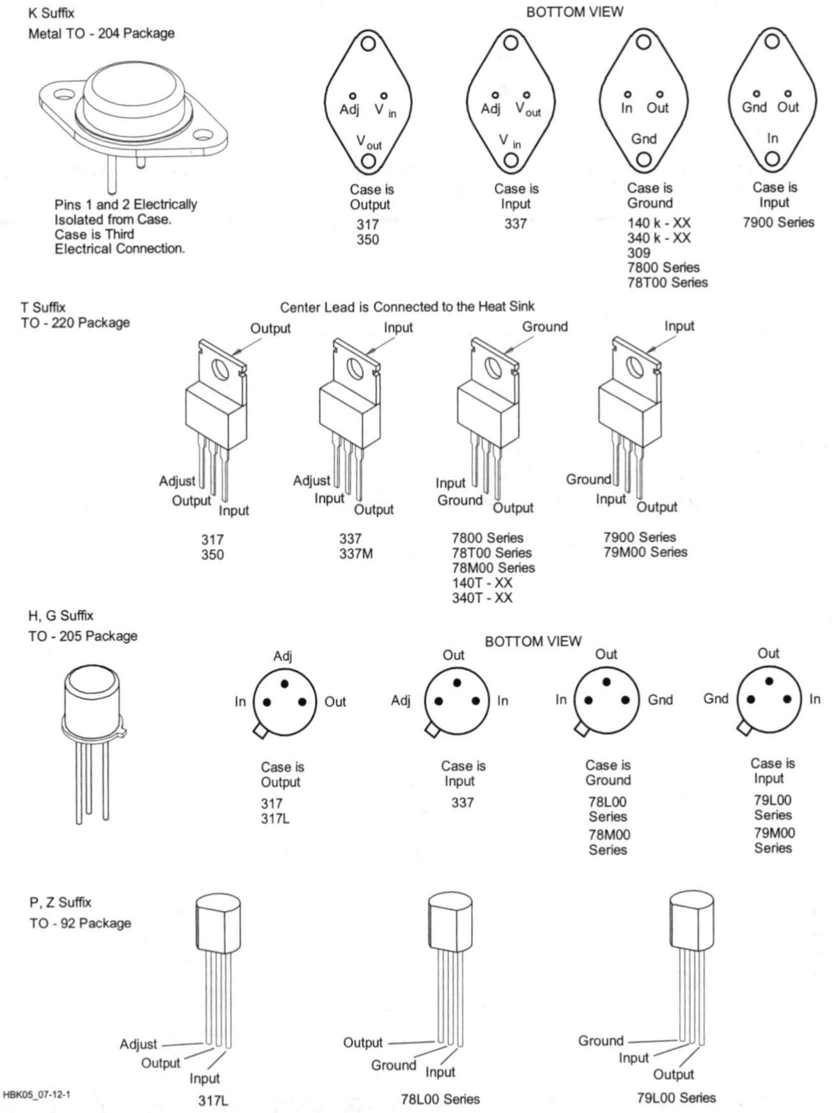

K Suffix
Metal TO - 204 Package

Pins 1 and 2 Electrically Isolated from Case. Case is Third Electrical Connection.

BOTTOM VIEW

Case is Output
317
350

Case is Input
337

Case is Ground
140 k - XX
340 k - XX
309
7800 Series
78T00 Series

Case is Input
7900 Series

T Suffix
TO - 220 Package

Center Lead is Connected to the Heat Sink

317
350

337
337M

7800 Series
78T00 Series
78M00 Series
140T - XX
340T - XX

7900 Series
79M00 Series

H, G Suffix
TO - 205 Package

BOTTOM VIEW

Case is Output
317
317L

Case is Input
337

Case is Ground
78L00 Series
78M00 Series

Case is Input
79L00 Series
79M00 Series

P, Z Suffix
TO - 92 Package

HBK05_07-12-1

317L

78L00 Series

79L00 Series

Coaxial Cable End Connectors

UHF Connectors

Military No.	Style	Cable RG- or Description
PL-259	Str (m)	8, 9, 11, 13, 63, 87, 149, 213, 214, 216, 225
UG-111	Str (m)	59, 62, 71, 140, 210
SO-239	Pnl (f)	Std, mica/phenolic insulation
UG-266	Blkhd (f)	Rear mount, pressurized, copolymer of styrene ins.

Adapters

Military No.	Style	Notes
PL-258	Str (f/f)	Polystyrene ins.
UG-224,363	Blkhd (f/f)	Polystyrene ins.
UG-646	Ang (f/m)	Polystyrene ins.
M-359A	Ang (m/f)	Polystyrene ins.
M-358	T (f/m/f)	Polystyrene ins.

Reducers

Military No.	Cable RG-
UG-175	55, 58, 141, 142 (except 55A)
UG-176	59, 62, 71, 140, 210

Family Characteristics:

All are nonweatherproof and have a nonconstant impedance. Frequency range: 0-500 MHz. Maximum voltage rating: 500 V (peak).

N Connectors

Military No.	Style	Cable RG-	Notes
UG-21	Str (m)	8, 9, 213, 214	50 Ω
UG-94A	Str (m)	11, 13, 149, 216	70 Ω
UG-536	Str (m)	58, 141, 142	50 Ω
UG-603	Str (m)	59, 62, 71, 140, 210	50 Ω
UG-23, B-E	Str (f)	8, 9, 87, 213, 214, 225	50 Ω
UG-602	Str (f)	59, 62, 71, 140, 210	—
UG-228B, D, E	Pnl (f)	8, 9, 87, 213, 214, 225	—
UG-1052	Pnl (f)	58, 141, 142	50 Ω
UG-593	Pnl (f)	59, 62, 71, 140, 210	50 Ω
UG-160A, B, D	Blkhd (f)	8, 9, 87, 213, 214, 225	50 Ω
UG-556	Blkhd (f)	58, 141, 142	50 Ω
UG-58, A	Pnl (f)		50 Ω
UG-997A	Ang (f)		50 Ω $^{11}/_{16}$"

Panel mount (f) with clearance above panel

Military No.	Style	Notes
M39012/04-	Blkhd (f)	Front mount hermetically sealed
UG-680	Blkhd (f)	Front mount pressurized

N Adapters

Military No.	Style	Notes
UG-29,A,B	Str (f/f)	50 Ω, TFE ins.
UG-57A.B	Str (m/m)	50 Ω, TFE ins.
UG-27A,B	Ang (f/m)	Mitre body
UG-212A	Ang (f/m)	Mitre body
UG-107A	T (f/m/f)	—
UG-28A	T (f/f/f)	—
UG-107B	T (f/m/f)	—

Family Characteristics:

N connectors with gaskets are weatherproof. RF leakage: −90 dB min @ 3 GHz. Temperature limits: TFE: −67° to 390°F (−55° to 199°C). Insertion loss 0.15 dB max @ 10 GHz. Copolymer of styrene: −67° to 185°F (−55° to 85°C). Frequency range: 0-11 GHz. Maximum voltage rating: 1500 V P-P. Dielectric withstanding voltage 2500 V RMS. SWR (MIL-C-39012 cable connectors) 1.3 max 0-11 GHz.

BNC Connectors

Military No.	Style	Cable RG-	Notes
UG-88C	Str (m)	55, 58, 141, 142, 223, 400	

Military No.	Style	Cable RG-	Notes
UG-959	Str (m)	8, 9	
UG-260,A	Str (m)	59, 62, 71, 140, 210	Rexolite ins.
UG-262	Pnl (f)	59, 62, 71, 140, 210	Rexolite ins.
UG-262A	Pnl (f)	59, 62, 71, 140, 210	nwx, Rexolite ins.
UG-291	Pnl (f)	55, 58, 141, 142, 223, 400	
UG-291A	Pnl (f)	55, 58, 141, 142, 223, 400	nwx
UG-624	Blkhd (f)	59, 62, 71, 140, 210	Front mount Rexolite ins.
UG-1094A	Blkhd		Standard
UG-625B	Receptacle		
UG-625			

BNC Adapters

Military No.	Style	Notes
UG-491,A	Str (m/m)	
UG-491B	Str (m/m)	Berylium, outer contact
UG-914	Str (f/f)	
UG-306	Ang (f/m)	
UG-306A,B	Ang (f/m)	Berylium outer contact
UG-414,A	Pnl (f/f)	# 3-56 tapped flange holes
UG-306	Ang (f/m)	
UG-306A,B	Ang (f/m)	Berylium outer contact
UG-274	T (f/m/f)	
UG-274A,B	T (f/m/f)	Berylium outer contact

Family Characteristics:

Z = 50 Ω. Frequency range: 0-4 GHz w/low reflection; usable to 11 GHz. Voltage rating: 500 V P-P. Dielectric withstanding 500 V RMS. SWR: 1.3 max 0-4 GHz. RF leakage −55 dB min @ 3 GHz. Insertion loss: 0.2 dB max @ 3 GHz. Temperature limits: TFE: −67° to 390°F (−55° to 199°C); Rexolite insulators: −67° to 185°F (−55° to 85°C). "Nwx" = not weatherproof.

HN Connectors

Military No.	Style	Cable RG-	Notes
UG-59A	Str (m)	8, 9, 213, 214	
UG-1214	Str (f)	8, 9, 87, 213, 214, 225	Captivated contact
UG-60A	Str (f)	8, 9, 213, 214	Copolymer of styrene ins.
UG-1215	Pnl (f)	8, 9, 87, 213, 214, 225	Captivated contact
UG-560	Pnl (f)		
UG-496	Pnl (f)		
UG-212C	Ang (f/m)		Berylium outer contact

Family Characteristics:

Connector Styles: Str = straight; Pnl = panel; Ang = Angle; Blkhd = bulkhead. Z = 50 Ω. Frequency range = 0-4 GHz. Maximum voltage rating = 1500 V P-P. Dielectric withstanding voltage = 5000 V RMS. SWR = 1.3. All HN series are weatherproof. Temperature limits: TFE: −67° to 390°F (−55° to 199°C); copolymer of styrene: −67° to 185°F (−55° to 85°C).

Cross-Family Adapters

Families	Description	Military No.
HN to BNC	HN-m/BNC-f	UG-309
N to BNC	N-m/BNC-f	UG-201,A
	N-f/BNC-m	UG-349,A
	N-m/BNC-m	UG-1034
N to UHF	N-m/UHF-f	UG-146
	N-f/UHF-m	UG-83,B
	N-m/UHF-m	UG-318
UHF to BNC	UHF-m/BNC-f	UG-273
	UHF-f/BNC-m	UG-255

Computer Connector Pinouts

(A)
Parallel Port (DB 25 pin)
Female

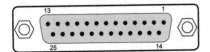

Pin	Signal	Pin	Signal
1	Strobe	10	Acknowledge
2	Data 0	11	Busy
3	Data 1	12	Paper Empty
4	Data 2	13	Select
5	Data 3	14	Auto Feed
6	Data 4	15	Error
7	Data 5	16	Initialize
8	Data 6	17	Select In
9	Data 7	18-25	GND

(B)
Parallel Port (Centronics 36 pin)
Female

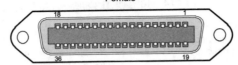

Pin	Signal	Pin	Signal
1	Strobe	13	Select
2	Data 0	14	Auto Feed
3	Data 1	15	N/C (not connected)
4	Data 2	16	Signal GND
5	Data 3	17	Frame GND
6	Data 4	18	+5 V Out
7	Data 5	19-30	GND
8	Data 6	31	Reset
9	Data 7	32	Error
10	Acknowledge	33	External GND
11	Busy	34	N/C
12	Paper Empty	35	N/C
		36	Select In

(C)
Serial Port (DB 9 pin)
Male

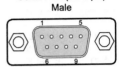

Pin	Signal
1	DCD (Data Carrier Detect)
2	RxD (Receive Data)
3	TxD (Transmit Data)
4	DTR (Data Terminal Ready)
5	GND (Signal Ground)
6	DSR (Data Set Ready)
7	RTS (Request To Send)
8	CTS (Clear To Send)
9	RI (Ring Indicator)

(D)
Serial Port (DB 25 pin)
Male

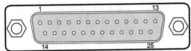

Pin	Signal	Pin	Signal
1	N/C (not connected)	20	DTR (Data Terminal Ready)
2	TxD (Transmit Data)	21	N/C
3	RxD (Receive Data)	22	RI (Ring Indicator)
4	RTS (Request To Send)	23	N/C
5	CTS (Clear To Send)	24	N/C
6	DSR (Data Set Ready)	25	N/C
7	GND (Signal Ground)		
8	DCD (Data Carrier Detect)		
9-19 N/C			

(E)
Ethernet Connector (RJ45-8 pin)
Female

Pin	Signal
1	Output Transmit Data (+)
2	Output Transmit Data (-)
3	Input Receive Data (+)
4	N/C (not connected)
5	N/C
6	Input Receive Data (-)
7	N/C
8	N/C

(F)
Ethernet Connector (RJ45-10 pin)
Female

Pin	Signal
1	DCD (Data Carrier Detect)
2	DTR (Data Terminal Ready)
3	CTS (Clear To Send)
4	GND (Signal Ground)
5	RxD (Receive Data)
6	TxD (Transmit Data)
7	GND (Frame Ground)
8	RTS (Request To Send)
9	DSR (Data Set Ready)
10	RI (Ring Indicator)

(G)
Mouse Port (DB 9 pin)
Male

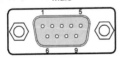

Pin	Signal
1	N/C (not connected)
2	Data
3	Clock
4	N/C
5	GND (Signal Ground)
6	N/C
7	RTS (12-9 V)
8	N/C
9	N/C

(H)
Mouse Port (mini DIN 9 pin)
Female

Pin	Signal
1	+5 V
2	X-A
3	X-B
4	Y-A
5	Y-B
6	Button 1
7	Button 2
8	Button 3
9	GND

(I)
Game/Joystick Port (DB 15 pin)
Female

Pin	Signal	Pin	Signal
1	+5 V	10	Button (B-1)
2	Button (A-1)	11	Position (B-X)
3	Position (A-X)	12	GND
4	GND	13	Position (B-Y)
5	GND	14	Button (B-2)
6	Position (A-Y)	15	+5 V
7	Button (A-2)		
8	+5 V		
9	+5 V		

(J)
PC-AT Type Power Connector

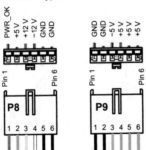

(K)
PC-ATX Type Power Connector
Viewed from Connector End

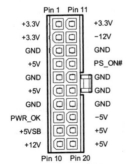

Pin 1   Pin 11

+3.3V	+3.3V
+3.3V	-12V
GND	GND
+5V	PS_ON#
GND	GND
+5V	GND
GND	GND
PWR_OK	-5V
+5VSB	+5V
+12V	+5V

Pin 10   Pin 20

(L)
Disk Drive, CD and Other Device Power Connector
Viewed from Connector End

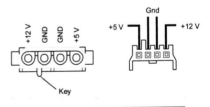

Note: All figures not drawn to same scale.

HBK0030

FEEDBACK

Please use this form to give us your comments on this book and what you'd like to see in future editions, or e-mail us at **pubsfdbk@arrl.org** (publications feedback). If you use e-mail, please include your name, call, e-mail address and the book title, edition and printing in the body of your message. Also indicate whether or not you are an ARRL member.

Where did you purchase this book?
□ From ARRL directly   □ From an ARRL dealer

Is there a dealer who carries ARRL publications within:
□ 5 miles   □ 15 miles   □ 30 miles   of your location?   □ Not sure.

License class:
□ Novice   □ Technician   □ Technician with code   □ General   □ Advanced   □ Amateur Extra

Name _____

ARRL member? □ Yes □ No

Call Sign _____

Daytime Phone ( ) _____ Age _____

Address _____

City, State/Province, ZIP/Postal Code _____

If licensed, how long? _____ e-mail address _____

Other hobbies _____

_____

Occupation _____

For ARRL use only	HOR ANT
Edition	1 2 3 4 5 6 7 8 9 10 11 12
Printing	3 4 5 6 7 8 9 10 11 12

From _____

_____

_____

EDITOR, HANDS-ON RADIO ANTHOLOGY
ARRL—THE NATIONAL ASSOCIATION FOR AMATEUR RADIO
225 MAIN STREET
NEWINGTON CT 06111-1494

— — — — — — — — — — — — — — — — please fold and tape — — — — — — — — — — — — — —